Praise for Glassbottom Days

WINNER! First Place Independent Publisher Award (2006)

"Island Magic... a home grown literary sensation...rave reviews for the quality of its writing and thoughtful insights... A coming of age story for Wilson, for island literary culture and for the Virgin Islands as a whole."

~ *Tanya Mannes, Virgin Islands Daily News*

"Beautifully crafted... excruciatingly readable."

~ *Shaun Pennington, V.I Source*

"When I saw I was near the end of Glassbottom Days, I began to read slowly because I did not want it to ever end.

Willie Wilson's Glassbottom Days gives the classic coming-of-age story a unique perspective by making it not only about a boy growing up as a "fish out of water" on St. Thomas, U.S. Virgin Islands, but also about a place and culture that were changing forever at the same time Willie was changing. The journey is simultaneously a gripping mystery, a nuanced romance and an enthralling two-family saga – all unfolded with humor and irresistible pacing. Wilson intertwines the events large and small that shape the boy, the place and the culture so that each one becomes a metaphor for the others and so that when the reader comes to the last page, the story ends but the richness of the storytelling lingers permanently. It is now on my lifetime list of "Best Books I've Ever Read."

With the author's permission, I submitted Glassbottom Days for consideration for the Pulitzer Prize for Non- Fiction, but the publication date made it ineligible. Nonetheless, the book's other prestigious awards reflect the high praise Willie Wilson deserves for this splendid literary achievement."

~ *J. Lowe Davis, Executive Editor of The Virgin Islands Daily News and Pulitzer Prize-winning journalist*

"... a poignant coming-of-age tale, a delightful tapestry of our island culture, a provocative crime mystery, and a gorgeous display of the English language."

~ *Rene Anduze*

"I suppose officially this isn't a novel, but rather a fictionalized coming-of-age memoir set in the Virgin Islands. But it certainly has the ambition of a Great American Novel, and offers complex characters, vivid locations and rich ethical dilemmas. How does one boy turn out just fine, while a neighbor down the street becomes a murderer and a fugitive? It's been a long while since I read a book that asks such big questions, or provides such satisfying prose and belly laughs along the way. I haven't been able to get this book out of my mind."

~ *Dr. L. Soutter (London England)*

"Books of quality like this one, books of resonance and tenderness and a kind of (gentle) outrage, are so seldom discovered... Damn fine!"

~ *Dick Jackson, Richard Jackson Books*

Also by Willie Wilson

Up Mountain One Time

—ᴡᴡ—

Praise for *Up Mountain One Time:*

GLASSBOTTOM DAYS

—ᴍ—

For Gladys –
who Auden felt
was a good poet! I
hope you enjoy this
Book. Best

Levine &
Karen

3 June 2012.
Matt and Amelia's Wedding!

Published by
Bonne Resolution Press
P. O. Box 1116
St. Thomas, VI 00804
wwilson@antilles.vi
bertrandkaren@hotmail.com

Copyright 2004, 2011 by Willie Wilson.

First Bonne Resolution Edition 2005
Second Bonne Resolution Edition 2011

Jacket illustration by Karen Bertrand
Book design by Karen Bertrand, Willie Wilson, Jen McQueen

This book is set in Galliard.

Title page image from 1850s lithograph *Denmark Hill* from
C. E. Bærentzen of Copenhagen.

Special thanks to Slinger Francisco (The Mighty Sparrow) for selected lyrics from
Benwood Dick and *Gunslinger* (also known as *Young and Strong*).

ISBN: 0-9763045-0-3

Printed in the United States of America.
DS Graphics, Lowell, Massachusetts

Acknowledgments

Labors of love can be long in the making. The following individuals have served along the way either as readers, helpers, or as inspiration. So, special thanks to Stanley LaBeet, Rick Simmons, Judy Soto, Salvadol Callwood, Dana Orie, Irving Paiewonsky, Dick Jackson, Lynn Franklin, Anne Sexton, Harold Bond, Tom Dillingham, Maurice Sendak, Scott O'Dell, Richard Dillard, William Maxwell, Thornton Wilder, Isabel Geffner, Peter and Sam Guzzardi, Lois Morris, Eric Hedin, Anne and Laurie Williams, Susan Crowther, Jane Wales, Carole Dudley, Elida Wassman, Sebastiano and Filippo Paiewonsky Cassinelli, Dane Perry, Carol Fava, Eric Zucker, Buzz and Kris McLaughlin, Suzanne Cavedon, H.D. Stevens, Glen Higgins, Kim Holdsworth and Bob Schmidt, The Mighty Sparrow, Calvin Emmanuel, Nick Russel, Ashley Merced, Per Fog, Shaun Pennington, Ken Anderson, Kathy Streibich, Roger Lakins, Barbara Birt, J. Lowe Davis, Jen McQueen, Chris Teare, Ann Key, the Rivara family, the Bertrand family, Mary Gilliam, Jim and Sally Soutter, Adele Sanger, Joan, Wendy, and Pam Wilson, Bobby VanCleave (wherever you are) and, most of all, to my wife, Karen, who always believed in this book's possibilities.

I would like to thank as well the Christa McAuliffe Fellowship Committee, the Virgin Islands Humanities Council, the Virgin Islands Council on the Arts, The University of the Virgin Islands Library, and Antilles School for the time and support they provided.

Finally, I thank my parents, Hack and Sallie Wilson, who will never read this book but who bravely chose to move to the islands all those years ago and, in so doing, enriched my life in more ways than I can fully imagine.

For Karen

Denmark Hill 1850s
lithograph by C. E. Baerentzen
(Crystal Gade at lower left)

GLASSBOTTOM DAYS

Willie Wilson

BONNE RESOLUTION PRESS
ST. THOMAS, VIRGIN ISLANDS

Author's Note

When one passes over a reef in a glassbottom boat, the splendid disorder offers competing shapes — brain coral, sponges, stag horns, anemone, sea fans — forms that seem to bear little relation to one another. In the shallows, it is as if one were too close to an impressionist painting to make sense of it. But viewed at a greater depth, the overall picture clearly reveals how different coral heads are invisibly connected by the underlying reef. Not unlike the way events form the geography of one's life.

Writers are often cautioned not to write about their own lives, particularly in a first book. Well, my first book was about a brave mongoose, who bears little resemblance to me. This book could also have been rendered as fiction (as some have urged), which would have allowed me to place myself at the scene of a murder, or aboard a hijacked airliner. Fiction might also have cast my adolescent romantic failings in a more favorable light, and helped provide a big kicker for the end. Tempting as that was, I have chosen to stick to real life, which has its own wonders. The names of certain people and places have been altered as a courtesy to real individuals, and circumstance has also required the occasional melding of faces, and the vague conjuring of forgotten conversations. The lines between memory and imagination are, at best, like those drawn in sand. But I have tried to be truthful; the essential events in this book actually happened, and that matters to me.

A GAME OF CATCH

—✺—

Mistaken Identity

A few years ago, I became curious about the origins of a street fight my father had when I was ten. I had witnessed the fight start to finish from the steps of our house. The house was on Crystal Gade on St. Thomas; the year was 1958, a few months after our move to the island. I could tell you everything about the fight. I could tell you, for instance, that the fight occurred in the early evening, that my Uncle Sandy was there, visiting from the States, that a man, Anton Merced, appeared at the gate calling for my father. Words were exchanged and the fight erupted and broke onto the street. It traveled down to the church on the corner and then labored back up the hill. At last my father gained the advantage and pinned Merced in front of our gate only to have three women begin to beat him over the head and back with broomsticks. As he rose to his feet, a boy appeared from nowhere and threw a brick into his ribs. My father went down on one knee. People slipped away and shutters above the street closed. These things I could tell you.

But there were, over the years, things I had also wondered about. In the first place, what had actually caused Mr. Merced to call at our house that night? Although I'd heard him accuse my father of hitting Merced's wife, I'd also heard my father tell him he had the wrong guy. Besides, I couldn't imagine it being true; like most ten-year-olds I'd believed largely what I'd been told. But all these years later, I've had to ask myself anew, What brings one man to the gate of another?

Looking back at that fight and the possible reasons for it has led me to see things a bit differently. At the time of the fight, seeing my father called onto the street like that confirmed my worst fears about island life. In the intervening years, however, the event has engendered, instead, a sense of belonging; and these words are, in part, a round-about way of making amends with the events of that night in 1958, the night Mr. Merced came to our gate.

An important part of this story has to do with what became of Jimmy Merced, the boy who threw that brick at my father. In 1972, 14 years after the fight, five armed men in fatigues and black hoods murdered eight people on a St. Croix golf course. The event, which came to be known as the Sweet Bottom Massacre, became world news overnight. One of the murderers was said to be Jimmy Merced who reportedly gave the orders and carried the machine gun, a gun similar to the one he'd used a few years earlier in Vietnam. After a lengthy manhunt, the five men were captured, tried and sentenced to eight consecutive life terms. Twelve years into that sentence, Jimmy Merced contrived to get out of prison for a court date, then hijack an airliner to Cuba, and disappear. He has not been seen or heard from since.

When the hijacking became national news in 1985, old memories about the fight resurfaced and with them, a few hard questions. I'd long viewed certain issues related to my father's street fight as unanswerable water-under-the-bridge concerns, because by that time my father was no longer alive. But then one day some years ago, I spotted Anton Merced walking out of the Charlotte Amalie Post Office, and it occurred to me that the man who had fought my father 35 years before was the one man I could go to.

—〜—

When I first went to Mr. Merced's house, I parked on Blackbeard's Hill, my wheels straddling the gutter, and waited with the engine running to see if other cars could squeeze past. The view was a fitting one for the occasion. The Merced house was a stone's throw below me on Bunker Hill. A short way across the valley, I could make out the house I had lived in as a child, its galvanized roof barely visible behind a neighbor's mango tree. The valley is one of the first settled on St. Thomas. On the west slope overlooking the harbor is the island's historic synagogue. Above it is Villa Santana, the former residence of the Mexican revolution's exiled leader. Higher still, its serene white walls separated from the world by acres of bush, is the Danish Consulate. In my youthful explorations, it was one place that was off limits; visible only from afar, it was remote and elegant, but somehow sinister.

Our house, like the Merced's, was located at a far lower, less distinguished elevation of, say, 50 feet, just high enough to see a slice of the harbor over the rooftops and, with any luck, catch the available breeze. Lower and you were on the floor of the valley. Here, among other things, lay the bakery, the butcher, two churches. At the base of our street was the Dutch Reformed Church and further up the valley, on Garden Street, was the All Souls Anglican Church. Between those churches, at a low point where the gut turns beneath the street — the approximate navel of the valley — was The Neptune, a decidedly less spiritual emporium, where schoolboys could, at certain hours, glimpse the commerce of flesh.

After a tour bus and a water truck managed to inch past my bumper, I started to walk down Bunker Hill. Though I had prepared Mr. Merced for my visit, I was still fairly certain he did not know I was the son of the man he'd fought on Crystal Gade. There was also still the possibility that he might hold a grudge. Knowing what I do now, it would not be surprising if, beneath the friendly veneer, Mr. Merced suspected me of being a Federal Agent interested in the whereabouts of his fugitive-hijacker son. But my interest in talking to him at the time had more to do with my father than with his son, and as I approached his gate, I wondered how best to broach the subject of the street fight he had with my father 30-odd years before.

These speculations were interrupted by a familiar arched wall above and across the street from the Merced's. It was the wall of the house where Pilar Bermudez once lived — Pilar, the object of all my sixth grade amorous yearnings. In this peach-colored house, Pilar once came and went mysteriously. In this house, she did her homework, had fights with her little brother, ate arroz con pollo, lay naked in bed. In this bed, I once wrongly imagined, Pilar lay secretly longing to be mine. The name on the gate was a new one, but a dog, as if being true to her memory, snarled at me from the porch.

Weeds sprouted from the gutter of the Merced house, and a scrap of wire held the mouth of the downspout to the cistern intake. The door at the top of the stairs was slightly ajar, but the windows were louvered shut. A last moment of misgivings. I looked again at the peeling iron gate and saw what I hadn't before. Just above my head, suspended on a new wrought iron hinge was an encouraging metal plaque with raised white lettering: Mr. and Mrs. Anton Merced.

"Inside," I called up.

"Coming," came from the room above.

Anton Merced appeared at the head of the staircase and gestured for me to come up. He was shirtless, shoeless, his shorts unbuttoned at the waist. I wondered as I headed up the stairs whether this attire was gauged to send a message, the informality meant to put me at ease, or, possibly, to telegraph a note of contempt, a sense that he had nothing to hide. Or perhaps this was just the way Mr. Merced dressed at home. He greeted me with a handshake and a thin smile.

Most houses in town share certain Danish West Indian qualities — a hip roof, covered gallery, hurricane shutters — and the Merced house showed from its position on the street and its stone foundations that it had been there for many generations. This, I vaguely knew, was the family residence, probably passed down from his father, but at the time he fought my father, Mr. Merced had lived across the valley on upper Raadets Gade, just around the corner from our house. The peeling paint on the outside of the house did not prepare me for the cool, carpeted calm inside. Though there were signs that an effort had been made to tidy up, it was equally clear that Mr. Merced, in his retirement years, was accustomed to a degree of comfort.

For a moment we stood side-by-side in the center of the room, each of us deferring to the other the choice of upholstered chairs. He was shorter than I'd imagined him, probably six-feet-two, still with traces of a well-muscled youth. His hair was wavy and dyed black, and his eyes, though wide and black at the center, showed around the edges a narrow circumference of blue. Above his lip, like a push broom, was a thin, rectangular, neatly trimmed mustache. For years after the fight, I'd seen this man at the post office window, always in uniform, always pleasant, sometimes smiling as he stamped parcels or doled out stamps, never a trace of hostility or even awareness. Did this man, this postal clerk, know who we were? My sister Pam and I often wondered. Did he know we were the children of the man he had fought on Crystal Gade, or was he just exercising the practiced self-control familiar to civil servants?

In the hour that followed, I learned that Anton (he insisted on first names) was 70 years old, that he had been retired from postal work for ten of them, that he had the same number of children as he had had broken bones (which was 19) from six women, three of them wives. I learned that he was not Puerto Rican (a time-honored assumption of our family) but descended from French ancestors who'd come to the island 200 years before and had once owned a large swath of land, lost generations later by Anton Merced's grandfather in a poker game.

As a young man Anton enlisted in the Army with his brother Hugo and both served in Puerto Rico as medics. Not all of their activities were humanitarian. After we had passed enough time to be comfortable with one another, Mr. Merced offered a few anecdotes about some of the less savory aspects of military life in Puerto Rico, having to do with barrooms and bare knuckles. These conflicts occurred on a regular basis. Merced's brother Hugo — younger, taller, perhaps meaner — was particularly adept at soliciting a brawl. If, upon entering a saloon, there seemed to be no lively prospects, a few discrete shards of ice tossed repeatedly at a neighboring table could usually be depended on to stir something up.

Anton Merced seemed neither proud nor particularly remorseful about these revelations, but the willingness to fight — whether provoked or not — seemed to stand as something of a family tradition. In talking about his father who was, among other things, a musician, a chandler, and a butcher, Merced revealed a revered and time-tested piece of family wisdom on the subject of fighting.

"Hit first."

The unstated but obvious corollary to this rule was not only to hit first, but to also hit hard.

During this discussion a child slipped through the room, brown, doe-eyed and about ten, and I calculated he fathered her in his 60s. Mr. Merced took the occasion to expound on his far-flung progeny. Of his 19 children, ten were girls. Roughly half lived in the States. He was particularly proud to have fathered such a generous array of colors.

"I got chocolate, coffee and cream, and some white like snow," he offered with a glint.

With the door partly ajar, I ventured to ask about Jimmy, the boy who had thrown that brick at my father. I wondered whether Mr. Merced had intentionally hastened the process with talk of his children. We talked about Jimmy at some length. We talked about Jimmy's childhood and his time spent in Vietnam, about the Sweet Bottom Massacre (and Anton's belief in his son's innocence) and we even touched a bit on the hijacking. But most of our talk that day was about growing up in town, about a Virgin Islands' childhood, about school days and other, more pleasant memories.

His father's willingness to discuss these things both surprised me and eased my misgivings about coming to talk to him in the first place. But of all the things that Anton Merced told me that morning, none surprised me more or put me more at ease than the revelation that came as a result of my opening attempt to identify myself.

"Mr. Merced," I'd started hesitantly, "Many years ago you and my father had a street fight."

He stared at me with clear, uncomprehending eyes.

I imagined him sorting through a mental gallery of rogues and victims looking for the father of the supplicant child.

"It was a big fight on Crystal Gade," I elaborated.

Something now registered.

"Your father was U.D.T.?"

"No," I answered, shaking my head. But in the same instant it occurred to me that my father might, at that time, have been mistaken for one of the Underwater Demolition Team members stationed on the island; he was stout, drove a jeep and, because of his work, regularly carted scuba gear around.

"Now that you mention it," I amended, "though he wasn't U.D.T, someone could easily have thought he was."

"And you say the fight was on Crystal Gade?" he asked, his memory now clearly coming into focus.

"Yes."

Mr. Merced allowed himself a smile.

"That wasn't me who fought your father. It was my brother, Hugo."

So basic a case of mistaken identity is a thing to wonder at. For 35 years I'd carried a grudge of sorts against Anton Merced, said unkind things about him to others, avoided his eyes on the street, assumed his dislike of my family. Come to find out, I had the wrong man. How much can one trust the siftings of childhood memory? In one instant, the name of a third-grade teacher, spoken a thousand times, slips away; and in the next, the scent of mud that clung to a sneaker one distant summer at a forgotten pond, percolates from a lost synapse, brought on by an overturned log. The attic photo reveals that the weeping willow was to the side of the house, not the back as memory had faithfully recorded, and the hill the house was perched atop was a slope and not a hill at all. Our memories recreate themselves, our imagination adding where it suits a purpose, and where it doesn't, taking away.

Another childhood memory I have no doubt embellished — stems from a question my father once asked me when I was young. Before that question I imagine my life to be a pond with a surface of glass. Into this pond the question falls from the sky like a pebble from outer space. The pebble breaks the surface and it makes a small splash, and from it concentric rings start their outward journey.

In this memory, it is 1957, the year before we moved to St. Thomas, and I am outside our home in Rye, New York, age 8, playing catch with Joe Castle. Joe is the policeman's son — black high-top sneakers, always handy with a piece of gum. Joe's a couple years older and better at grounders and high pops and has a tendency to burn it in a bit too fast. The afternoon of this particular memory I imagine it to be spring. Somewhere, the sound of Mr. Gillespie mowing his lawn. In the dog-wood tree, two birds. We are practicing grounders. The pond's surface is still and unsuspecting; the pebble, from outer space, is on its way.

"Give me a one-hop," Joe says.

I bobble one out. He scoops it up and fires it back. The sound of the leather echoes off the neighbor's porch.

"Not so hard," I say.

"How about a pop?"

I lob one over his shoulder and he gets a glove on it. This time he takes something off the throw, and just then I hear the screen door and see my father crossing the lawn. The birds stop their chase and the lawn mower fades away. The flickering sunlight in the leaves holds still as my father crouches on the curb, puts his hand on my shoulder and brings his face level with mine.

With eyes bright he says my name, and then, "How would you like to move to the Virgin Islands?"

Kerplunk. Splash.

"Sure," I say knowing dimly that this is the correct answer, the required answer. I get a pat on the shoulder and he heads back toward the house and I wonder what it is I have just agreed to.

"Grounder to the side," Joe calls.

I bounce one his way and he burns it back and the thwack of leather brings the sound of the mower back, the afternoon light. The birds are in the dogwood tree and a pebble now sits at the bottom of the pond.

At dinner that night I expected to have things fleshed out. After *Howdy Doody*, the set went off and my mother put the food on the table. We were eating early because my parents had someplace to go and my sister Wendy had a date. Pam was talking about summer camp and my father wanted to know about Little League, but there wasn't a word about the islands whose name I had already forgotten. By the time Jell-O rolled around, I'd begun to think, to hope, that it was something I'd imagined or misunderstood, and by the time my parents rushed off to the club or wherever, the lump of uncertainty had begun to dissolve. I decided not to ask either sister, thinking it might be a secret entrusted to me. I was also afraid that mentioning it might make it real, might give it a life it didn't already have. .

Wendy's date came and once they were gone, Pam rolled up the sleeves of her T-shirt and headed down the hall to her room. I followed her to listen to Elvis and watch her do chin ups on the bar installed across her doorway. Pam was 13 and the neighborhood tomboy, known to leap from trees to right wrongs and dispense hard-knuckled justice. In an attempt to curb these manly instincts, my mother bought her three nice white slips. That same night Pam cut them off into T-shirts.

But that was in sixth grade and she was now in seventh, and Mike McKinney, the class heart-throb, was showing interest in more than just her punches. I watched her knock-off a cool dozen chin-ups with one for good measure while *Don't Be Cruel* crooned from the Victrola. Then she invited me into her room, which meant for the moment she could trust me. We were shipmates thrown together by circumstance, alone in the house at night. I was reminded about the island thing and I wondered again if she knew.

"Want to see something?" she asked.

"Sure."

She went to her bureau and produced a cigar box with a charm bracelet and a few cherished baseball cards. Then she pulled something out and held in behind her back.

"Promise not to tell Wendy?"

"Sure."

"Cross-your-heart-hope-to-die?"

"Yup." This was serious business.

Then she revealed it, an actual photograph of Mike McKinney. I studied it not showing my disappointment. There he was, an eighth grade Elvis looking over his shoulder, T-shirt sleeves rolled, a comb jutting smartly from his back pocket. When he first came to the house he'd arrived in a lime-green Cadillac (the "Caddie" Mike called it), my parents smiled but later there was talk about the car. A person could be excused for selecting a poor color but not, apparently, for having chosen a Cadillac. Our own car, a sensible brown Chevy, may have lacked glamour but was not, we were told, entirely without taste.

On the back of the photograph were the words, *to Pam — Love, Mike*. Pam really was going out on a limb to reveal this dark treasure. Maybe this was the time.

"Pam?"

"What?" She was tucking the cigar box beneath some sweaters.

"Did Pop tell you anything, lately?" I ventured.

"Anything like what?" she asked, giving me a queer look.

How could I say it without revealing it?

"Anything about moving ... or anything."

"Yeah, to the Virgin Islands."

The casual answer was a cold steel blade. She knew. Everybody knew. She read the stunned look on my face.

"But don't worry," she said closing the bureau drawer, "we probably won't be going until next year."

Don't worry. I didn't like that.

"Where are the Virgin Islands?" I asked bleakly.

"It's kind of down below Florida," she replied, showing me the geography by raising her elbow and dropping her hand. I knew that Florida already hung down beneath everything else. What in the world kind of place were we going to?

"It's tropical," she explained. "You know what a palm tree is?"

"Yes."

"Bingo."

The palm tree I was most familiar with was the one rendered in comic strips. It grew on an isolated mound of sand. Under the palm was usually a man with a note and a bottle. Pam raised an eyebrow, the eyebrow of a doubter.

"Why are we going there?"

"Pop's going to have a new job."

My father, I vaguely knew, sold insurance which was something he carried in his briefcase that wasn't really there. Twice a week he went to Poughkeepsie. He worked for Fireman's Fund which did not have to do with hoses or sirens or putting out fires. It was all in his briefcase.

"What kind of job?"

"He's buying a glassbottom boat."

"Very funny."

But Pam wasn't laughing. She was looking in the mirror; feminine, muscular.

"What's a glassbottom boat? I asked, the words like marbles in my mouth.

"A boat with a glass bottom, stupid."

"What if the glass breaks?"

In the mirror the eyebrow went up, then the shoulders. Not a good sign.

Later I lay in bed turning it over. I had a nighttime habit of putting a shirt under the covers to twiddle the buttons with my toes. I shoved a favorite flannel down to the foot of the bed and put my toes to work. The only boat I had any familiarity with belonged to a Westchester playboy named Jack Rafferty who cruised the beach clubs on Long Island Sound. He always had a young girl or two onboard and usually a third skiing behind. My father thoroughly disapproved of these antics. That Jack Rafferty was handsome, tan, dashing and single were further marks against him. I had never been asked aboard his snappy runabout, but I had seen it carve turns and marveled at the way the hull parted the water. But my father's boat was to have a bottom of *glass*. I imagined this peculiar craft to be bigger than Jack Rafferty's with a cabin or some sort of covering. I remember lying in bed, my eyes closed, my toes feverishly working the buttons, and stepping onboard. The engine rumbles alive, and the craft surges forward and starts to plane. My bare feet rest on the glass floor so I cling to the rail to support my weight and keep from crashing through. The hull cuts into the water, the glass growing thinner, the blue racing beneath my feet.

In my bedroom there was a window at the head of the bed. On windless nights the streetlight on Rye Beach Avenue had a way of playing the shadows of the dogwood tree onto the windowpane, creating a shadowy face behind me. Often, looking up and seeing it was enough to send me running from the room. I looked at the window now, searching for the familiar fear I could chase away by going to the kitchen and opening the refrigerator door. But wind was moving the branches and the face wasn't there. The boat carved ahead, the glass thin as ice, a speeding blue gash in the water.

The Post Office Steps

A few years ago when my father was in the last months of a six-year battle with cancer, I sat down with him and a tape recorder. Like most sons, I was arriving late at the parental going away party, showing interest in things that should have interested me years before. I knew the highlights — his athletic youth, his war years as a bomber pilot, prison camp, his participation in the 1948 London Olympics, the time he wrestled Torpedo Joe. But now I wanted to record his own words, to hear things as only he could tell them, so that years after he was gone I could still hear his voice.

We were on the porch of his home on Vieques, a small island off the east coast of Puerto Rico where he moved after his years on St. Thomas. There was the predictable awkwardness of the tape recorder, the black box between us, and an unspoken urgency visible in his skin, his teeth, his loss of hair. Listening to the tape now, my own voice seems transparently buoyant, too intent on being upbeat. His is raspy and often unintelligible, made that way by a recent bout of chemotherapy.

I think now my father was a bit gun-shy. Though our first words covered mostly familiar ground, I think he sensed, correctly, that there were other questions laying in wait. I did want to cover some new, perhaps forbidden ground but our session ended with barely one side of the tape recorded. He said he was tired and I accepted that. But there may have been an unwillingness to delve deeper. Though I knew he was willing to clarify some mysteries, there may have been those he preferred to preserve and others he still, at the end of his life, had no answers to.

He did answer one question that day posed by an old photograph I'd discovered between the pages of a termite-ridden volume called *The Love Junk*, about an island couple and their converted Navy barge. The photo shows my parents looking slender and tan, younger and happier than I'd ever seen them. They are standing at a beach bar, drink in hand, a friendly looking West Indian in white shaking up the next round. My father identified it as 1954, St. Thomas, their mid-30s, second honeymoon. This was their first taste of the Virgin Islands. The photograph, my father confided, was taken a day or two before a particularly important moment in his life.

They had gone to St. Thomas to visit a childhood friend of my parents, who, after years as a foreign correspondent, had chosen to settle there. Knowing someone who actually lived on the island may have helped stir some curiosity. Their second day on St. Thomas, my father went to the Charlotte Amalie Post Office to mail some postcards. It was early in the morning, he told me, and it had begun to drizzle lightly in the sunshine. Standing on the post office steps, he watched the easy flow of islanders starting their day. In the drizzle the sunshine dazzles the red rooftops and glistens the palms. He is 36. He is looking out at a St. Thomas hillside.

Few people chose to leave Rye, it seems, and those who did left more to escape the rigors of keeping up with the Jones than out of any real desire to be somewhere else. In our case it was possible, still, to belong to a couple of clubs and in that way put a good face on things. But the stiff upper lip must have been increasingly difficult to sustain. Our house, situated between the policeman and the butcher, was a nice house by most standards but modest in Rye. Pam and I were going to the public school and not to Rye Country Day, where the better-heeled sons and daughters learned their Latin declensions. And Pop's job at Fireman's Fund was not a fast track to the executive suite.

To move to a different town — say, upstate — would have been a conspicuous retreat. But a move to the Caribbean might be viewed more an adventure than a withdrawal. Old chums with three-car garages and pressure-cooker careers, might more likely view such a departure with admiration and, possibly, envy. In fairness to my father, there was more to it than social and financial calculations. What my father saw from the post office steps — in the sun, in the red roofs and green mountains, in the bright drizzle and lazy pace of things — struck a quixotic chord in him.

When my parents returned from their 1954 vacation, my father brought the matter up with my Uncle Rutledge. If he could only find a way to make a buck down there, was the way he put it. Rutledge was a bachelor, a self-made entrepreneur, a make-happen kind of guy. The kind of guy who, a year or two later, might call with an angle, or a friend of a friend, or a glassbottom boat.

This from the Distant Connection Department: After my first conversation with Anton Merced at his house on Bunker Hill, we decided, having sniffed each other out, to meet again for lunch the following week. We ate at a quiet northside garden restaurant, both of us ordering a West Indian plate of kingfish and fungi. Our conversation lasted three hours and ranged seamlessly from his family to mine, from one generation to the next. One thing in particular offered me a new perspective. When I mentioned my father's moment of clarity on the steps of the post office that would, years later, lead to our move to the islands, he smiled to himself.

"What year you say that was?" he asked

"1954, I think."

He timed the moment well, taking a sip of his beer.

"I probably sold him the stamps."

One Overlook

Summer in Rye drew to a close, and certain comforting fall rhythms resumed, and the move to the Virgin Islands seemed to recede. Camp and Little League yielded to Cub Scouts and third grade. Pam went off to Rye High for eighth grade and Wendy to her first year of college — nursing school in New Haven, Connecticut. The house had started to empty, and for the first time I began to view my surroundings as something less than permanent, as something that could be pulled away.

Our house at 1 Overlook Place was a short walk from my school, which was located on Milton Point. It wasn't on the point, exactly — The American Yacht Club was — but at the base of the peninsula, near the fire station and the Luncheonette, the old Friends Meetinghouse. That neck of Rye was the most interesting and varied. The coast, on the bay and along the sound, was mostly ringed with beach clubs and large estates. But the base of the peninsula (near our house) was bordered by the Playland Parkway, a short artery designed to funnel outsiders straight to Playland, our homegrown, genteel amusement park offering every-thing from a dragon coaster and bumper cars to a Tunnel of Love. In summer, chrome cruisers from New Rochelle and the Bronx, entered our world with blasting radios and curvy girls in tight pink pants. The prox-imity of our house to this pleasure palace was a source of some discom-fort to my father. Still, by amusement park standards, it was hard to fault the place; the village elders had seen to it that there were ponds and weeping willows, lawns and white ducks, and parapets to view the sea. Often we walked the dog in the adjoining park or on Rye Beach, and in the winter we skated at Playland's large indoor rink.

I was just as interested in the other side of Milton Point where Blind Brook empties into the bay after passing the old Purdy Cemetery and the town dump. There, also, was Disbrow field, home of my many Little League strikeouts, and some woods and a greenhouse and a cattail swamp. All in all, 1 Overlook Place was well situated, with plenty of things for a boy or girl to do.

Looking back to that year, 1957, I imagine certain events auguring our move to the islands. For one, Bobby VanCleave was also moving away. Bobby was my best friend, a boy's boy who had come to Rye only two years before and swept our class by storm. He had come from a far-away place called California. "Back in California ..." Bobby used to say, and you listened because Bobby, the first time he played kickball with us, kicked the ball over the same fence none of us had ever even hit on the fly. In dodge ball, he was always last to get hit, often forcing the teacher to end the game and start anew. Now Bobby was going away.

That year, in a house across from his, something happened that broke on Rye like a nightmare. Randy Alsworth, a high school junior and a pretty regular guy, called his father to the head of the stairs and unloaded a shotgun on him. Then he coolly reloaded and blew his mom and kid sister away. He only winged his brother Tim, a lean, likable fellow with a bristling blond crew cut, who was in my sister's eighth grade class. I think (or have I created this memory?) Bobby's parents were across the street washing their car when Tim flew out the front door holding his shoulder. On our walk home from school after that, we were always aware of the house but careful not to get caught looking. But from Bobby's bedroom window we would eye it and try to imagine the gory events that happened behind the drawn curtains. Little white house, tidy green shutters, all that blood.

The grizzly news made the New York papers which provided some of the gruesome details the staid *Rye Chronicle* had chosen to omit. The blood-splattered wallpaper was of particular interest. Pam and I dwelled on the subject once too often, and my father forbade further talk of it.

There were other stirrings that year, further harbingers of change. Girls, creatures I had long secretly admired and shyly wondered at, had become a small but important part of my day. Even in the worst of times, called out on strikes or sent to the corner of the class, a passing smile from an Andrea or a Nancy would carry me home. I had seen enough things on TV to give my pillow a proper kissing, and the year before, my sister, during another baby-sitting confidence, had taken it upon herself to give me a good talking to. The talk had concerned the Facts of Life. The facts were few and pertained entirely to a single unthinkable act not even distantly related to the smothering pillow kisses I preferred — a looming responsibility that confirmed my darkest notions of adulthood.

If the boat with the glassbottom failed to go away, Nancy Lawton, like Bobby VanCleave, would be lost. Actually (and this was worse), they would both go on living the same lives in more or less the same world and only I would be lost, alone on an atoll, a single palm arching over my head. I was secretly in love with Nancy. One day in October, shortly after parent conferences, my teacher, Miss Carlotti, (who my father had pronounced a "hot ticket" at the dinner table) called the class' attention to a photo in our social studies book. The unit was about the native customs of a remote Pacific isle. The photo showed a glistening loin-clothed native casting a net into blue shallows.

"I think there may be someone in this class who will see this kind of scene soon," Miss Carlotti revealed.

"Who?" we all wanted to know.

No one answered. I wondered myself. Everyone looked around until they noticed that the teacher was smiling at me. There was a sudden something, thick and twisting at my center.

"Didn't I hear someone say you're going..." she hinted.

I looked at her, lost, readying myself for the punch.

"To the ..." she hinted again, her eyebrows arched and smiling, her teeth now over her lower lip showing me how to shape the sound. I cannot bring myself to say the words, afraid to breathe life into them.

"To the Virgin ..." she tries again.

"To the Virgin Islands," I blurt, copying her smile.

All jaws drop as young minds try to connect me and the loinclothed fisherman. I fear talk may turn to glassbottom boats and am relieved when the lesson resumes. But now I see that my mother and father have actually spoken to my teacher, and everything is completely real.

That afternoon, walking down Milton Avenue, Nancy Lawton, the most beautiful girl in the world, did not turn left onto Purdy Lane as usual with Winston Lord, the class artist.

"I know a way your way we both can go," she said brightly.

Was this a dream?

"Across Blind Brook," she explained, "through the cemetery and the cattails."

So we walked the quarter mile down Milton Avenue to where the little footbridge crosses Blind Brook. Approaching it, I must decide whether to turn off at Rye Beach Avenue or to go officially out of my way. I continue walking with her. In the middle of the footbridge I stop to show her my "alligator" a slender sand bar half submerged in Blind Brook. It is here, on the footbridge, that she asks about the islands I am going to, and I realize that it is this that has caused her to veer my way. Our walk continues into the forest where the old Purdy gravesite lies. On a rise in the woods, littered now with autumn leaves, are tombstones of clay-colored slate, most of the names and dates flaked off or mossed over. I do not tell Nancy about my interest in the stones or that I imagine Quaker-like people moldering in their graves, everything turned to dust but the buckles on their shoes. As I recall, we passed that section of forest in silence. Perhaps she was thinking as I have always thought that that was the place to kiss her or at least to take her hand. But fear seized the moment, and the path came out of the forest and started into the cattails.

Everything is bright and unfamiliar, and so, suddenly, am I.

"Isn't it wet in there?" I ask sensing this is where I should turn off.

"No, I go this way all the time," she answers bravely, her books under her arm. Then she waves and turns to go. I watch her disappear into the cattails, her pleated skirt slapping at her knees. I am in a movie. The camera is behind me, the girl gone, the cattails touching the sky.

After the classroom episode off the net-casting native, I was ready to start asking questions. I remember putting the first one to my mother that same afternoon. She was at the kitchen sink scrubbing a pot.

"It's like Port Chester," she explained with a wan smile.

Port Chester! What in the world did she mean by that? Port Chester housed the servants of Rye and Greenwich. It had a Life Savers factory on Main Street, and each day the town could smell what flavor they were making. Port Chester was the gothic location of my dentist and where my father bought hot sausage from a fat Italian woman.

"It's different, really," she elaborated. "The buildings are kind of the same though, and there are lots of negroes," she added turning back to the sink.

"You mean like ... Amos Jackson?" I asked forlornly.

"Yes, like Amos," she answered.

Amos was the one black guy at Milton School. He was very well-liked. But he was black. Now I was to be among lots and lots of Amoses. I was having difficulties piecing together my fragmented notion of island life. First, and most abiding, was the comic strip made real of the guy out of luck on an atoll, one arching coconut tree over his head and a bottle with a note. There was also now a net-tossing native of the Amos Jackson variety, a boat with a bottom of glass, and a tropical version of a Life Savers factory. These fragments were not far off the mark if someone had helped interpret them or piece them together. I wonder whether there was really so little discussion or whether I've experienced selective memory loss. It seems a brochure of a beach or some keen talk of sunny days would have put a more optimistic spin on things, but in this kitchen incident — the only one I remember — Port Chester and Amos Jackson are the two things that stand out. I think now that may have been my mother's way of preparing me and of letting me know how she felt about the move.

It was announced one night in early December that Pop would be "heading down" after Christmas. He would be away for a while, but he knew we would be well behaved and help Mom and wait until he got things ready. The announcement was made in a matter-of-fact manner as if the separation was something we'd long awaited and fully expected. I sort of remember our mouths wide, our soup spoons poised over our bowls.

"How long will it be before you tell us to come down?" Pam asked getting right to the point.

"Well, as soon as I settle some business matters and find ourselves a place to live. At the same time, your mother will be trying to sell the house and you will be helping her get things packed up."

I think there was mention of us not expecting as big a Christmas as years past and that we could think of our plane ride to the Virgin Islands as our late Christmas gift. It would all be very exciting and we would love the new place we were going to. This last sentiment was added in a way that sounded a bit like a decree. Pam and I caught each other's eye.

"What about my friends?" I asked him.

"You'll make new ones."

We were selling the house. I did not know at that age the meaning of burning one's bridges, but if someone had taken the time to explain it, I would have seen at once that the selling of our house was just that. Someone else would be living here, someone else sleeping in my room. Soon there would be no trace of us; no dog, no grandfather clock, no me.

When I went to bed that night, I saw the face in the window. I got up and closed the curtain and went back to bed. But the streetlight continued to play the leafy shadow on the curtain like a screen, and now and then the shadows would connect into the momentary configuration of a face. I called out, and my mother came and tucked me in and parted the curtain and showed me, sure enough, no face — just the dogwood tree and Rye Beach Avenue. But when she closed the door, the face came back and a branch must have brushed the windowpane because I screamed. My father came this time and walked me into the warm living room light. Mom was curled up on the rug and *The Honeymooners* was on the tube with Ralph Cramden telling Alice how one of these days he would punch her right in the kisser. My father could get misty-eyed over Ralph's optimism and his ability to muddle through. We cuddled in the blue glow and canned laughter and waited for the end (my mother's favorite part) when all their problems would be solved and Ralph would tell Alice, "Baby, you're the greatest."

Then my mother gave me a kiss and my father walked me back, and the face in the window was gone.

In his wallet, Anton Merced carries various family photos. The most prominent is a post office employee identification card taken probably in the 60s with Anton sporting a swashbuckling mustache. Two of the photos in the wallet are of his son, Jimmy, one showing him astride a horse, age ten, and the other a year or so later cleaning a fish. The photos provide my only glimpse of Jimmy Merced before I knew him, before he threw that brick at my father, and they have become a part of my sense of who he is. The boy who squints up at the camera — the gills of a grouper in one hand, a knife in the other — is not someone I could have easily identified. He seems serene, almost poetic in this photo, the glinting sea forming a kind of halo around him. The photos say a lot. Jimmy spent most of his summer days over at Rosendahl on the north side of St. Thomas where the family had several horses. Often he and his cousins went hunting with pellet guns for thrush or dove or, on occasion, ducks. Some weekends, Anton and Jimmy trolled the south bank for wahoo and kingfish in a 14-foot pram. An adventure of this sort requires leaving before dawn in order to get back before the seas pick up, and a failed outboard can spell disaster. Those two photos show me how different Jimmy's early years were from my own. Not better or worse, just different. Compared to this island world, my own *Howdy Doody*, Cub Scout, country club, Little League environment seems a bit anemic.

The microfilmed pages of *The Virgin Islands Daily News* from 1947 offer an interesting glimpse into that world, the world Jimmy Merced was born into. The islands in 1947 had been an American territory for only 30 years, and slavery had been gone almost a century. The island still had no radio station and TV was years away. *The Daily News* in 1947 is four pages long and sells for the monthly rate of 75 cents. The content of the paper offers a stark contrast to the pages of the *Rye Chronicle*.

Articles during a week in August, the week Jimmy Merced was born, include a lead article decrying the traffic problems caused by peddler's pushcarts. In another, a truck has collided with a telegraph post and a girl, 5, has been struck by a bicycle. A man's chickens worth 40 dollars are reported missing, and a donkey has made the news after biting and fracturing a boy's arm. The island, this particular week, is playing host to a "throng" of 40 visitors arriving on the steamship *Alcoa Cavalier*. On St. John, readers are informed, an old-timer has been mourned at the Lutheran Church. Hymns included *Abide with Me, We Shall Gather at the River* and *There is no Goodbye in Heaven*. A vast multitude filed by the casket.

When news is lacking, the editors of 1947 *Virgin Islands' Daily News* are enterprising. A lengthy front-page article that week features the details of a local custody battle (he would return "under the influence" and beat her. He shot her in the leg and, presently, she is living with her mother). The public is also informed of a case where a woman awoke to a body on top of her. When she screamed, the body said, "Don't call out, it's me, Steve." He was last seen wearing only underpants, and the police are investigating the case.

Also that week in 1947 are a number of news items that defy the sleepy-town stereotype. Terence Todman (one day American ambassador to a half-dozen countries) has been commissioned 2nd lieutenant. Virgin Islander Andres Wheatley has won first prize in a Paris music competition for execution and general artistry. Doris Galiber (mezzo soprano) will be giving a summer concert, and J. Antonio Jarvis has just completed a play in blank verse. A V.I. veteran is pictured receiving a medal, and there is an item about local champ Kid Canton, who will be taking on visiting pugilist Battling Nelson (164 wins, 45 by KO). Also that week, a local student has been accepted at Xavier College.

These achievements are contrasted in the same pages with other events that may be more germane to the kind of Virgin Islands world Jimmy Merced was born into. In one case that week, a man has stabbed himself in the chest with an ice pick after a disagreement with his mother. In another, a woman has been brutally beaten with a broomstick and a third has ended her life in a rage of jealousy. Bones found on St. John may help solve the mystery of a missing girl. A Tortola convict has escaped after seriously wounding a woman with a machete. Certain residents are complaining about stones falling on their roofs at night. An eight-year-old boy has stolen two dollars to buy a BB gun, and another boy, 14, has wounded a boy, 16, in the head with a stone. At the Normandie Bar, a man accused of tickling his friend has been beaten over the head with a 2x4. This is one week in 1947, all in a town of less than 15,000.

In those microfilmed pages, I am surprised to find both the Apollo and Center Theatre already well established. That week in 1947, at the Center Theatre one could see (for 20 cents) a twin bill: *Lady on a Train* starring Deanna Durbin, "Lovely Deanna on a manhunt — her most delicious role," and *Deadline at Dawn* — "a pulse-pounding romantic crime drama." At the Apollo Theatre readers are told not to miss the twin bill of *The Monster and the Ape* (Episode 7) and *Heading West*, featuring plenty of gun slinging. Later in the week the Apollo has an unusual offering — *Night in Moscow* with Laurence Olivier followed by *Saps at Sea* with Stan Laurel and Oliver Hardy.

A newspaper ad informs residents they can fly to Puerto Rico on dependable DC-3s for a round trip fare of twelve dollars. The corner store is doing well, it seems, with Betty Crocker soup now available at 49 Charlotte Amalie groceries. At Walter Pennyfeather's Emporium, north of Bakery Square, there are ties, belts, shirts and school supplies available.

On the facing page, an editorial compares our Virgin Islands' 1848 slave uprising with the American Revolution. In 1776, while Americans were celebrating their freedom, Virgin Islanders were still living under Danish colonial rule. Runaway slave leaders, the article informs readers, were to be pinched three times with red-hot iron, then hung. A regular runaway was to lose a leg or (if his master wished) an ear with 150 "stripes." If you were black, upon meeting a white you were to step aside. The article also bows to the women of Frederiksted who, led by "Queen Mary," marched into town with straw and matches and threatened to burn the island to its foundations.

Alongside this 1947 editorial is an ad for Pepsi with the bottle in the hands of a winsome blonde in a low-cut dress. Another blonde sells Ponds for "ungreasy kissable lips." The price of Milk Stout is going up to six cents a bottle, but Pepsi is holding at five.

I don't recall my father's departure to St. Thomas. Perhaps I shut it out or maybe we were so accustomed to his regular departures to Poughkeepsie that only the duration of his time away brought the loss into focus. He was setting things up for us. Life went on and weeks turned into months, and the house seemed to grow smaller. My mother, who worked part-time at a real estate firm, was in charge of selling the house, but she wasn't getting many bites. Because Pam and I were at school, we never saw the people who were supposed to have looked at the house but would hear some days later that they'd found something else. I wonder now whether Mom was really putting her heart into the island move, or hedging her bets.

We still went through the winter routine. I remember dancing school, held Wednesday evenings at the Rye Country Day School gym, white gloves de rigueur — the waltz, the fox trot, the lindy, the Mexican hat dance and (the only one I could get the hang of) the bunny-hop. We were trained to say our hellos and to save our complaints of stepped on toes for the ride home. Pam had recently progressed beyond discussing toes, and the issue now was where her partner placed his hand. Ever since my older sister had shamed her into a training bra, Pam preferred the boy's hand on the small of the back. Her impatience with partners whose hand went too high was lessened a bit after a new student — a swarthy ninth grader with whiskers — put his hand too low.

Usually Mom and Pop were there in the balcony with the other parents at the end of the session, but that winter with Pop gone Mom came alone to pick us up. She kept smiling through the balcony scene for a while, but Pop's continued absence inspired too many polite wonderings and rehearsed answers. Soon she started waiting for us in the car.

Another weekly social event was Sunday service at Christ Church. Pam and I were both in the choir as were other friends and relatives. After the service, we were trotted off to Sunday school taught by a sweet high schooler named Candy. Candy was the pubescent niece of Reverend Thornton Withers and had, in recent months, given added meaning to her assortment of V-neck sweaters. She read to us from a book that showed pictures of colorful miracles: Jacob's ladder, David and Goliath, Daniel and the Lion's den, blue-eyed shepherd boys and their blue-eyed sheep. Candy even showed us, her pert red lips mouthing the letters, how to J-e-s-u-s spell Jesus.

It seems the last couple of years in Rye my parents spent the two hours of service and Sunday school reading the *Herald Tribune* on the living room floor — or at least that is what they were up to when we got back. I wonder now about their choice to stop going to church. The subject comes to mind because of a letter discovered while sorting through some of my mother's belongings after her death. The letter was in a small envelope that bore the insignia of Christ Church. I expected to find a copy of a baptism or confirmation certificate because it was in a box of other assorted keepsakes. Instead, it was a letter. A quick glance at the bottom showed me it was from the Reverend Thornton Withers himself.

August 13, 1956

Dear Mr. Wilson,

Not only have you been a regular member of the church, but you have also been a faithful usher in recent years. However, your disgraceful conduct at our recent church supper has prompted several longstanding members of our parish to remind you that these suppers are not designed for members to overindulge to the extent that their presence becomes an embarrassment to others.

In closing, I only hope that your future conduct more closely reflects your presence during our Sunday morning services.

Sincerely,
Rev. Thornton Withers

I wonder about my mother's choice to save this letter, to tuck it away. I am also curious about the exact nature of my father's "disgraceful conduct" and wonder at a more distant remove whether this letter, this event, might have been partially responsible for my parents' decision not to attend services, or even part of what soured my father on Rye. Some misjudgment or over-reaction, some social snit that put his nose out of joint.

Questions about the nature of my parents' relationship never much occurred to me until we had actually moved to St. Thomas where certain events forced the issue. Like most sons, I was inclined to worship the heroics of the father and to see my mother in relation to them. She was devoted to my father; I seemed to know that much. Later, when I did grow more curious about her, I learned from Pam that my father had not been the answer to my grandparents' hopes for their Greenwich daughter's bright future, not the kind of match that would help reverse the Lippincotts' diminishing fortunes. When she developed a crush on him, they were both only 15. This time in my parents' life would have been hard to imagine had it not been for a certain discovery.

One summer afternoon at my uncle's house in Rye (I must have been

visiting in my mid-20s) while putting away a trunk in the attic, I spied a
stack of old picture albums. I pulled a chair up to the attic window. Most
of the albums were from my aunt's side of the family, but in one album
of snapshots mounted on black construction paper I recognized my
mother's handwriting, her neat white lettering identifying people in the
photos. This was her album, a kind of baby book, but one that followed
her all the way through graduation. I examined each page, seeing my
mother before she married my father, proof (I seemed really to need it)
that she had once been truly young and very pretty. Here is Mom, age
four, hugging a lamb named Wully. Here again looking wobbly on a bike,
her parents on their Greenwich lawn measuring her progress. In many of
the early photos there is a dog — a Scotty named Orville, a Great Dane
named Jaguar, an unidentified Dachshund and a shepherdy-looking mutt
named Robbie. In the more posed pictures, she is often at the end of a
descending line of older brothers and, below, her letters: Harlen, Sandy,
Tobias, Sam, me.

At about age twelve the photos begin to show the young lady. In one
she is coy on a summer swing in Mattapoisett. In another she is a thousand miles away in Vero Beach among adults. A third shows her in
Provincetown. The photo is of the weathered carcass of a large sailing
vessel beached long ago in a storm. From the forward hatch peeks my
mother at 13, her eyes bright with this little adventure, a world turning
to driftwood.

Further on in the album she is attending Miss Porters, a Connecticut
boarding school. One snapshot shows her in a playful mood lying on the
grass in a light sweater and wool skirt. She is on her stomach, her elbows
propping her up, her legs bent at the knees so that her uplifted soles form
a stool upon which a classmate sits holding Mom's hair as one might reins.
In another it is summer again and her head, shoulders and arms show
above a worn wooden fence. A strap over a shoulder and another loose
over an arm suggest a bathing suit. Her hair is tousled and a bare limb
shows over the fence. There is a sultry, sun-drenched look about her.

Two of the last pages of the album in my uncle's attic show my mother with friends lounging on the dorm steps in their graduation gowns.
There is much camaraderie and clowning in this series. My mother's feet

are of particular interest, here crossed in a casual, carefree way, there coy and turned out, but never truly flush on the floor. In one photo the others smile at the camera but Mom's eyes are averted, preoccupied. She might, amidst all the gaiety, be remembering something sad or far away. Thumbing through those black pages, I see in her eyes the same doleful look of her childhood dogs being held in place for the camera.

The album ended with those graduation photos. If one were to add a few more pages to that album the mood would change. In a matter of months a careless bit of lovemaking would lead to premature vows, and an unfamiliar world would descend overnight. Old friends of my parents have assured me that sooner or later they would have been married anyway. Perhaps. I only regret that it was sooner, that their lives were derailed by that microscopic event of biology. But without that misfortune, I would not be here to wonder or lament.

One day in March, two months before our departure to the islands, Bobby VanCleave told his classmates he was leaving and a week later he was gone. Back to California. His sudden disappearance seemed to confirm my own. I had a recurring dream in which I found myself swooping beneath our dogwood tree and ascending, already flying away. I had created a vision of my future self — something I borrowed from a newsreel — with me on the tarmac turning to wave to my assembled friends before entering the silver fuselage. I was creating a memory of an event that had not yet occurred, and there was a bit of daring-do as I waved to the flashing cameras in my new blue suit and tie-up shoes.

That spring I began to spend more time at the dump. With Bobby gone and other friends soon to be lost, these excursions became private outings with Mom packing me a sandwich. I think she thought I was going down to the ballfield or the park, but it was the dump I liked the best. I had developed a fondness for discards, an empathy for castaways. Some days I'd smuggle home a wayward sneaker or a broken clock, or rescue other items drifting to oblivion while still feeling for the rusty spring, the frozen padlock, the things passed over. Certain items I assigned to a hollow in the woods beyond left field and beside the old Purdy gravesite where an ancient oak offered rest. From a low limb I could hear the faint sounds of spring training and speculate further on the ways of worms and graveyards.

A final memory from that spring of getting ready to fly away was the revelation that there were drawings of near-naked women in the house.

"Where?" I asked my sister.

"I shouldn't tell you."

"Please."

"I'll give you a hint. Laundry."

Laundry. The only thing I knew about laundry was that at times it hung from lines out back. It seemed like an unlikely spot for drawings of naked women, but I went there anyway and parted the grass, looked behind the gas cylinders and across the path for any evidence of something buried. It suddenly occurred to me that Pam could have made it up and was, at that instant, peering out the kitchen window, laughing. I went back in.

She was still reading.

"There aren't any pictures," I announced.

"Didn't take you long to look, did it?" she said with a smile.

"They're not there," I repeated.

"Where'd you look?"

"By the clothesline."

"Not *there*, Willie. By the washer and the sink. In the cellar."

The *cellar*!

The cellar was where the furnace was. It was also home to an expensive toy electric train that turned boring circles on the rare occasions that I chose to start it up. In one corner of the cellar was a small bar and a dusty piano and, on the walls, weathered posters of European saloons — the whole set-up a totem, I think, to my father's war years. In the corner beneath the stairs was the washing machine, a workbench and some drawers. First I looked in the washing machine. No naked ladies there. Then, with trembling hands, I opened the top drawer. Nails, screws, hinges, sandpaper.

This could still be a trick. In the second drawer, there are saw blades and bar items. I am thinking of Annette Funicello hiding in my basement when I open the third — to disappointing prospects: rags, instruction manuals, a calendar. I turn the calendar over.

There, in living color is a luscious blond automotive assistant, her sleeves rolled up, a smudge on her cheek beside her pouty red lips. Her fingers are wrapped around a lube gun, and the straps of her lavender overalls are set wide to accommodate her breasts causing her nipples to strain against the delicate fabric of an old and rather damp T-shirt. A quick flip through the calendar reveals the other months and their automotive themes. I put the calendar back the way it was, and with racing pulse, tiptoed up the cellar stairs. I peeked into the living room. Pam was still reading. I had not played with my electric train in months because its numbing circles tired me, but I now took renewed interest in going into the cellar to switch it on. Those women in their smoldering automotive circumstances helped a bit to reconcile the grim facts of life as expounded by Pam with my own pillow-kissing ardors.

In May, a few weeks before we were to set off to the land of the glass-bottom boat, my father made the mistake of sending us a picture of our future house. I have only the vaguest recollection of seeing this photo (Pam reminded me of it), choosing perhaps to ignore it. Pam could not afford to. Until that time, she had maintained a composed, rather muscular attitude toward the future. The photo was like a kick in the solar plexus. Any house in Port Chester would stand like a palace next to this, our future domicile. It was a peeling three-story structure (the landlord on the bottom), tin roof with gutters, a sagging balcony, the front steps onto the street over an open gutter. The letter, which accompanied the photo, spoke of the place in rather glowing terms. In fairness, we too would come to like the place after a few months of tropical conditioning.

Once we got the plane tickets the house began to feel like it was afloat, and we, like survivors in a lifeboat, adrift. June 16th was set as our departure date. With school out, there was nothing left to keep us there. As the final days ticked away, Mom started to lose it. I was not, at my age, and with my own worries, really aware of this. I only remember the little yellow pills she was supposed to take and how her two brothers were helping give her the final push — Harlen seeing to the sale of the house and Sam to the packing and shipping of our belongings. There were boxes on the floor at the end and the grandfather clock lay in a crate, and the spirit of the house seemed to be lifting away. The china was wrapped in white paper and when the paintings were pulled from the wall, the faint ghost on the wallpaper showed where they had hung.

When I imagine myself those last days in Rye, when I create a memory of that time, I think of things like pillowcases and pajamas, Little League practice and Playland. I imagine the dogwood tree to be in blossom, though I doubt it was. It is the memory thing of what is real and imagined. I imagine my head still comforted by a feather pillow and my dreams populated by cemetery Quakers. I imagine, also, something like an angel watching over me. It is the Angel of Things to Come. In the silent summer night beneath oaks and elms I am being rested, being made ready. Soon I will know how best to flick lizard droppings from my pillow where they have come for the mosquitoes that feast on my blood, and I will know the name of the local coffin maker and the name of the palsied man with one leg who comes to our gate. I will have learned how to filch mangoes from the neighbor's tree, and when to flush, and when not to. Soon I will pass happy hours racing corks and popsicle sticks in the gutter with a friend with skin like chocolate, and at the beach my eyes will study a certain girl in the purple bikini. At nights I will fall asleep to the sounds of the steelband a block away where my father is tending bar and just around the corner will be the house of Anton Merced and his family, and in the morning we will hear the same roosters and donkeys, and the same aroma of fresh bread from Lockhart's bakery will find its way into our rooms.

I imagine another angel of sorts watching over Jimmy Merced, another Angel of Things to Come. At that time, the summer of 1958 when we moved to St. Thomas, Jimmy was twelve years old, tall for his age and wiry. He had a job that summer working mornings with his Uncle Hugo, a heavy equipment operator, out in Bournefield where they were mending a runway apron and leveling an old barracks. After lunch he could cross the fairway of the old Navy golf course to the thicket below the water catchment and find his pony, Butterscotch. Sometimes that summer Jimmy would take Butterscotch down to Brewer's Beach for a swim. I imagine them slipping bareback into the shallows then swimming into deeper water. Butterscotch snorts and Jimmy takes her over the drop. He holds on to her neck and lets his feet float out behind him as she swims, her nostrils flared and snorting against the salty mist. The angel looks over him. Looks over Butterscotch.

That fall Jimmy would be going into the sixth grade. When Anton talks of Jimmy, these are the years he likes best to remember, before certain events in Jimmy's life and his own. He likes to recall the boy who still came to games when Anton was pitching at Lionel Roberts Stadium. The boy who was a good student, a good fisherman and hunter, a boy who was at times given licks for misbehavior. But not often. Anton says Jimmy was a good boy, and one who never lied.

The subject of lying had come up between Anton and me on a number of occasions. We had talked about the art of the lie, and lies sometimes being better than the truth, and we had laughed at the lyrics of a famous calypso song about a liar. And in my early talks with Anton there was always the unstated possibility that we might be lying to each other and that I was undercover trying to get information about his son. Anton often repeated Jimmy's words spoken from his cell at Fort Christian shortly after the golf course murders. According to Jimmy, it was another group who had worn the slitted hoods and pulled the trigger on the golfers.

Once, Anton spoke of a particular jail cell conversation.

"Daddy, I didn't do it," he said, repeating his son's words.

At the time I asked Anton whether he had attended the trial and was surprised to learn he had chosen to follow events in the newspaper. Later, when I knew more, I would be able to remind him of the signed confession and the machine gun found in the outhouse. But at that time, the word "Daddy" pulled me back. Anton's words and the way he delivered them forced me to ask myself whether there was any possibility that Jimmy Merced *was* innocent. Framed in some way. Scapegoated, perhaps. My actual knowledge of the crime was pretty sketchy when it came right down to it.

At the time of the Sweet Bottom Massacre, I was 24 and living in Peru. Although I had heard only bits and pieces about what had happened, it had not prevented my mind from creating its own imagined view of events. In it, eight golfers are passing through a meadow by the side of the green when five armed men burst from a spray of bougainvillea and mow them down. For years I carried this imagined picture of events, never having cause to wonder at its accuracy. Only when required to come up with a few basic facts — found in the microfilmed pages of *The Daily News* — did I discover how far off these imaginings were.

That day in the library I chose not to go straight to the day of the crime but to delay instead with the week before, setting the scene, reminding myself what the island was like 20-odd years before. The microfiche is equipped with a clicker to advance and reverse at variable speeds. I stop in the classifieds and remember the store that used to be across from the Jolly Roger and the face of the man who sold candles by the market. I savor each image and notice, playing Father Time with the clicker, blurring the screen and stopping, blurring and stopping. A moment of time, illuminated, observed, drawn back into the spool. I am wondering if there is, hidden in the listings, some silent portent. I see a follow-up article to the Munich Massacre, masked killers only the week before.

The front page on the day after the crime shows a large photo of a terrace glistening in spots as if from an afternoon shower. The pools that wander and collect are not water but blood and the tiny white flecks in the pools are golf tees used to identify the location of the bodies. The terrace is at the clubhouse on the 18th hole placing the crime not on the putting green as I had pictured it.

Further "memory" corrections: The eight killed are not all golfers, nor are they all male, nor all white. Three victims are women. There is an electrician who happened to be doing some rewiring with his black Kittitian helper, also murdered. One of the dead is a woman in the pro shop who was filling in for a vacationing friend. Another is a groundskeeper. I look for the eyewitnesses identifying Merced but find none. The five were wearing fatigues and black hoods with eyeslits, making positive identification impossible. And the group is not quickly apprehended in the way I had imagined it. A week after the crime Merced and two others last seen entering the bush, are still at large — this despite an islandwide manhunt with 150 police, FBI agents, sharpshooters, SWAT teams and helicopters combing an island of less than 80 square miles, much of it criss-crossed with roads and dotted with neighborhoods.

Sitting in that library, twenty-odd years after the event, my mind speculates across the landscape. I see Jimmy in the bush hiding in the hollows of an old tamarind tree as the helicopter passes overhead. He is older than the boy I knew, a hybrid Jimmy made from memory and photos. He is in big trouble. I see him scrambling up a gut, and when he turns to look back I cannot make out his face and I remember how, even as a child, I often mistook him for someone else. He is already beginning to disappear.

FACES IN THE WELL

—◊—

First Flight

O ur flight to the islands left New York's LaGuardia Airport
around mid-morning, a DC-6 to San Juan. I don't recall too
much except that, unlike my boyish reverie of waving to the
assembled well-wishers, I entered the silver fuselage with no fanfare. This
was my first time in a plane, a big four-engine prop at that, bigger even
than the B-24 my father had flown during the war. There was very little
English being spoken by the passengers. My mother was sedated and my
sister had instructions to remind her to take another Miltown about an
hour before landing in San Juan. The cabin door closed, and one by one
the engines were started and the pilot came on with certain instructions,
which were followed by translation and a life jacket demonstration. As
the engines powered up for the final taxi, the corpulent señora across the
aisle broke out the rosaries and started into her Hail Marys. Later in
the flight, the same lady would expose a big brown nipple to silence a
crying child.

The landing in San Juan touches off an explosion of applause and cheering. At the sweltering baggage claim area throngs of relatives press against the security bars shouting greetings and instructions. They are here to welcome the missing ones, to hear stories of life up north. I am still wearing my blue suit and tie, my lace-up shoes that were meant to complete the picture of my newsreel departure. The connecting flight to St. Thomas does not leave for another three hours due to a shortage of passengers, but we have our luggage and seats on the 7:15 flight. Slowly, the airport empties. We sit on a bench. I fish my sneakers out of a bag and roll up my jacket and tie and stuff them in where the sneakers came out. I wonder now what a photograph of the three of us would have to say about our mood. For my mother, who chose not to take the second Miltown, it was a time of reckoning. Although she has at least seen the island and has some physical sense of what awaits her, there are other concerns. It seems that sitting there I might have had a thought or two of my own, but my capacity for the unfamiliar had already been exhausted and I'd surrendered to the not knowing, left to think instead about the coin jammed in the airport soda machine and the money already lost at the candy machine, where familiar faces — *Hershey's, Chuckles, Milky Way* — called to me from behind the glass but failed to appear when the lever was pulled. The candy wrappers offer me silent assurances that I have not yet fallen off the planet.

Our connection to St. Thomas is aboard a sturdy Caribair DC-3 — board in the rear and walk uphill toward the nose. When the plane lifts off, San Juan spreads like a wide blanket of light beneath us. When the wheels touch down again in half an hour, I will see my father for the first time in six months. Looking out the window, the comforting twinkle gives way to a string of scattered lights along the coast, distant pockets glowing inland, and, beyond those, the faint silhouette of a mountain range. Soon Puerto Rico falls away and we enter the darkness. Only one light remains, a small red one near the cockpit door, and all I can see in the blackened window is myself, my face framed in the red glow of the cabin. Pam is looking out her window as well, and no one has anything to say.

Before long the pilot starts to feather the engines and the pit of my stomach feels the belly of the plane begin to drop. We are going down but there are no lights. The plane drops and levels, drops and levels. Still no light. Where is the island? I begin to wonder, fearing the plane is running out of fuel. Soon the landing lights go on and I can see dark water rushing beneath the sleepy propeller blades that seem to spin in reverse. The water is coming closer and closer, faster and faster. I feel the squeeze of my mother's hand. Then, at the last possible second, the wing crosses a dirt threshold. Lights. Runway. First one wheel, then the other give a quick screech on the tarmac and the tail comes down and we're rolling. We speed past a big metal hanger. In the slanting light of the hanger I think I see my father. He seems to be wearing shorts and a brightly-colored shirt.

The drive into town is in the back of a jeep, Pam and I sitting facing each other on the metal seats, the luggage and George Patrick, our white Persian, in a cat carrier between our knees. There are few lights. I see palm trees, overturned boats, tin shacks. Along the waterfront, large sailboats and cargo line the apron. My father is pointing something out, and I nod because the jeep is too loud to hear what he is saying. We enter an area that is clearly town, and Pop turns into a section of buildings and trees. Left again and a corridor of buildings closes in. Then a right heading even deeper into it. At the second corner, we turn onto a roller coaster hill and halfway up come to a stop.

"We're home," my father announces yanking the emergency brake. "Watch out for the gutter."

The house I fear is ours, is. It is a three-story structure, the bottom floor (the landlord's) masonry, the top two wood. It has a lopsided look to it brought on in part by the slant of the street. This is the house captured in the photo Mom had shown Pam. The stoop in front of the gate arches over the gutter. The gate is wrought iron and painted a dusty green. Negotiating the luggage across the street and up the stairs I am in a geography book, a faraway slum where clotheslines color the sky. My father is just now reaching through a broken louver to open the front door from the inside. The door swings wide to reveal the living room of my new home. There are no rugs and nothing hangs on the walls.

Everything smells of fresh paint. The boards on the floor are gray, the walls white. There are two straw chairs and a straw mat. The dining room table has shiny aluminum legs.

"The place will look like something just as soon as the furniture gets here," my father assures us.

"What's out here?" Pam asks.

"Our very own balcony. Very fancy."

We all go out on it and immediately the landlord's chained mongrel in the yard below starts to snarl and bark. Next we are shown the kitchen and, beside it, a pantry that can also serve as an extra bedroom. A huge cockroach scurries into the rusted bottom of a prized freezer. To the side of the stairs leading up from the living room is a bathroom with blistered cement walls that are covered with a dark red paint. My father points to a fixture clamped to the showerhead.

"This little gizmo will give us hot water just as soon as its fixed. And this," he said with a nod to the stairs, "is Mabel."

A slinky black cat stops on the landing, takes one look at the situation, and continues on its way.

"Mabel just walked in one day," my father explains.

"I wonder if George Patrick will like her," Pam mused.

"Cut from different bolts," my father said. "Still, the local toms find her charms quite irresistible."

From the landing the stair turns up another ten steps to the wide second-floor hall. First door on the right: Pam's room. A bed, a table, a light. On the wall, a travel poster. A second door leads to my room. A single bulb hangs on a wire from the ceiling. A mattress on a fold-up bedspring. Two windows looking onto the street. New, sill-high shelves along one wall. Fresh paint everywhere. A second door opens onto the hall. Across the hall is my parent's bedroom and a white-tiled bathroom with a tub but no shower.

After soup and sandwiches we are sent upstairs to bed. Pam and I exchange our first under-our-breath comments about the accommodations and say goodnight. I turn out my dangling light bulb and go sit on the shelf by the windows and stare out. It is my first chance to really look. There is the jeep. I see the canvas top is torn in parts and the front bumper has huge carbuncles of rust and the license plate is secured with a piece of wire. There is the gutter — deeper on the far side of the street, forming a kind of moat around a building, which, because of the boarded-up shutters, appears to be abandoned, a tumble of green growing beneath the eaves and clinging to the downspout. There is no more than a foot of space between that building and the one beside it. At the corner, a single streetlight shows where one steep road intersects our street so that a car turning there would go from steep uphill to steep downhill with a turn of the wheel. The street is very narrow, no sidewalks. I hear voices and soon two men and a boy pass our gate and turn down the steep side street. They are black. There is laughter and I wonder about it. I get up and in the half-light from the street take a few things from my suitcase and put them on the shelves. My shirts and socks seem lost on so vast an open expanse, so different from the cozy bureau drawers in Rye. The room itself is bigger than my room in Rye, stark and hollow, and, like my socks I feel dwarfed by the emptiness around me. I lie on my bed for the first time and the springs make the metallic sound of my weight. The streetlight casts a pattern on the ceiling. I listen for some sound coming from Pam's room and wonder if she too is staring at the ceiling.

Then I hear the cry of a child. I go to the window, but the street is empty and I figure someone has just passed carrying a crying infant. I return to my bed and the crying starts again and I jump to the window and again see nothing. But then there is a terrible prolonged cry. It is coming from the gutter. Clearly, someone has abandoned an infant in the gutter and I am hearing its death-cry. I go into the hall. Light still shows beneath the door to my parent's room. From the hall I tell my father about the child in the gutter.

"It's not a child," he replies. "What you're hearing is a cat."

This is not a cat, I am certain.

"No it isn't. It's a baby. Come listen."

Just then a blood-curdling cry went up, joined by another, equally frightening wail.

"Cats don't sound like that," I say. Cats meow.

"They do down here. Now go to bed."

The strange sounds that I fell to sleep with were there in the morning in the form of donkeys and roosters whose calls bore little resemblance to the barnyard hee-haws and cock-a-doodle-dos I had been led to believe in. Then came the bells. Somewhere up the valley bells sounded non-stop for what seemed an hour. It was Sunday. I heard sounds coming from Pam's room so I knocked and went in. She was finishing making her bed. Neither of us had heard any movement from our parent's room so we sat like hostages behind her closed door and spoke in whispers until we heard footsteps going downstairs.

"That's the Mad Bellringer," my father explained in answer to Pam's question about the bells.

"Who's the Mad Bellringer?" I asked.

"Someone who has spent too much time in a belfry," he replied. "Look, I need to concentrate on breakfast. Why don't you two take a walk or something. Breakfast will be ready in about 15 minutes."

Pam chooses to do some unpacking upstairs and I venture onto the landing outside the front door and stand looking over a bleak windowbox filled with rubbery-looking shrubs. Mabel is curled up on the wall in a spot of sunlight, snoozing off a wild night. Overhead, along a stretch of power line, alien tufted plants grow without roots, with no connection to the earth and confirm the strangeness of this new world. Nothing in the street seems particularly inviting. Does my father's suggestion to take a walk mean to actually venture *outside*? I wonder.

"You have to give the gate a good yank," he calls from the kitchen as if in answer to my question.

I walk down the few brick stairs, give the iron gate a yank and step outside. Summoning my courage, I hazard across the street to peer into the gutter, site of last night's cat wars. This street called Crystal Gade is even steeper than I thought, and from the street I can see that not all of the houses are like ours. Most are made of stone and appear to be quite old and well kept. At the bottom of the hill, the street disappears into rooftops scattered across the floor of the valley. I go up the street to where it connects with the cross street going down and see for the first time a bright and unfamiliar blue, a chunk of harbor. Floating in it, framed on either side by buildings and galvanized rooftops, is a huge ship anchored in the bay but looking in size and direction as if it is coming right up the street. The ship is green, a freighter I suspect judging from the thicket of cargo booms and cranes sprouting from its deck. It is fair in size as freighters go, and its bow wears a trail of rust seeping from the eye socket where the anchor usually hangs. It has been to distant lands I feel, and though I have no real knowledge of such things, I like the ship's lines and what its bulk and rust seem to be saying to me. The message, if I could have decoded it at the time, was roughly this: Despite the aging jeep, the empty shelves, the strange animal sounds and all the other uncertainties, this place, this island, this new world offered the prospect of adventure. I remember that view, that feeling, that sense of impending adventure. And it has only recently occurred to me that the foreground of that very picture would have included a house — small, yellow, wooden, second one on the left — belonging to the family of Anton Merced.

The rest of the day was closely choreographed, perhaps to ease our misgivings by putting the island in the best possible light. We drove into the hills above town for a panoramic view of the harbor and then headed east into the country. We saw herds of goat, mango trees, people in their Sunday best, roads in desperate need of repair (Pop brought a couple of boat cushions to soften our bouncing on the metal seats), and stunning vistas of distant islands. At a point far to the east, we pulled into a beach where the trees parted and an iridescent blue jumped out at me, and I didn't immediately realize what it was. It was water. The blue was edged with sand that looked like sugar. Another feature of this beach was the number of white people who congregated at the bar and along the terrace, and I suspect now that our going there was meant to give us a reassuring sense of the world we had come from.

By the end of the afternoon I had snorkeled over a reef, eaten a West Indian meat pate, seen an iguana, the pulsing dewlap of a lizard, a darting mongoose, several well-appointed bikinis and an inebriated dowager being shoveled into her waiting car. I had witnessed the bloated body of a dead dog, the tumescent shape of a termite nest, the circling of a chicken hawk and the plunging artistry of a pelican. I had also walked alongside an American warship. On the ride home my father stopped at a local roadside bar to get a beer and asked me to come in ostensibly to help carry something to the car. But there wasn't anything to carry. I think my father wanted to measure my reaction to this rather squalid structure and to show me there was nothing to fear in this strange new environment, this unknown culture. The friendly man who served us was named Webster, and the Happy Inn Bar and Rest was clearly a regular watering hole for my father's return trips from the beach. The glass display case contained jars of familiar sweets in a sticky state. The walls were covered with metal signs for Malta and Tennants Milk Stout and Coke and 7-Up. In the corner were two ice coolers — one for beer, the other for soft drinks. I noticed light could be seen through cracks in the wall. Mr. Webster asked me how old I was, whether or not I was a good student and if I liked girls. I lied about girls, and he smiled and said, "All in good time, M'child", and winked at Pop. Mr. Webster, I noticed, was missing two fingers from his left hand. He also had a notch gone from his right ear, eyes that were red and clouded over with cataracts, and more than a few missing teeth. Mr. Webster shook my hand, offered me a Mary Jane, and wished me well.

"With God help you go grow to love this island of ours," he smiled.

Of all the stops that day, of all the sights and new experiences, Mr. Webster and the Happy Inn taught me the most.

That night Jack and Doris, two of my father's friends, came for cocktails and supper. Pop laid the flank steak my mother brought from the States right on the coals and, along with it, the tail of a lobster he'd caught a few days before. After that, the drinking kicked in, and Pam and I said our goodnights and went up to our rooms. Before she closed her door, Pam said something that stayed with me. It was about Pop's red-haired lady friend downstairs.

"Didn't you think she was rather friendly?"

"Uh-huh."

"Toward Pop I mean."

I took in the probable meaning of this remark.

"I guess. But he wouldn't like her." This said more like a question.

"Oh really. Why is that?"

"She's kind of fat, isn't she?"

"Lively too." She raised the eyebrow. "I'm going to sleep."

I was tired and unlike the night before had no trouble falling asleep. But I was awakened later by the same cat business as the night before. This time I was prepared. A small pile of stones was neatly placed by the window sill for just this occasion.

But instead of throwing in the direction of the sound right away, I took time to really listen. Two cats were arguing. One, on closer examination, was clearly the tortured voice of a cat. The other was still the sound of the dying child. There was a certain beauty to this primal conversation, but the pitch was moving toward a fight. I lobbed a stone in the direction of the noise, and for a second the sounds stopped. Then they resumed at a terrifying pitch, and I put some zing into the throw and heard the stone ricochet in the gutter. I followed it with another and another until the sounds stopped and the cats went away.

It was some days later that the landlord stopped me on my way out the gate. The people around the corner had complained about someone firing rockstones at night. I probably denied any knowledge of this and, at that time, would have had no way of knowing what neighbors he was referring to. But all these years later, the memory of that conversation has resurfaced and offered an unexpected slant. Given the stones' trajectory and the ricocheting properties of that gut, it's fairly likely the complaint came from the Merced family. Where, I wonder now, did I think those missed throws and ricochets went to? Because I couldn't see around the corner and because I probably exercised the judgment typical of most ten-year-olds, I didn't give it much thought. But I see now, over 40 years later, how within 48 hours of our arrival on St. Thomas I may have unwittingly managed to antagonize the neighbors, the family of Anton Merced.

Our second day on the island, Monday, was not as tightly choreographed as the day before. Being a workday, it was, for better or worse, our first opportunity to see the boatyard and the much-imagined boat with the bottom of glass.

The day got off to a rocky start when my father, eager to show us the wonders of having a maid, introduced us to Ida who was instructed to make breakfast. We had never had a maid in Rye, and I was having some difficulty balancing the conflicting images of poverty and wealth. The eggs came out first, scrambled, but the bacon, which Ida had been instructed to "cook," took longer. Ida was from Tortola and on Tortola, we were soon to learn, cook means boil. My father, his show of domestic niceties ebbing, grew impatient once the eggs were consumed. He explained to Ida that the idea was to serve the bacon and eggs at the same time.

"I sorry Mr. Wilson, the bacon ain' finish cook as yet."

"Well, we're in a rush so bring it the way it is."

One seldom has the opportunity to see a pound of bacon that has been boiled a long time. Drained, it is something otherworldly, a white and gelatinous semi-transparent pudding. Something to draw back from and grimly dispose of.

Pop carried his breakfast table mood to the jeep for our drive to the boatyard. His jaw was set. Mom and Pam were sympathetic to Ida's failings; it was a matter of language. Mom found the whole thing laughable. Imagine poor Ida, told to boil the bacon. What wretched creatures we must appear to be.

The boatyard was located two miles west on the airport road. When we left the house it was not yet eight o'clock but town was already humming with activity. Shopkeepers were opening their doors. On the waterfront, small crowds of people brought fresh fish while cargo loaders stacked boxes on the waterfront apron and stray dogs sniffed around looking for handouts. At the west end of the waterfront, we passed through Frenchtown, a cluster of shacks and fishermen's shanties, and further west, the cemetery. The closer we drew to the boatyard, the less promising the environment became. Pam and I exchanged looks in the back of the jeep, but I still held out hope that the bumpy road would miraculously deliver us to a glistening white cabin cruiser with a Cinderella bottom of glass.

At a bend in the road, Pop turned off the potholed asphalt road to a bumpier dirt one. He got out of the jeep and unlocked the gate of a chainlink fence. On the fence was a large sign, light blue with red letters:

Virgin Islands Pleasure Boats
Glassbottom trips at 10, 11, 2, 3, and 4 o'clock.
Harbor Cruise, Skiing, Water Sports.
Call 932.

The dirt road was bordered by towering guinea grass over six feet tall, making the boatyard invisible from the road. About 200 yards down the rutted track, this jungle parted to reveal, at last, the family business. By most measures, the boatyard was a pretty unpromising thing to behold. The main building was about 30 feet long, plywood on a 2x4 frame. Out front, was a small covered terrace and bar and, leading out from it, the dock. Inside, there were nautical maps on the wall, a display case with a shell collection, and a small side office with a swinging waist-high door. There was also a small bathroom and, out back, an equipment room with diving gear, ropes, anchors, and an engine or two in a state of repair or being cannibalized for parts. There was no gleaming cabin cruiser anywhere to be found, but there were, in various states of repair, a total of six different hulls in the water.

My father set about being busy, self-conscious I suspect, as his family — absent for six months — took silent stock of the situation. Yesterday we had been treated to a taste of the icing; now we were beholding the underlying cake. While Pop opened doors, got the cashbox out of the safe and brought several canvas chairs from inside, we sat on the terrace feeling somehow in the way. The obvious thing to do — I now realize — was to show interest, to go out on the dock and look at the boats, to lend a helping hand, to utter an enthusiastic word. And why none of us chose to do those things, I can't say. Perhaps it was because I had never been to a place like this. Maybe there was danger on the dock or rules about children going out on it or one of us would do something wrong and be scolded for it. He was in a grumpy enough mood. Perhaps in this setting my father was feeling more acutely the weight of having made the decision to come to the islands, to sell our house, to leave our friends, to expose ourselves to incalculable risk, and the whirlwind of purpose he was presenting to us was designed to obscure those facts. But he must have wondered at our inability to respond, to say something nice, or better, to be thrilled with the adventure, to charge uncontrollably on to the dock to gee and golly all over the place. What was required was a short period of adjustment.

"Which one has the glassbottom?" I thought finally to ask.

"The two tied to the dock," he answered, disappearing out back.

When I looked I realized how pathetic the question was; both boats had, written on the stern, Glassbottom I and Glassbottom II. Pop swept out with an armful of boat cushions.

"Why don't you take these out to Glassbottom II," he said to me. Then, turning to Pam, "You could sponge the table and the top of the bar." Then he asked Mom to lend a hand with sweeping the terrace, this said with a trace of annoyance — for not volunteering fast enough, perhaps.

I took the cushions and walked out on the lumpy concrete pier — the concrete had been poured atop a long pile of stones — to the small wooden dock that extended out from it. Glassbottom II was on the left side, smaller than I had imagined it, its gunwale below the level of the dock. I looked in. My heart sank. The bottom of the boat was wood, not glass. Under a covered midsection, benches were arranged around a table. Had I made some mistake? Rather than ask a stupid question, I checked the other boat on the opposite side of the dock. It was older but of a similar construction and it, too, had no bottom of glass. I returned to the first boat and put the cushions on the benches and looked to see if the floor could somehow be raised to reveal glass below. It could not. Only at that point did I become suspicious of the central table which was more like a large box. I heard my father call something out and, looking back, saw a large, muscular black man striding out on the dock with an outboard motor in each hand. He was singing *Rock of Ages* — double time.

"Good morning, Mister Willie."

"Good morning."

"My name is Salvador — Sal for short. Let me just put these motor in."

"You want me to get out?" I asked.

"No, just step to the bow."

When he stepped aboard, his weight and the weight of the two outboards caused the entire boat to list. He lifted a rear hatch and exposed the transom, then attached first one and then the other engine. Sal wore only tattered shorts and a pair of flip-flops. He was hugely muscular, the kind of muscles I had seen only in Superman comics.

"Those engines look heavy," I said.

"They only look so. One day you could lift them, too."

That day, I was certain, would never come.

He finished tightening the clamps and said he was going for the gas tanks. Then he noticed the cushions.

"Is you put the cushion them out so nice?"

I nodded.

"That's good. You do a good job."

"Sal? This is the glassbottom boat?"

"Yes. What, you ain see the glass up to now?"

"No."

"Man, come let me take this cover off for you," he said. He lifted the tabletop which was hinged in the center and stowed it forward with the anchor.

"See it there."

There it was, a rectangular piece of glass about 3x6 feet. Through it I could see what looked like mud. Sal stood to one side, hands on hips, like a proud father.

"I going for the gas tanks," he said stepping on to the dock.

I stared into the well at my own reflection. This was it. The glassbottom. A small silver fish swam through my head and disappeared into the near side of the glass. In the far corner, a crab of some sort burrowed beneath a shard of tin sending up a small brown billow. I looked back at the boatyard. My father had commandeered the broom from my mother who was, in turn, standing to one side of a barge-like boat drawn up on shore. Large faded letters on the barge's stern spelled its name: *Love Junk*.

No one showed for the nine o'clock except the captain, a sandy-haired 40-ish Nova Scotian named Dan McDougal. Dan, I would later learn, had all the requisite skills of a glassbottom captain — a license, a vague idea of how to fix an outboard, the ability to pilot the boat over two area shipwrecks, and a limited knowledge of fish and coral names. Dan smoked a pipe, which showed the quaver in his hands but helped cover his breath that otherwise smelled of the Cruzan Rum he kept squirreled away in a mayo jar in a paint locker above the rotting scuba gear. After saying hellos, Dan slipped out back to tinker with an outboard while Pop led us to see something out back. There, hidden from view by the guinea grass, was a huge rectangular concrete tank which looked something like an aborted swimming pool. Above it was a timber trellis that may have once supported a roof. Some waterlogged flotsam floated in about six inches of brackish rainwater. The apparent attraction was two smallish alligators marooned on an isle of weeds in the center of the tank.

"They don't look very happy," Pam remarked.

"Alligators seldom do," my mother replied.

Just then the phone started to ring and Pop trotted across the parking lot. One of the alligators snapped at a dragonfly, and Mom, with Pop gone, allowed as how the poor creatures were a very long way from the Everglades. Later we learned the wife of a previous glassbottom captain had put them there. This woman, a former alligator wrestler in Florida, had hoped to set up a little sideshow in the parking lot.

"Four lively ones for the eleven o'clock," Pop called across the parking lot.

At about 10:30 Dan emerged from the equipment shed looking very nautical in a white shirt with epaulets. At the same time Sal went out to the glassbottom to clean the glass and roll up the canvas rain flaps. The first couple showed at about ten of eleven, looked at the shell collection and had a coke. We sat on the terrace studying a map laminated on the tabletop and Mom struck up a conversation. They were from Columbus, Ohio, on their second honeymoon. Shortly after eleven the woman asked us if we were the other passengers.

My father explained that we were family.

"Oh. We thought...you said there was a party of four and I thought ..." She looked at her watch.

"Well, the others called from Bluebeard's," my father explained, "so we'll give them a few more minutes."

The few minutes stretched on. Pam and I, feeling the couple's impatience, found things to occupy ourselves. I followed a large land crab beneath the *Love Junk* and watched it scuttle into one of the many holes surrounding the boat's hull, which brought me into my first contact with Reluctance, the yard burro. Pam, meanwhile, talked to Sal about Jesus, and Dan, puffing furiously on his pipe, headed out to check the engines. I saw him lift the lid of the transom and, after a few pulls, a cloud of blue smoke went up.

At 11:15, Pop gave up on the group of four, and we marched out and boarded the boat. With just two paying passengers — a total of five bucks — this was not a very profitable morning. Still, Pop, in an effort to console the delayed couple, instructed Dan to take the boat over both shipwrecks.

"Two shipwrecks for the price of one," my father beamed.

"Oh, well thank you very much," said the man from Ohio.

Sal cast off and the boat slid past the dock. Dan, squinting into the sun, the wind in his hair, gunned first one and then the other Evinrude, and the glass came to life. It wasn't the gleaming cabin cruiser I'd dreamed of, but it was new and exciting and my father, standing at the end of the dock, was giving us a parting wave.

"You won't see much for about five minutes," Dan said leaning forward out of the sun, his hands on the roof, his foot steering the outboard. Then, pointing toward a nearby island, "The reef we're going to look at is along the north side of Water Island."

As he said this the bottom started to fall away. We could still see vague shapes for a while but the blue deepened in the channel where we saw only the reflections of our own searching faces. The water here was about 60 feet deep we were informed, with a mostly sand bottom. This did not seem to be of great interest to the couple from Ohio. Pam gave me the pained look, and the five minutes stretched on. Finally Dan cut one of the engines and slowed the other and faint traces appeared in the glass followed by polka dots suggesting the sea urchins I had seen snorkeling the day before. Not exactly spellbinding stuff.

Then, in the space of a second, the ocean floor jumped from 60 feet to about 18 inches from the glass. A coralhead, magnified even closer, appeared ready to crash through. All four of us looked up at Dan.

"Is it always *this* close?" Pam asked.

Dan put the engine in neutral and allowed the boat to drift over the reef.

"Don't worry," he assured us, "the bottom of the boat is flat. There are always at least a couple of feet between the glass and what you're looking at."

Then he began to name the things that came into view. Antler coral, sea cucumber, yellowtail, redman, lizard fish, brain coral, old wife, angel fish, grouper, sea fan, gar, fire coral, staghorn coral, sergeant major, three-eyed butterfly, sea anemone, snapper, grunt. The glass drifted over a blue canyon where we caught sight of a barracuda and a school of tarpon. Dan spun the boat around trying to pick up the tarpon again, but they had disappeared. We drifted a while longer over a second section of reef and then headed into deeper water on our way to the first shipwreck.

No one had spoken to me about a shipwreck before. Or had they? I had in mind the fishtank miniatures I had seen — the bulging Spanish galleon, its hull spewing doubloons, the masts trailing canvas gossamers from their spars. And it was this that I was looking for when Dan slowed the engines and the speeding bottom began once again to crawl. We passed through a dense school of sprat invisibly choreographed by our twirling props, and I peered through their darting transparency looking for a mast, a crow's nest. The sprat cleared and the bottom showed.

"See anything?" Dan asked.

"No."

"We should be right on top of it."

I saw what looked like a metal pole.

"There's something," the woman said.

"Oh! There it is!" the man exclaimed.

I saw what looked like slabs of metal. Dan stepped forward to look.

"Just where I thought we were. I'll swing around and take another pass."

It took several passes to piece it together. This wreck was not a treasure galleon but a Navy supply ship that had run aground only 30 years before. The big colorless slabs were the side-plates that had, over time, collapsed from pressure and surge. Only one torqued section of the hold offered any sense of volume, and out of its looming darkness came the thick-lipped head of a huge grouper. The stern section seemed to have wandered off on its own, separated from the rest by 30 feet of sandy bottom and a scattering of wreckage — a cargo boom, a hatch cover, a spool of cable.

The second wreck lay off the northwest coast of Hassel Island. It was more recognizable than the first, and older. The name of the boat was *The Brindicate* and Dan said it had been left there by the receding tidal wave of 1867. The wooden ribs were still connected to the keel and one mighty head of brain coral, like a huge malignancy, sprouted from its belly. Further encrustations of fire coral coated the rudder and the stern. Several ribs torn from the keel had been largely digested, melding with the sea bottom. We hovered over the remains of the vessel like medical examiners at a postmortem.

After several passes of *The Brindicate* we headed back to the dock, the glass showing only a bleak sandy plain with an occasional urchin or sea cucumber. I recall feeling a bit tired, numbed by the relentless unfamiliarity of those watery depths. When I think back to that day, think of my skinny arms resting on the well of the glassbottom, my sister beside me, I remember being as struck by what I couldn't see as by what I could. The broken glimpse of a passing fishtail that slipped out of our sights pulled at our vision. With all we were given to see, we were tempted most by what we could only wonder about. To my mind, the greater mystery always seemed to linger to one side or the other of that glass, seemed always to have eluded us and, at the same time, to beckon. In this new island world we were, ourselves, like that looking glass — peering, curious, and, at the same time, unknowing. And the island, like the sea floor and the life that inhabited it, seemed to look back at our strange staring heads, disembodied at the top of the well.

16 Crystal

As far as I could see there were few neighborhood kids my age who would likely end up being my friends. I had seen in the adjoining yard and coming and going from the gate two boys, two brothers a few years younger than I. There were also two girls Pam's age who lived near the top of Crystal Gade and a few young faces around the corner in the Merced family who I had seen playing stickball in the lot across from the bakery. Certain kids tooled through the neighborhood using a stick to move a bicycle wheel along, and a crop of others danced in the vapors behind the mosquito flit truck. But I made no real effort to strike up an acquaintance with these children. I did not know their names, and they were darker and spoke a different way than I did.

The first true candidates for new friend status showed up on our doorstep a few days after our trip on the glassbottom.

"You must be Willie," one of them said.

That a white child my age on the island actually knew my name might have been reason to celebrate. Instead, it was immediate cause for suspicion. These two smiling faces were Bradley and Seth, the sons of my father's business partner, sent no doubt on an obligatory mission of welcome. They stayed as long as seemed proper and then departed with promises of future beach outings. I went to the pantry window where I could see them turn the corner and, once out of sight, heard their laughter echo up the street. Was their mirth caused by something we had said or done, I wondered, or by our predicament of living in this house? I did not know where I would find my friends in this new world, but I sensed uneasily that I had, perhaps, met my first enemies. Pam, who was older than either of them, had been quite pleasant during their visit, returning their social civilities in full. When I returned to the living room, she looked up from her book and uttered her pronouncement.

"Creeps."

One evening a few days later, Pam and I were sitting in her room when a strong beam of light shined in on us through the window. We closed the louvers and then the shutters and looked at each other. The light seemed more curious than threatening, a kind of practical joke. But who was playing the joke? The light, when we reopened the shutters a while later, was gone.

The next morning, we could see that the light had come from a porch landing at the top of a stone staircase that ascended from an alleyway adjoining our yard. Most of the house was hidden behind a wall of banana leaf, but it was clear that the house was large and well kept. That afternoon, quite by chance, I noticed a boy sitting on the top stoop tinkering with a car battery. I ran to get Pam and we hustled upstairs to her window.

"Excuse me," she called across the rooftop.

The boy looked up. He had mixed skin, copper-colored with freckles.

"Are you the person who was shining a light over here last night?" she inquired.

The boy gave us a blank look.

"Well," Pam said after taking in his silence, "if you are the person — just if — don't do it again." My sister had spoken. In our neighborhood in Rye, this order would be fair warning.

That night after dinner, the light went on again. Or, rather, a different light. If the first was powerful, then this was perhaps a car headlight hooked up to a battery, a blast of light that illuminated Pam's room like an incendiary flare that angled into the hall, out the window and onto the building across the street.

I don't recall for certain how I first crossed into friendship with Niles. I remember the event but not the specific invitation to come up. I imagine him calling across the rooftops an invitation to come over. To go to his house I would have had to leave our house and walk down Crystal Gade to an alleyway with stairs that doglegged through patches of banana leaf. At the top of the stairs was a large green wooden gate set into a concrete archway. I remember struggling with the latch and the gate opening on to a leafy landing, walls on three sides and two sets of stairs leading in separate directions. The boy stood halfway where the two stairwells converged and instructed me to latch the gate. As I struggled again with the unfamiliar latch, I sensed impatience.

"Come," the boy said.

I followed. The subject of each other's names was ignored. I was following a boy who was bigger and a year or two older than me, who knew exactly what he was up to. It occurred to me that the business of the shining light had not been settled and that the likely perpetrator was now leading me through a leafy passageway to some unknown place.

"Wait here," he ordered.

He headed down a kind of courtyard and disappeared into a shuttered door. Around me were several other smaller structures — a cistern, a cook house, a cellar, a retaining wall, a chimney, more stairs. He reappeared holding a box of kitchen matches and gestured for me to follow up the final flight of stairs. At the top, things began to crowd in. More doors, a tight alley overgrown with vines. The boy stopped in the alley and turned to me.

"Oh yeah," he said looking at me for the first time, "you want to see a haunted house?"

"Sure," I heard myself say.

"Wait here." He opened and closed a tall shutter and disappeared into a dark room. I heard noises coming from inside, and I wondered if on the other side of the door there might be a rough and ready group of his chums ready to pounce on me. It was not too late to run. The structure didn't look like much of a haunted house, I assured myself — a low stone and brick building two maybe three rooms long. I comforted myself with quick memories of the Haunted House at Playland — a barge ride through a pitch black tunnel with sudden scenes of gore, archetypal villains, goons rising from coffins, Blue Beard hacking away at his newest bride. That haunted house cost seven tickets (35 cents) and ended up where it started just across from the cotton candy man. Haunted houses were not real, I reminded myself, and I was something of an authority on the subject. I was feeling better.

The shutter opened and the boy reappeared shielding his eyes.

"O.K.," he said, "once we're inside, there's no turning back."

"I'm not afraid," I lied.

"Good. I'm going to have to blindfold you."

This I did not like.

"O.K., then close your eyes the first few seconds until I get the door closed."

I back in, eyes closed, the boy holding my arm. Then the blackness closes in and I am told to open them. I am facing the door I came in made visible by flickering candlelight. I am instructed to turn around and see on the floor the outlines of a body. The body is that of a large man dressed in jeans, rubber boots and a checked flannel shirt. His feet sprawl toward the center of the room, and his head and one arm are caught in the slammed lid of a large treasure chest from which necklaces and pearls ooze into a pool of jewels and coins. The picture of the treasure and the man is made complete by the blade of a huge kitchen knife plunged between the man's shoulder blades. It is a tale of greed and revenge. I take a moment to appreciate the scene's finer points. The tip of the carving knife has passed through the chest causing a glistening island of blood to collect. Out of the dead man's sleeve pokes the nose of a rat. A store-bought spider dangles from a gossamer behind the chest and in the flickering light, the ghostly carapace of a land crab laps at the banks of a bloody tributary.

"This way, please," the boy said, parting a curtain to one side.

In this room different themes competed — a shrunken head, various rubber insects, a rubber bat suspended by black thread angling in on me. There was also a stump and an axe and more red lacquer to make the point. On the stump was a bent porcelain pan with severed chicken parts, a goat hoof, a root, beads, a rubber snake, a die, certain seeds and some small orange and red peppers — obeah items I would come to know by heart. Finally, at the door out was a grave composed of yellow brick and selected bones laid on top to resemble a skeleton. At the head was a crucifix and, encircling the grave, an assortment of small candles.

Outside, I was told to wait — presumably for him to blow out the candles — and I wonder what I was thinking, standing in that overgrown alley, about the boy whose name I didn't know. He reappeared and we went down the stairwell, across the courtyard and through a shuttered door into the kitchen. The boy put the matches over the stove.

"Want a Coke?"

I don't recall what happened after that, but I think the visit was brief. He may have chosen to show me his room or his models or his guns or his closet darkroom, but I think all those things came later. What I do remember is catching a glimpse of his grandmother, an old black woman with a clear West Indian accent, talking to someone on the porch.

That night Pam was moody and reading a book. She listened to my description of the haunted house distractedly until I got to the gorier details and she finally put the book down. She let me know that my new chum was exhibiting the symptoms of a certifiable nut case and to watch out I didn't end up with my own head in a chest.

"What's this guy's name?"

I hadn't thought to ask.

That night I went to sleep relieved, knowing I had found a possible friend — nut case or not — who lived, as luck would have it, right next door. He was also, I would later learn, a cousin and classmate of Jimmy Merced.

—❧—

One morning at 16 Crystal, I was sitting on the straw rug in the middle of the room playing with the cat and a marble. It was mid-summer, and entertainment was catch-as-catch-can. Mom had a real job selling china and cuckoo clocks at the Continental and, without adult supervision or camp or Little League or The Club, we were pretty much left to our own devices. Often I went to the boatyard to help out or just to go on the glassbottom. There were also the occasional invitations to the beach or mornings spent picking and eating mangoes from the neighbor's tree. I had, by that time, learned to jump from the roof to get over to the house of my new friend, whose name was Niles, Niles Vanterpool. But Niles was often off on his own or out hunting with his uncle. Sometimes, I raced Dinky Toys in the gut outside the house, or, when it rained, corks. I knew the best gutters and had tracked my cork rafts over rapids, through tunnels, under streets and, currents permitting, into the harbor. It was not hard to stay amused.

On this particular morning, I was amusing myself with Mabel (the cat) and a marble, when I heard the jeep drive up. This was unusual. Mom had already left for work, and Pop seldom returned from the boatyard before six. I jumped up and peeked over the flower box. Sure enough, Pop. And the way he cut the engine and pulled the emergency didn't sound happy. There was still time to run upstairs, but then he might think I was still sleeping. I started for a broom I knew to be in the kitchen but stopped halfway realizing how transparent that would be. I ended up right where I had started, in the middle of the room.

"Hi," he said entering the doorway.

"Hi."

His eyes fell to my feet where Mabel was batting the marble. The marble rolled across the straw rug, continued across the floorboards and ricocheted off the foot of the stairs.

"Where's your sister?"

"Upstairs, I think."

Just then we heard Pam's door shut, her feet starting down. Pop went into the pantry to pick up a couple of regulators and a weight belt he had forgotten, which explained his mood. Pam appeared on the landing with a squirt gun in her hand and I sensed she didn't realize Pop was there. Pop rounded the corner and looked up at her — barefoot, cut-offs, T-shirt, squirt gun.

"I want you to take this list to your mother and tell them the Elliots are coming to dinner. Maybe you can go to Clinton's to pick up the bread and milk."

"O.K."

"And make sure you get the peas with the green label."

He leaned on the table to add something to the list. When he looked up, Pam was standing there with the squirt gun in her mouth shooting streams of water. A stunned look crossed his features.

"Get that thing out of your mouth," he said, his voice quavering and the look we feared showing in his lip.

"It's only water," Pam said.

"I don't give a goddamn *what* it is!" he bellowed, slamming his hand on the table. We both jumped as did the wooden bowl, which continued to rock in the ebbing silence.

"That's the green can. Not the big peas, the small ones. And don't go to the Continental," he added, "until you've put something decent on." The gun had begun to leak in Pam's cut-offs.

He gathered up the gear and headed for the door, then stopped just outside and looked back at me.

"And what are you up to today?"

"I think I'm going to do something with Niles," I answered.

"Well, stay out of trouble," he smiled and in as pleasant a voice as he could muster, "We'll see you both later."

We waited for the jeep to start and listened to it turn down Raadetts Gade toward the waterfront. Pam looked at me and then at the squirt gun. My father seldom raised his voice, and it usually required a far greater sin than a squirt gun. He was firm, but fair, my father — predictable in a scary kind of way. But this outburst had caught us by surprise.

That night I was sitting on my bed fashioning a noose from the spine of a palm frond to be used to catch lizards. Pam appeared in my doorway.

"I just got it," she said looking through me.

Whatever it was, it was deep.

"Got what?"

"Why Pop blew up."

"Why?"

"Something Wendy once told me that I'd totally forgotten," she said sitting on the bed, a distant look coming over her.

"What?"

She stared at me. "Pop's father committed suicide."

These were two new words side-by-side. From the look on her face, this was a very unpleasant matter. But what did it mean?

"He killed himself, stupid."

Killed himself. Committed suicide. It had never occurred to me by age ten that a person would choose to do such a thing or that a word even existed to describe the event. I could see from the look on Pam's face that this was a ghastly business. Commit suicide. But what did that have to do with my father blowing up at us?

"Don't you see?" she said putting her finger in her mouth, "I had the gun in my mouth."

My father's father was born in 1885 in Brooklyn where his father, my great grandfather, owned a number of pharmacies. I know little about my grandfather's youth except that he was an only child and that his foot got caught in the wheel of an ice cart. The injury gave him a slight limp for the rest of his life and relegated him to the sidelines of the sports he adored.

The only person alive who knew my grandfather at that age was my Great Aunt Babe, who died recently at the age of 104. She described my grandfather as handsome, engaging and fun-loving and, perhaps, overly dapper. He entered Harvard in 1903. An old college photo shows him bowler cane and spats, one eyebrow arched and quizzical. At Harvard he got on with a fast crowd of rich aristocrats. He got along with these people, Aunt Babe said, but the association "turned his head," leaving him with glamorous but vacant memories.

He married my grandmother, Helen Peacock Rolston, and then had two children, Adele in 1912 and my father in 1917. They lived in Rye at a house on Purchase Street, and he worked at a bank in New York. Things were all right at first but then his drinking began to be a problem. By the time my father was seven and Adele twelve things had become intolerable. There were fights and nights he spent in the city — usually at the Harvard Club. Several short separations resulted in an ultimatum: She would move to Paris to live with Aunt Babe and, unless he stopped drinking completely, she would have to ask for a divorce. This was strong medicine because she still loved him and because in 1924 divorce was a socially disastrous last resort.

They stayed in Paris for several months. A photo survives showing my father, age 8, his sister Adele, age 13, and their two cousins Jerry and Brown on a front stoop. The three boys wear long smocks in the photo, some kind of French school uniform. My father also wears knee socks, cap and gloves and a slightly impish grin. My grandfather sent letters of protestation along with assurances that he had quit the bottle. Only after receiving confirmation of this from friends and relatives did my grandmother relent and pack up the kids for the return home.

Things improved for a while even though he had not, in fact, stopped drinking. He managed to keep the lid on through concealment and occasional nights in the city. It was at this time that Adele recalls happening upon a pistol in the bottom of her mother's sewing basket. Soon enough, things boiled over in the worst way, and my father and Adele boarded a train with their mother for the long trip to Reno, Nevada.

"We are going out West," she informed my father. "Where you will see lots of cowboys and buffaloes."

The oddity of this sudden departure in the middle of third grade didn't dawn on him. Adele, five years older, was her mother's confidant and knew exactly what was going on. She welcomed a way out of her father's tyranny, for her mother's sake more than her own. My father, searching the plains for cowboys and buffalo, was kept in the dark until the true meaning of their western journey was revealed one day near St. Louis when a man asked to join their table in the dining car. My grandmother, then 38, consented.

"Where you folks headed?" the man inquired.

"Reno," Mrs. Wilson replied.

"Oh, a divorce."

They stayed in a small rooming house and began the long six-week legal process. My father told me he remembered very little of the stay except the time when several neighborhood bullies pulled down his pants. He remembered also that the divorce was never completed but that one day they packed their bags and abruptly headed home.

Adele was there the day Western Union came. She was alone in their Reno boarding house rooms, a gaudy western affair with mauve wallpaper and crinoline curtains. Her mother and brother had gone to the lawyer, which meant two hours of solitude and the luxury of dancing to the victrola, time enough to dance, shower, re-hang the dress and still be reading *Les Miserables* when her mother returned. There was a mirror in the foyer and she had slipped into her one good dress to waltz and twirl in front of it in the stifling desert afternoon. The song was *Lazy River*, over and over again. Shortly, there was a knock.

Her heart tripped. She hurried to the victrola to turn down the music.

"Who is it?" she called through the door.

"Western Union."

She opened the door. An old man smiled down on her having heard the music and seeing now the perspiring girl in the party dress.

"Telegram for Mrs. W. A. Wilson," he said.

"She'll be back soon," Adele answered. "I'll take it."

She closed the door and held the envelope to the light but could see nothing. For a moment she debated the matter. Then she went into the kitchen to start a pot for tea. When the water began to boil, she held the envelope over the kettle spout and steamed it open. With unsteady hands she unfolded it. It said:

> Bill died suddenly yesterday.
> Come home at once. Love.

Adele stood in that boarding house kitchen, her fancy dress damp with dancing, the fan turning circles overhead, and took in the meaning of these words. She refolded the telegram and put it back in the envelope, then lit a candle and used a thin smear of wax to reseal it. This she placed on the entry table beneath the paperweight. She was then free to return to the victrola, turn up the music and dance again.

The exact circumstances of my grandfather's death I learned only a few years before my own father's death, and not from him but from Adele. The telegram, it turned out, was not exactly correct. He had not "died yesterday." He had been found at that time. In fact he had taken his regular room at the Harvard Club and turned the Do Not Disturb sign. The maids, ever respectful of the member's wishes, obliged until an unpleasant and suspicious odor prompted a call to the concierge. My sister's squirt gun suspicions were correct: He had shot himself in the mouth.

—∞—

About a month after our arrival my father started bartending a few nights a week at The Gate whenever the steel band played. The band, The

Shooting Stars, played their pulsing rhythms in the wide stairwell that connected the bar and dance floor with the rooms upstairs. For hours at a time, Pam and I stood on the stairs watching the fast confident hands work up a good calypso. The band was comprised mostly of high school students. They played the occasional *Yellow Bird* or *Island in the Sun*, but it was a mixed crowd that wanted to hear the popular local tunes as well, Mighty Sparrow songs like *Young and Strong* and *Benwood Dick*, songs I already knew by heart.

Also observed from those stairs were the mysteries of the dance floor offering a rapid education on things not taught at the Rye Country Day Dancing School. Some danced a hygienic meringue, but as the night wore on there were other, more personal, gyrations where participants seemed joined at the hip. These I watched furtively and with dark interest while Pam kept score on just who was dancing with whom — particularly when the matchings involved tourist girls and taxi drivers.

One afternoon, I was helping my father set up by sweeping and sponging off the tables. He sent me upstairs with a burlap bag to get a block of ice from the freezer on the upstairs landing. As I lifted the lid of the ice chest I was startled to hear the sounds of a fight in the corner room. They were the grunts and groans of a violent wrestling match. I turned to run downstairs for my father when one of the groans became, instead, a giggle. I froze. The groans grew more regular, louder and louder, faster and faster, ending in a prolonged and languorous wail from the throat of the woman. I held my breath and eased the block of ice into the sack. Soft sounds of laughter and the deep resonance of a West Indian voice covered my retreating footsteps.

An hour later, I was watching the band set up when a young tourist woman came down the staircase with a local cab driver and part-time calypsonian named Manchester. I remembered this lady from the night before talking to my father about her family's summer home on Lake George. Her civilities then were different from the sounds I'd heard coming from her room. To my surprise, she waved at me and called me by name as she sat with Manchester at the bar. She wore a modest white linen blouse with a bit of lacy embroidery on the sleeves and neck. I studied her lips as she sipped her iced tea. This woman, I realized, was the kind of woman I'd seen gracing the pages of the calendar I'd discovered in the basement in Rye. A creature of wildly opposing natures. Or were all women, secretly, no different? From the shadows at the end of the bar, I regarded her darkly. Soon Manchester rose to go and touched her creamy neck with his huge black hand. She looked up at him and smiled. The future was a frightening thing.

By the end of the summer, I had grown closer to Niles. He had shown me his darkroom, the archeological excavations in his backyard and the secret to mixing good gunpowder. I had, by that time, gone hunting with him and some of his chums and had seen how small dead birds can lie like little soldiers in a knapsack. Of particular interest to my parents were the pottery shards, clay pipes, pieces of china, and coins — some dating to the eighteenth century — that he was unearthing in his back-yard. On several occasions, I heard my parents explain to other adults in slightly disbelieving tones about this kid next door.

While I told everyone about the stamp and coin collection, the mod-els under construction, the taste of his grandmother's West Indian cook-ing, I was sworn to secrecy about things like the catapult and the bomb. The catapult was a three-foot high slingshot made from the crotch of a sturdy wild tamarind. Each band of the sling comprised one hundred interlaced rubber bands connecting at a leather pouch. Strapped to their wrought-iron porch railing, the catapult was capable of launching a green mango a couple of blocks. The bomb was an aluminum pipe, crimped at one end, which he was packing with his special gunpowder mixture. He had a supply of yellow sulfur, plenty of fresh charcoal, and he was buying incremental amounts of potassium nitrate (salt peter) from the island's two drug stores. Soon the tube would be full. All that remained after that was the making of a satisfactory fuse.

When I described current projects at the dinner table, I often used the word "we" a little loosely, and it amused my mother. In the Rye Cub Scouts, I had scarcely been able to tie a proper knot and here I was talk-ing about how we were mounting the engine on the model or we were considering using the pontoons of a wrecked seaplane to make a boat. Niles undertook his archeological excavations with exquisite patience and a small spade where I would have worked with a pickax. His models of fighters and vintage cars came with meticulous and baffling directions. I participated by looking over his shoulder, by holding the glue. It didn't matter to my parents that I was merely an accessory to these events. Something, however small, might rub off.

One afternoon while I was following Niles from place to place, something unexpected occurred. He was salvaging an old ship model of his uncle's, a sea-worthy 40-inch gaff-rigged sloop. First it was into the shop for pliers and vice to mend the anchor chain. Then to the kitchen to melt paraffin to make the cloth sails look more like canvas. The hull, freshly sanded, lay keel-up on the courtyard bench, ready for a fresh coat of varnish. Next it was off to another house on a lower landing to cannibalize a miniature block and tackle from a termite-infested model of his grandfather's stored there in a damaged glass case. He stopped first in the kitchen to get the key dangling from the board beside the pantry door.

But when we got to the door, the lock — a huge, ancient, heart-shaped affair, wouldn't open. Niles examined the key with disgust.

"Coming back," he said heading again to the keyboard.

I stood, or leaned rather, against the papaya tree, one foot up on the planter wall.

"Hi," I heard from overhead.

I looked up to see the face of a very pretty girl looking out the window of a tangerine wall in the adjoining yard. Incredibly, this girl appeared to be talking and smiling at *me*. This requires some word in return, but the sudden dark eyes, the tangerine wall and papaya tree have me in a place I've never been.

"Hi." I manage at last.

"You living over there? " she asked.

"No, this is my friend's house."

"Oh. I see you there looking like you deep in thought."

This makes me smile. She is Latin in coloring and has a local lilt to her voice. Her name is Pilar. She asks me my name and where I'm from and whether or not I like St. Thomas.

"I like it." And suddenly I am liking it a bit more.

"Really?" Her face shows a slightly disapproving look, as if, given a choice, she might prefer living elsewhere. When she asks me what part I like best I want to say — "You Pilar, I like you best" — but there is a look in her eyes that seems already to know this. I tell her I'll be attending All Souls and she reacts with genuine excitement because that is the school she goes to. But just then she looks back into the window and disappears for an instant, but I can hear her talking to someone. I try to think of something else to say to extend the conversation.

"I have to go, " she says reappearing. She smiles and waves and I hear the sound of my name on her lips, and I stammer something about seeing her when school starts but she is already gone. Just then I hear Niles returning with the key. He gets inside and starts to de-rig the sails of the old model to get the block and tackle he is after.

"Who lives across the way in the tangerine house?" I asked him.

"Here, hold this," he said, ignoring me.

Pilar Bermudez did not live in the tangerine house I would later learn, but across the valley in a pink house on Bunker Hill, the house just across from where Anton Merced now lives. The tangerine house belonged to her uncle, Santana, the butcher. Pilar was a year older than me and a grade higher. Looking back, I see how that first encounter was a perfect metaphor for my subsequent efforts: The vision, the longing, the disappearance. Swallowed by a tangerine wall.

Leaving Niles one afternoon, I heard what sounded like newborn kittens somewhere in the alley just off the street. I listened at a neighbor's wooden gate to see if the sound was coming from inside. It wasn't. I looked in the drainage ducts of the retaining wall and in the crawl space beneath the stone staircase. Leaving the alley the sound of the kittens became metallic and I grew suspicious of a garbage can. It seemed an unlikely spot for a litter of kittens. I lifted the lid.

The can had been recently emptied and had only a ring of swill, a few of yesterday's mango skins and five tiny kittens, eyes closed, looking more like wet slugs. I replaced the lid and for a moment stood there. That someone had intentionally thrown these little creatures away took a minute to sink in. They were unwanted, meant to die. This was none of my business was another thought, a thought that would likely be given expression by my father if I dared take them home. This was Mrs. Thomas' garbage can and her gate. It was not my gate. I was just innocently going on my way. None of my business.

I opened the lid and looked closer. The light flooding into their prison and through their closed eyelids gave rise to a mighty ruckus — as if, sensing light, they also sensed survival. There were, in all, five newborns, but only three of them were moving. I reached in and poked the two unmoving ones. They were dead. The others would soon be joining them. I scooped up the wiggly ones, put the lid back on and headed up to the house.

Within an hour, Pam and I had them cleaned up and fed — using an eyedropper to force-feed warm, thinned-down Pet Milk. One of them was so weak it managed only to lick a few drops off its lips. Without their mother, Pam didn't think they would make it. Pop came home in a hurry — between the boatyard and The Gate — and, after a quick shower, headed off again. He didn't have much to say about the kittens, but he wasn't going to banish them back to the garbage can. At least not immediately. Our German shepherd, Schoern, was taking an unhealthy interest in these new arrivals and, to prevent them from becoming a meal, we put them in the pantry off the kitchen in a high-sided box atop a ratty old flannel blanket. Before we headed off to The Gate to listen to the steelband, we closed the pantry door and gave Schoern an extra can of dog food to help keep her mind and appetite away from the kitties.

An hour later, between sets, I ran back to the house to check on things. Entering the kitchen, my heart sank; the pantry door was ajar and there were no kitten sounds. I braced myself and turned on the light, fearing the worst. The box was on its side and over in the corner lay Schoern looking at me with hang-dog eyes.

The little ones were not being digested but were, instead, tugging away at her nipples, their mouths too full of canine flesh to make a sound. Schoern's look of guilt deepened. I felt certain I was witnessing something horribly wrong, something bizarre and grotesque, nature gone whacko. For a moment I watched, mortified by the sight of these squiggling garbage can slugs growing out of Schoern's belly like misshapened appendages. Slowly, as if some spell might befall me, I backed out of the room and closed the door. Then I tore down to The Gate.

The band was playing but the bar was not too busy. My father, measuring my concern, got someone to cover him and went back to the house with me. When I opened the pantry door, he turned on the light and we stood there staring at Schoern — caught in the act. I looked up to see how my father would handle it. He had a stunned look on his face as if he, too, didn't know what to make of it. The kittens were tugging furiously at her nipples, their paws making muffins of her flesh. Slowly my father crossed the room and crouched by the dog and Schoern's look of guilt multiplied. Then my father's hand reached forward and stroked the dog's head.

"Good girl," he said in a whisper, "good girl."

Schoern leaned forward and gave the kittens a few rough licks. She had come to us spayed and had never had a chance to have puppies. She had them now.

The cats I named Rin, Tin and Can after the garbage can they'd been found in and because of their German shepherd nurturing. Schoern moved her litter to a crawl space beneath the stairs, and from time to time she'd venture out to collect one that had wandered off and carry it back in her mouth, only a head and tail visible. The crawl space was a storage locker, a closet of sorts with its own little door and light and rug and I would go there to be with the kittens or to read a book or to stage mock battles with my assortment of plastic soldiers.

Some days when Niles was elsewhere and the beach or boatyard too far away, I lay alone in my room in the stifling summer heat staring at the ceiling and wondering what would become of us in this place. At moments like this I longed for old friends, green lawns, cool evenings. At night I sometimes squinched my eyes closed until the 40-watt bulb hovered like a distant star. And at times like this I felt like I had fallen into a deep well with only a small circle of light at the top, the place I had come from calling down to me. For companionship, I sometimes went downstairs to borrow a kitten or two from Schoern to take back upstairs.

Those kittens, who had survived the garbage can and had quickly grown feisty and strong, those kittens gave me hope.

Early one evening a few weeks after moving to the island, Pam and I were walking up to the house from The Gate when I noticed a boy sitting on a stoop with his little sister. The boy was probably a year or two older than me, a face from the neighborhood. As we passed the boy spoke.

"Dirty white cat scunt."

It seemed unlikely that someone I didn't know would say something like this to me, or to Pam.

"Are you talking to us?" I asked, slowing.

"Kiss your white mother scunt."

Pam grabbed me by the wrist and gave me a yank.

"Let's go, " she said.

Although I had no way of knowing it at the time, the boy I'd just met was Jimmy Merced. Soon he would throw a brick into my father's ribs. Twelve years later, he would be convicted of machine-gunning the golfers on St. Croix. Later he would escape from prison, hijack a plane to Cuba, and disappear. But for right now, he was just a kid with an attitude, sitting on a stoop with his little sister.

One evening about a month later, my father sent me from The Gate to pick up some French bread at the bakery. I went along Back Street past the offices of *The Daily News* and the back of the Apothecary Hall then left to Lockhart's Bakery. At this hour, near closing, most of the goodies in the display case were gone but there were plenty of the warm and doughy three-cent breads. I got the dozen required and the lady gave me the crumbling remains of a guava tart from a tray. On the way out I decided to cut through the empty lot across the street. The far side of this lot fronted on the backside of the Merced house (though I didn't know this at the time), and the path I was taking cut alongside it. I was eating the guava tart and could hear the steel band starting up almost a block away when I also heard what I thought were muffled shouts. I slowed and looked behind me and tried to locate the sound. Through the trees at the back of the Merced house I saw a boy in the twilight sitting beside a fish trap. It was the boy who'd called me a cat scunt the week before. I wondered about his sitting in the dark like that, and as I drew alongside the Merced house, the shouting I'd heard seconds before started anew. A man and woman were having a big fight. Someone's parents, I guessed. And it occurred to me that maybe that's why the boy was outside, sitting alone in the dark.

The Dragon Slayer

One afternoon I went to my window to see what all the yelling and honking was about. Parked on the hill was a dilapidated truck heaped to the brim with our Rye belongings — everything from my bicycle to the grandfather clock. The clock appeared to have been thrown atop everything else. The movers, we soon discovered, viewed the antiques, old and wooden, as junk. On the other hand, a fold-up aluminum card table, which in Rye had resided in basement obscurity — had now been elevated to a new position of importance; it alone had been wrapped in a blanket to prevent it from becoming dented.

To my mind these relics from our past confirmed in the most severe way our position as castaways. When the major pieces of furniture — the grandfather clock, a highboy, a china cabinet, an old writing desk — were positioned in the living room, they failed to produce the desired effect. Mixed with the straw rug and chairs, bamboo curtains, the uneven floorboards and the other items my father had found to furnish the house, the antiques looked ungainly and out of place. To my way of thinking, the straw chairs seemed bewildered, the antiques, dismayed. The grandfather clock, its innards broken and beginning to corrode, was still the tallest thing in the room, which allowed it a measure of dignity.

The one item I had great plans for was my bicycle. This gleaming Raleigh three-speed acted on me like a life preserver, which both reaffirmed and transmitted my identity from Rye. But I quickly learned that even it did not translate very well to the local terrain. Unlike Rye with its flat contours and smooth blacktops, St. Thomas was all up and down and to get almost anywhere required an ordeal.

But not knowing this, I set out that first day to show the world a thing or two. I tooled down Main Street and up to Market Square imagining people viewing me as I viewed myself — casual, sporty, unconcerned. I turned south coolly going against traffic on the one-way street, then onto the waterfront looking for another audience. Instead, I attracted a retinue of barking dogs unfamiliar with the singing spokes of a bicycle wheel. One dog went after the pedal and I came crashing down right in front of the audience I'd intended to impress, a fish-buying throng assembled at the stern of a native sloop. My bloodied shin and bent fender were cause for a bit of stifled jubilation.

Within days, my bike riding plans were further dashed when the bike, which had been parked up behind our gate, was stolen. Eventually the police were called, and they asked the predictable questions and cautioned me not to leave it out in the future. When the bike turned up a week later, it was almost unrecognizable. The thief, in an attempt to conceal the stolen merchandise, had painted it with red enamel. Everything was red, the spokes included. The red enamel had gunked up the gears and brake cables and gotten into the chain. My father thanked the police while I wept. I never found out who stole it, but I would later have my suspicions.

Around the time the grandfather clock arrived, we were paid a visit by an old friend of my father's from boarding school days who'd surfaced on the island for an extended visit which, in the end, would last many years. Diz was very large — particularly around the middle. His wife Ruby was like Popeye's Olive Oyle, thin as a twig. Diz was a terrible slob, a fat slob who happened also to be filthy rich. For some reason, he chose to live in a converted trailer near the airport with a view of quonset huts, junked car lots and directly in line with the ascending underbellies of aircraft. The trailer was littered with paperbacks, cigarette cartons, booze, empty glasses and general filth. Ruby seemed too weak to keep up with him. When we visited, Diz often greeted us in his underwear and, only after extended protestations from Ruby, would he slip into something slightly less revealing from which his scrotum would invariably put in an appearance. Diz lived in his underwear because of a skin condition — huge circular rings of redness — that itched terribly. While I had been told not to pick my nose or scratch in public, Diz could get away with extended scratching in the most private places. On these occasions my father could barely suppress his repugnance. He liked Diz, but at times he seemed to resent him, probably because he'd lucked into a huge inheritance.

The place they had known each other was St. George's, a boarding school near Newport, Rhode Island. The school is situated on a tapering down, its centerpiece the church's lofty Gothic spires, visible for miles. The walls of the dorms and commons room are fieldstone, brick and ivy, flanked by playing fields and tennis courts. There is a track and a hockey rink, and, on the coast nearby, a boathouse with racing shells and sail-boats. In the commons room, filled with long oak dining tables, hang medieval shields, banners and lances elaborating the Arthurian theme. There is a painting of St. George, himself, slaying the fire-spitting drag-on. On one staircase, a medieval knight — helmet, mail and velvet — guards the door.

At St. George's my father was a dragon-slayer, dressed not in armor but in herringbone and flannels, button-downs and Oxfords. Often I had paged through his yearbooks and marveled at how many times he was pictured in various organizations and sports. It was, along with the Olympics and his war experiences, an indelible part of who he was. I have sometimes wondered if St. George's — for all its virtues — hadn't done for my father what Harvard had done for his father by surrounding him with an unrealistic landscape. What reason was there not to believe that further success and ease of life awaited him beyond the campus, as it did in affluent Newport only a mile from school where princes and movie stars cavorted in Roadsters? It was only a step away, a seemingly logical extension of St. Georges.

Now, on St. Thomas I was seeing another product of that esteemed institution — Diz. A look back at the 1937 yearbook showed me Diz — or, rather, Edward Astor Stanton III — as he once was, handsome, smil-ing, and not particularly plump. Although my father did not hide the fact that he and Diz had gone to the same school, he chose not to dwell on it, preferring, perhaps, not to tarnish St. George's image. It may have been a bit galling to him — trying as he did to put a good spin on our tropical circumstances — to know that of all the faces in those yearbooks, only two had washed up on these shores, and Diz was the other. Of course, and this was the rub, Diz had the financial resources to wash up anywhere he chose.

Part of my fondness for Diz had to do with our grandfather clock. When Diz came to dinner one night he saw it in our living room for the first time, silent of course. It was similar to a clock he had grown up with, he announced. He walked over to it, opened the glass door to the clock's filigreed face and mechanical calendar insert and poked at something with his stubby fingers. Then he opened the door to the pendulum and weights, and started to fiddle around. My father watched skeptically and with mounting impatience as Diz stuck his head in and the whole clock tipped to one side. Rolls of fat quivered and sweat dribbled from this minor exertion. But then, a minute later, we heard the familiar and heartening tick-tock we had known so long, and we listened, unbelieving, for a moment expecting it to stop. It didn't. My mother rose and gave Diz a big hug then headed into the kitchen. Pam followed to help set the table.

Later Pam told me she had found Mom bent over the cutting board in tears. When Pam asked her what was the matter, Mom pointed to the onions on the cutting board. But the knife had not yet made the first cut.

All Souls

In August several shops in town filled up with school uniforms, so Mom and I went down to get mine. The dry goods store was transformed by uniforms stacked to the ceilings like gigantic multi-colored caterpillars. Each school had its color. All Souls was green and white; Catholic was blue and white; Lincoln school yellow and khaki. Then there were maroons and plaids and even pinks. Soon all the uniforms in my neighborhood would make the morning streets look like confetti. Niles was light and dark blue. Jimmy Merced was going to Lincoln School, he was yellow and khaki; and his friend Bappo who went to Commandant Gade, yellow and green. The two living by the mango tree were going to Lutheran School, maroon and white. When Mom and I got back from shopping for my uniform that day, I put it on and checked myself out in the mirror. Mom, in anticipation of a growth spurt, had gone with the larger size. I looked like a scarecrow lost in green folds and my head, sprouting out of my white short sleeve shirt, seemed unaccountably large. This is how I would present myself on my first day of school.

In early September, my mother took me up the valley to register for classes at All Souls, the island's Anglican school. Pam, it had been decided, would be better served at the Catholic school where nuns would be able to keep close tabs on her moral deportment. Though I had grown weary of summer, I did not look forward to a new school and a sea of new and searching faces. Chief among my concerns was the fact that the vast majority of these faces would be black. I felt I would be further reduced by the one thing we all had in common — our green and white uniforms.

Mom accompanied me opening day and left me at the parish gate where the principal, Mrs. Brenner, was directing people and answering questions. I knew already that I was getting in deep. At registration the day before, I had had my hopes for a school vastly inferior to my school in Rye dashed when my question about long division was answered in the affirmative: yes there would be plenty of that.

Standing at the gate that morning in my green pants and white shirt, I studied the swarm of new faces, many of them already masters of the one mystery that had cursed me the year before. Suddenly one of my fifth grade classmates, a girl — is directing me to my classroom to meet my teacher, Mrs. Howell, who is black. So, too, is everyone else except for one, a silent and frail boy in the third row, and another, a girl, talking in loud and flawless West Indian to two black girls. Clearly, this is not her first year here. I feel a small measure of comfort, therefore, knowing that at least one white child has survived this experience intact.

Soon we are trotted off to the Parish Hall, an old wooden structure similar to a barracks, where we sit on benches. Here we are all made to stare at Mrs. Brenner's nose, which is white except for the end, which is red from where she is poking it. Finally we are all silently staring at the red end of her nose, and her hand drops and there is a short prayer. Then on three — one, two, three white fingers — we all, except me, sing:

> *Good morning to you,*
> *Good morning to you.*
> *We're all in our places*
> *With sun-shining faces.*
> *And this is the way*
> *To start a new day.*

The collective voice of the assembled classes is strong and rousing. We all feel a little better. Now there are certain announcements before we head back to our classes in straight lines.

By the end of the day, I have yet to face my first onslaught of long division. I have, on the other hand, learned the basics of marbles, tasted my first saltfish and dumplings, and had my first religion class. No unkind word has been spoken to me, and no stone-throwing youths have hurled anything at me on my way home. I have also that first day caught a fleeting glimpse of Pilar, the girl from the tangerine wall.

I would not be exempt from hurled stones for long. One afternoon a week or so later, I would take the shortcut home past the rectory and, turning the corner across from the Emporium, spot two unfamiliar boys my age or a bit older sitting on the steps leading to High Road. They have yellow and khaki uniforms and say nothing as I pass. I think to make eye contact but don't, and this is probably a mistake. So is the choice not to look back. A block later two stones caromed off the building I am passing, one whistling by my ear. I run around the corner and up the hill to the house and look back from the gate but see no sign of them. They probably ambushed me from the mouth of the side alley. I try to recall their faces but can remember only that both are lanky and coffee with cream. I do not wonder if this is pay back for some offense I have given. The ambush, I assume, is because I am white, a curiosity, and an easy target.

It quickly became clear that school in the islands was not much different from school elsewhere. Perhaps the most distinguishing characteristic was the business of religion. Church on St. Thomas was not something reserved for an hour once a week when one saw the same faces one saw an hour later at the country club. Here, we were reminded of the Almighty every morning for 20 minutes and for an hour on Wednesday when a full and formal communion was held and the altar boys swung their boats of incense causing some to gag long before the body and blood were drawn from the tabernacle. Twice a week, we attended religion classes where we learned to recite various biblical passages along with the Apostles' Creed. Failure to perform satisfactorily often resulted in swift retribution administered by Father Nibbs in the form of a zealous rap on the knuckles with his yardstick or, worse, with a homework assignment of copying an entire chapter of the Gospel. And there were no blue-eyed Jesuses anywhere to be found.

On the one occasion that both my mother and father went to church, things ended badly. It was on All Souls Eve in early November, and the school was trying something new called the Feast of the Candles. The church — a large, rather handsome structure built in the 1820s — was packed with parents and parishioners. Just before the start of the service, all the lights were extinguished leaving the cavernous nave steeped in darkness with only a single candle flickering in the pulpit. As Father Nibbs read passages of scripture chronicling the lives of Saints and Apostles, individual children representing those lives entered the church, each carrying a single candle. I was to be St. Stephen. Like the others, I was to enter when told, cross to the center aisle, genuflect, and stand behind the altar rail in my appointed position. We had rehearsed this twice during the day — without costumes and with unlighted candles. We were told how beautiful the church would be with all the candles and our shimmering, smiling faces illuminated in the glow.

My costume was less elegant and flowing than some of the other saints but that was because I had been poor and a martyr, killed for my beliefs (stoned to death, I seem to recall) and that made me feel incredibly saint-ly. By the time the passage about my saint was read, half the characters and their candles were already in place and the effect was dazzling. It was all very exciting — being a martyr and what not — with my parents right there in the church to see me.

Mrs. Howell nudged me forward as I heard my name read. While the congregation heard of my many good deeds, I crossed, bare feet and burlap, to the center of the church. There, I turned — careful not to spill any wax — and, facing the altar, gave my best genuflect (my parents had never seen this little trick). Then with a slight wobble I proceeded to my place behind the altar rail. I tried to scan the congregation for some sign of my mother and father, but the glow of the candle blinded me from seeing beyond the first few pews. Father Nibbs continued to drone on about the other saints, saints lesser than myself, and things seemed to be moving very slowly. The flame in front of my face was making a halo, the aperture of which was narrowing and growing furry. I remember my feet beginning to tingle — strange little pinpricks — and wanting to scratch them, but St. Stephen, immune as he was to torture, would not be one to go around scratching his feet, particularly on so solemn an occasion.

But the tingling began to move up my leg, and I suddenly started to feel lightheaded. There were still a dozen or more passages to be read, saints still waiting in the wings, and my hands were beginning to go numb. I decided that if things didn't improve at once I would, against all my saintly good judgment, have to genuflect and leave the church. It is a monstrous turn.

The next thing I know I am being carried from the church. It is dark and cavernous, and I am horizontal and men in dark suits and worried faces are carrying me away. Suddenly I understand that I am at my own funeral, living the tale of the boy accidentally buried alive. Soon the lid of the coffin will be slammed shut. I scream and break free of some of my captors, but one of them is shaking me by the shoulders. He owns the feed and grain store in town near the lumberyard. What is he doing here? There is his wife. And Mrs. Brenner. And there, suddenly, is Mom. I am not dead I tell them, but they already know. Other students are beginning to turn green, and I hear Mr. Clifford, the science teacher, explaining that the candles are consuming the oxygen beneath people's noses. Mrs. Brenner runs in and catches little Liza Scatliffe just as she keels over.

On the walk home down Garden Street, I am between my parents, delighted to be alive and nursing a lump on the back of my head where it is said my noggin hit the altar rail. My parents have not failed to grasp the humor of the situation.

"Well, you *were* a martyr," my mother said.

It is a mixed compliment but there is something a bit heroic about it. How did it look, I wanted to know, seeing myself now in a slightly cinematic light. My mother had not seen my collapse, she said, but my father had.

He put a hand on my shoulder. He was proud, beaming.

"You went down like a ton of bricks."

Almost at once I found myself imitating the lilting calypso I heard around the schoolyard. This was not a conscious effort at first but one that insinuated itself. In class, certain expressions struck me. If a child was unable to do, say, a math problem, he or she would say "I can't get this do" instead of "I can't do this." On the playground to tell someone to stand back one said, "move from there" or, to say "I'm over here" one said instead, "See me here, no." To accuse someone of a lie, one said, "You untruth" (pronounced on-troowt). Certain of these expressions I could say at the appropriate time with something approaching the right accent. But I could not, at first, sustain a conversation. To start to speak St. Thomian and trail off into standard English was not good form. I could hear for myself how only a few "continentals" spoke with a good accent and most did not.

Being able to converse in St. Thomian — or at least willing to try — had a considerable bearing on how quickly one was likely to be accepted by the others. Although the desire to speak like the locals stemmed primarily from the pleasure I derived from hearing these things come from my mouth (and at home the looks of dismay such sounds produced from my parents), acceptance was definitely part of the equation. And the principal reason acceptance was essential had to do with fighting.

For lack of any organized sport, there were three activities that occupied us outside the classroom: marbles, rock throwing and fights. The local penchant for fisticuffs was alien to me and deeply disturbing. I don't recall ever having seen children in Rye get into fights after school, but here it was an almost daily preoccupation. I was determined, if at all possible, to avoid confrontations — certain, from things I'd seen, that I would be bloodied and humiliated by a pummeling of black fists. In hindsight, I suspect the local penchant for fisticuffs derived from the steady diet of cowboy movies at the local cinemas, offering countless Wild-West situations where disagreements are settled with someone getting walloped through the upstairs banister or out a saloon door. To many classmates, this was the appropriate way to settle those pesky little schoolyard grievances.

My fear of fighting did not exempt me from the same voyeuristic curiosity that afflicted everyone else. When fights erupted in the schoolyard, non combatants watched, silently evaluating the abilities of those in conflict. Some had a wild windmill style of throwing punches, others a peek-a-boo style of fending off and firing blows. I chose always to watch from a safe distance, fearful that I might otherwise become entangled. If one or another of the combatants showed the slightest reluctance, bystanders could always be depended on to jump-start things by pushing one person into the other. On one such occasion a white friend, Danny, was thrust unwillingly into a fight with the class bully, a boy whose taut black skin and bulging muscles I secretly coveted. I watched, transfixed, as this child, Leroy, pummeled my friend — who was, himself, stronger than me — into a cowering ball. Even more amazing, and a little disappointing, I witnessed Danny get up, dust himself off and pick up his books. Like the others, I'd wanted to see a Wild-West knockout

I was by now, and by necessity, a student of the language of fighting, one schooled in the nuances of provocation and how to avoid them. If in marbles, there was a dispute, a phrase like "M'son, don't get me vex here today" was fair warning. If, on the other hand, the phrase was, "You want me bust you one cuff?" or "I'll fire a clout in him, you know," it was time to either back off or follow with one's own threat. These threats were not idle, and there was no easy rejoinder. "I go tell the teacher" was a certain loser. Finally, if one was very angry, confident, or insane, one could insult the anatomy or occupation of the other's mother. Anything containing the words "your mother scunt" was the guaranteed tripwire onlookers yearned for. From this, there could be no turning back.

Not wanting to get into a fight or to expose my as yet inexact accent, I chose the safest route and said nothing. If that failed I would linger in class at the end of school until my tormentor had gone down the road. Then I would go home and give my toughest face to the mirror and practice my lines.

"You want me bust you a cuff?" the face in the mirror might ask.

"You think I 'fraid you?" I'd respond. "Come your ugly scunt."

Then I'd grab the villain (myself) by the shirt collar and throw him against the wall. I practiced the sudden look of surprise and fear my tormentor would show as I stood ready to "clout him up."

Lying in bed at night I often played over the day's events in my mind, searching for the right language, the right combination of words, trying out new words I was just getting the hang of. Lying there I might arrive at a good construction, a string of words I could unleash the following day to achieve a momentary level of St. Thomian-ness and, thus, acceptance. Waiting for the right moment in art class, I would then blurt out, "All you people like to skylark too much, you hear." The end of a sentence like this needed to be punctuated by the sucking of one's teeth, an expression of annoyance or disgust.

If only my old friends in Rye could see me now.

If someone at this time had asked me how or if or why I liked St. Thomas, I would have likely given the typical inarticulate response expected of any ten-year-old. There were things about St. Thomas that I liked and things about Rye that I missed, but looking back now I doubt I could have, at that age, given clear expression to my conflicted feelings.

A small photo survives from those first months on the island, a photo I cherish and one that seems to embody my gradual absorption into the culture of the islands. The photo was taken from the steps of The Gate — probably by Pam — and it shows me playing one of the Shooting Stars' steel drums. Behind me and to one side are the real band members, coal black, in carnival shirts with ruffled sleeves. I could not, at that time,

have been able to do much more than sound out note-by-note a few of
the songs they played, and the photo was no doubt taken between sets.
The band probably tolerated me because I was the bartender's son. In
the photo, the steel drum I am plinking away at is at chest level and seems
almost as wide as I am tall. I look very white in this black-and-white
photo, and slightly skeletal, my eyes lost in shadowy sockets and my
mouth open wide, as if in a state of suspended wonder.

That sense of wonder (though I would not have thought to describe
it as such) I experienced those first months in the islands is, itself, a thing
to wonder at. In the case of the steel band, it is not surprising because it
was a thing I had never seen or heard before and the loud pulsing
melodies — particularly in the echoey stone stairwell of The Gate — traveled straight to the marrow of one's being. But there were other, less
obvious wonders that accrued over time.

Something as basic as geography. In Rye, one sensed one's physical
location by one's relation to certain familiar things — in the comforting
shadows of oaks and maples, the familiar contours of this lawn, that
building. George Washington slept here, the sign read. And the sign by
the ramp said, This way to New York City, that way to Boston. You knew
where you were because you were told or because the map on someone's
lap showed the blue and red arteries leading in different directions, the
contours of the coast showing Long Island. You knew where you were
because all those dark-suited men with their briefcases standing on the
platform or emptying from the New Haven Railroad seemed to know
where they were coming from and going to.

On St. Thomas, geography is not something inferred or assumed.
Visible all around you, it simply is. The island's contours, its valleys and
hills, its harbors and bays, its twisting ridges — all offer views of itself,
undeniable panoramas. It is also a geography that constantly reminds you
that you are surrounded by water, and alone — no comforting blue and
red lines leading to one city or another. On the horizon to the south one
can see St. Croix, and to the east, the British Virgin Islands, and, on a
clear day, Puerto Rico 50 miles to the west.

Also on the horizon and heading one's way was the weather. Should I
do my errands now, one might ask, and looking out to see a squall

moving in from the east, decide to wait 15 minutes. Or, later, when one had a more refined sense of these things, one could see from the angle of the wind that the shower would pass to the south — fine for errands, not so good for the cistern. In Rye, rain appeared out of nowhere and water, just as mysteriously, poured from spouts. It would always pour from the spout and who could say just where this water came from? What's more, who really cared? On St. Thomas, the cause-and-effect relationship of weather and water was altogether clear: it fell on your roof, ran into the gutters, down the downspout and into the cistern. And you had better care. Because when the faucet started to sputter, and you checked the cistern and saw the silt and lizard skeletons on the bottom, it was time for the water truck, time to take the military showers you should have been taking all along, time not to flush until the bowl was brimming. In Rye, the mildly sinister bathroom plunger gathered dust beneath the cellar stairs; here that black rubber mushroom was a trusted friend, always close at hand.

There was also the matter of gutters that ran alongside every street. In Rye, rainwater carried leaves and bits of debris into storm drains, never to be seen again. Where did all that water go? The question never occurred to me nor should it have. On St. Thomas, there was no mystery. This gutter led to that one, which converged in the valley with other gutters, all emptying into the main guts which, in turn, emptied into the harbor. The corks I raced in those gutters cleared that mystery up for me. There was also the issue of electricity. Although I didn't understand it any more on St. Thomas than I did in Rye — except that it traveled in the lines strung overhead — I certainly knew that the plant down in Krum Bay was responsible for producing it and that several times a week, when something went awry, the power could be depended on to cease and, before long, the things in the freezer to rot.

Finally, there was the business of sex. In Rye, sex was something alluded to, revealed in minute doses, in baby sitting confidences, in waltzes with white gloves, in glimpses of my Sunday school teacher's cleavage, in calendar girls hidden away in basement drawers. On St. Thomas, where flesh bulged beneath sweat-dampened fabric, curves were not suggested or concealed, and, at the beach, it was not a question of how little but of how much could be revealed. On the dance floor, little was left to the imagination and in the words of calypsos, nothing at all. One song of particular interest was *Benwood Dick*:

> *Tell your sister to come down quick*
> *I got something here for she.*
> *Tell she tis Mister Benwood Dick,*
> *the man from Sangre Grande.*
> *She know me well -*
> *I do she already, oh,*
> *she must remember me, oh.*
> *Go on, go on,*
> *Tell she Mister Benwood come.*

This was not Pat Boone crooning about pink carnations. At the movies, audiences sighed and jeered with contempt for cinematic swoons and embraces. "Only that?" they cry or "T'ain kiss she want!" or "Gi' she d't-ing, no." And if the sounds I heard coming from the upstairs room at The Gate — the sounds of the taxi driver and the tourist lady from Lake George — left any room for interpretation, the almost daily sight of copulating dogs helped mightily to clear things up. Though one seldom saw cats in the act, the nightly battles, the spine-curdling caterwauling, left little doubt about the issue involved. Those cats had the last word of the day and cocks, whose crows punctuated the dawn, the first. Then, there were the donkeys, the jackasses whose piercing hee-haws occurred at any time of the day, and whose huge dangling phalluses evoked, at first, averted looks of dismay and, later, ripples of mirth.

These things, again, were not consciously wondered at, comparisons not deliberately made. If one had been asked how the issue of, say, water differed between St. Thomas and Rye — it would not have been beyond our capacity to describe because somewhere these vague, internal calculations were taking place. What was less obvious was that some invisible polar re-alignments were also underway.

The first time I became aware of these realignments occurred around the time the photo was taken of me playing the steel drum. A family from the States — friends of friends of my parents, I believe — were staying at

The Gate. There was a son — my age — and a daughter, Pam's. We were on an upstairs terrace waiting for our parents to finish their eggs bene-dict and bloody Marys (in addition to bartending, Pop was now helping in the kitchen) so that we could head off to the beach. Cindy, the daugh-ter, was commenting to Pam about how lucky we were to be living in the islands, and Pam, being polite, was saying that the place had its draw-backs and that there were things in the States we both missed. Cindy brushed this off and continued to list the island's virtues. Though we had heard this kind of thing from friends of our parents, we hadn't heard it from someone our age. I felt, in a small way, uplifted.

Later at the beach the boy, Thayer, and I were roughhousing at the water's edge. Things then got a little out of hand, and the playful jostling turned real and for me a bit desperate. In a minute, much to my surprise, I pinned him. Nothing was made of this and our play resumed. But later, sipping Cokes at a picnic table, I detected an edge. He started talking about how much he was looking forward to getting back to the States, talk about snow skiing in Vermont and missed programs on TV. I think I must have countered with some one-ups-man-shipping of my own, possible talk of scuba diving, maybe some baloney about sunken treasure. Then, contradicting the feelings expressed by his sister earlier in the day, he started in on how hot it always was here, not to mention things like mosquitoes and cockroaches. He had never seen such huge roaches. I began to take offense, began, to my own surprise, to defend St. Thomas. There was tit for tat. Then he said he couldn't see how I could stand liv-ing in a house like ours, tin roof and all.

"Man, kiss your scunt," I heard myself say.

"Fuck you, asshole."

"Oh yeah? Well fuck your ugly white mother scunt."

One day coming from the Continental where mom was selling jewelry and cuckoo clocks, store owners started closing their doors and, turning, I saw a funeral coming down the street. A couple of trombones from the Community Band were doing their usual dum-dum-dedum-dum-dedum-dedum-dedum thing. What was unusual was the number of familiar faces. Two of my teachers were there and Father Nibbs. Also to the rear of the procession were various All Souls students including Pilar Bermudez all in black and, walking beside her, Jimmy Merced and his brother, Noah. The coffin was lavender and placed on palms in the back of a pick up. A sign in the truck window said Christensen, and it dawned on me that Jimmy and Pilar might be related. Jimmy had a black cowboy shirt on with a bit of white piping. He and his brother were walking with his mother and his aunt (the same ladies who would, in a less somber moment, beat my father over the back with broomsticks and mop handles) and with Pilar and her younger brother, Aldo. As they drew alongside Creque's Alley where I was standing, Jimmy said something to Pilar that made her smile. At that same instant her eye passed over me, and I thought she was about to get off a little wave but she checked it and turned back to Jimmy who was saying something. When they'd passed he looked away, and she tossed her head and pulled her hair back and in that gesture found my eye and gave me a smile. The procession shuffled by heading for Western Cemetery at the edge of town. When they were gone, the shop doors reopened and everything returned to normal, except me. Pilar had chosen to look back. Had troubled herself to turn her head and use her hand to move her hair. And she had done this for me. I continued down the street in the opposite direction the funeral procession had gone, my feet carrying forward, my head full of grinning, happy thoughts. Someone had died and, because of it, I now had Pilar seriously on my mind.

The Bomb

One Sunday morning at around 9:30, when most people were in church, an explosion rocked our neighborhood. I was down at the boatyard helping my father haul a boat at the time, and Pam was at a friend's where she had spent the night. Mom was the only one home, taking advantage of the empty house to sleep late. The explosion almost blew her out of bed.

Minutes later the police, who had heard the blast down at Fort Christian, cruised the neighborhood looking for the epicenter. Because so few people were around at the time, no one could say for sure where the blast had originated. My mother, who had been asleep, told the police that she, too, was uncertain. But she had her suspicions.

"Your friend Niles hasn't been fooling around with explosives, has he?" she asked when I got home.

"No," I lied. "I don't think so."

Later, when they were taking an afternoon nap, I snuck over. Since the start of school I'd seen less of Niles because he was in a higher grade and a different school. I assumed the explosion was the pipe bomb he'd been packing with his homemade gunpowder mix. But that was months ago, and I'd almost forgotten about that project. Later, he showed me the eight-foot crack the bomb put in a backyard retaining wall.

When Pam heard about the blast I confided in her. The event deepened our curiosity about Niles, who had become a kind of shifting jigsaw puzzle to us. Though I knew him quite well by now, I seemed not to know him at all. The most abiding mystery was the matter of his parents. Where were they? Why did he live with his grandparents — both in their 70s? I may have innocently asked him early on — or perhaps Pam did — but never received a satisfactory answer, and the longer the question, asked or unasked, remained unanswered, the more awkward the question became. At first we imagined they'd been the victims of some tragedy, a plane crash perhaps. Murder was another speculation. But then we learned from someone that Niles had a sister somewhere and that his parents were alive. So why were they nowhere to be seen? Was someone in jail? Even my parents wondered.

There were less spectacular mysteries as well. Behind the main house was the bathroom. The room was quite large — not originally a bathroom — and contained, among other things, a number of gun cabinets with rifles, shotguns, pistols, ammo, Army surplus belts, packs and canteens. Across from these cabinets was a walled storage area where Niles had created a tiny darkroom. The business end of the john — toilet, sink, medicine cabinet — was situated farthest from the door. One could see where the modern plumbing had been steered to one side, the pipes side-by-side tunneling through the two-foot thick masonry wall. In the medicine cabinet Niles, kept his Wild Root Cream Oil and beneath one of the floor's green tiles — three from the west, nine from the north, which he had laboriously picked away at, removed and replaced — was a time capsule in a cigar tin, buried for some future archaeologist. Two small arched windows with bars were set high on the wall where the south light streamed in. To lock the door from the inside one had to use a huge three-foot steel hook.

The most intriguing aspect of the room was the amount of time Niles spent in there. Often when I visited unexpectedly his grandmother would tell me he was "out back," which usually meant the structure that housed the toilet, guns and photo enlarger. Seeing the door shut, I would call to him and he would yell "coming" in a business-like manner, but not emerge for several minutes signaled by the deep clanking sound of the bar being unhooked. He'd then brush past me and brusquely order me to follow, heading swiftly to his room or up to his digging area and away from the room. If I asked him what he was up to in there — (developing photos, cleaning guns, making rocket fuel, shitting?) the answer was always the same: "Nothing." This kind of unsatisfactory answer, like the choice never to reveal anything about his parents, engendered in me a sense that, although I was tolerated as a friend, I was not a real confidant, not someone who could be completely trusted. His choice to detonate the pipe bomb without informing me added to this sense of exclusion.

It would be 20 years before I learned the truth about Niles' parents and, when I did, I would learn it from Niles' wife. Why we chose to remain in ignorance may have had to do with our notion of social niceties. Instead we relied on conjecture and were willing to abide the mystery and at times to encourage it. One early piece of information came from a third party and a fairly reliable source who claimed Niles' father was one of the guys who invented the Atomic Bomb. This fit rather nicely. It explained his love of explosives. It explained all the secrecy. It was the missing key and for years to come the whispered explanation that was certain to raise eyebrows and utterances of disbelief. It was, as well, only distantly related to the truth. Although Mr. Vanterpool was an associate of Oppenheimer, involved peripherally with the Manhattan Project, his area of expertise was not in making things go boom. Mr. Vanterpool was interested in the nuclear isotopes and their effect on organisms.

The Vanterpools had come originally from the island of Saba, a volcanic stump located 100 miles southeast of St. Thomas. Visitors to that island are always struck by the immaculate streets and stairways, the tidy agricultural terraces, and the rugged self-reliance of its people. The island has only one export: a steady supply of able seamen. In his youth, Niles' grandfather served aboard various square-rigged vessels plying the waters up and down the eastern seaboard. Some of these were legitimate Merchant Marine ships; others carried contraband. At one point he ran guns up Haitian rivers for the U.S. Navy and similar subcontracting for the Coast Guard and Marines. Later, he moved to St. Thomas and for 30 years served as a Harbor Pilot, becoming the island's Harbor Master in 1947, responsible for maneuvering huge cruise boats and military vessels into Charlotte Amalie's famous harbor. Captain Vanterpool, during his years on St. Thomas, fathered four sons all of whom grew up in the house on Crystal Gade. The oldest of these was Eric, Niles' father.

Eric was valedictorian of the 1934 graduating class of Charlotte Amalie High School and went on to Swarthmore and ended up with a Ph.D. in zoology. Upon graduation, one of his professors — an expert in radiation — urged him to go to Chicago where he was sure he could find him a job. Eric, then 26, decided to move and had been working in a lab for about a month when he was summoned into a room and given an oath of secrecy. When he later learned that various teams were looking for trustworthy foot soldiers in the cause, he managed to get jobs for his two brothers. One, Allen, spent the war serving as a courier shuttling small heavy containers from Midway Airport to a place in New Mexico called Los Alamos. Neither of the two brothers knew exactly what the top secret project was. But there they were, three sons of a Saban sea captain, helping to usher in the Atomic Age.

After the war, Niles' father married a young schoolteacher from southern Indiana. Within a year, the young bride gave birth to a daughter,

Kelly, and, two years after that, to a son, Niles. By this time Eric was teaching at the University of Illinois. When his wife began to behave strangely, he at first attributed it to postpartum depression or to strains resulting from the recent move to Bloomington. Later, when he called her family to report what he suspected was a nervous breakdown, they were saddened but not particularly surprised.

Hadn't she told him that schizophrenia was common in the family?

No, she had not.

Nile's father returned from the lab one day to find the house completely empty — rugs, furniture, the works. The two children, Kelly and Niles, had been left with a neighbor who told of the moving van that had backed up to the house earlier in the day. A caretaker was hired for several months until Eric's parents telegraphed from the Virgin Islands offering to take the children until he could see his way clear. He drove to Miami and put them on a plane. Perhaps Mr. Vanterpool's nuclear work prevented him from holding on to the children, and perhaps, coming as he did from a Saban family tradition of fathers being off at sea, it was easier to surrender the children to his parents. And perhaps the grandparents, then in their 50s and having raised four boys, welcomed the renewed child-rearing responsibilities. Whatever the case, that year, 1947, was a big one for Niles, then a year old. The loss of the mother, the drive to Miami, the end of a family.

I doubt Niles could have told us much of this history at the time we lived on Crystal Gade, and I doubt his father went at great lengths to explain. Though his sister may have confided some things in him, I sense Niles may have known only in the vaguest way what had become of his mother and why he had been sent away. But at the time, all we knew was what a third party had told Pam — probably a year or so after we first met Niles — that his father had been one of the mad scientists who'd created the Atom Bomb. A mad scientist was something we could work with. Of course — and we had no way of knowing this at the time — it was not his scientist father who was mad but his schizophrenic mother. And Niles was carrying those hidden genes, a bomb of another sort, silently ticking away inside.

—〰—

ISLAND BOY

Stepping Outside

Madness was not something unknown to us. Our own family — particularly my mother's side — had more than its share, mostly of the manic depressive variety. One of these cases, my mother's brother, Uncle Sandy — along with Aunt Vivian — came to St. Thomas for a visit that April. I had only met Uncle Sandy once before when he came up from New Orleans to visit us in Rye. On that occasion, we had been instructed to be particularly polite to him because he was slightly "off his rocker" (I think he was recovering from an episode at the time). I gathered from these anticipatory instructions that Sandy was a little nuts. But I misunderstood the expression off his rocker as "off his rocket." I therefore had, at age five, a kind of Buck Rogers sense of a man on a lunar mission careening through space, lost among the stars. So I was surprised when the man who showed up at Overlook Place, dressed in a checkered jacket, turned out to be wonderfully kind, and playful and funny. This was my first introduction to what madness was all about.

During their St. Thomas visit, Sandy and Vivian were staying at The Beachcomber and had been on the island for several days the night Mr. Merced came to our gate. My father was grilling flank steak and lobster tail on the charcoal. He was shirtless at the time, wearing only a pair of Bermudas when I heard someone calling from the street.

"Inside," the voice repeated before I could get to the front door landing. There, outside our gate, was a man who was only vaguely familiar, someone from the neighborhood. He was Latin-looking, quite tall, sporting a mustache and a faint snarl to his lips.

"Tell your father come," the man said.

Pop had just laid the lobster tail on the coal pot so I knew this was not a good time. But judging from the man's demeanor, it was better that my father convey that message. I went back into the house.

"Pop, there's a man out there who wants to see you," I informed him. Then, thinking it better that he be warned, I added, "He doesn't seem to be very happy."

My father went to the landing wiping his hands on a dish towel.

"Yes, may I help you?"

"You hit my wife," the man said.

"You got the wrong guy, pal."

"You hit my wife," the man repeated, this time raising his voice.

At this point, Mom was on the landing with me, and Sandy and Vivian, who'd heard me say the caller wasn't happy, were watching from the doorway. Pam, I later learned, was looking on from the upstairs window.

"I don't know what you're talking about," my father said, dropping the dish towel in the flower box. The gesture carried with it an edge, a sense that his patience was wearing thin.

"You want to step outside?" the man asked.

"You're goddamn right I'll step outside," my father replied.

If, by some cosmic sleight of hand, I could step out of myself and go back to that moment in my life, I would set myself up in a window directly across the street. From there, I would be able to see my mother with me beside her, both of us looking over the window box, the window box with those ridiculous rubbery plants. I would see my sister in the window above and, in the shadows of the doorway, my Uncle Sandy and Aunt

Vivian. I would see, also, 16 Crystal, its sagging gutters and blistered paint, and the faint outline of the hillside in the twilight. And I would want, given this luxury of time travel, a moment to stop the tape, to study this particular frame and to look into my own unfathoming eyes.

I would also want to study Merced to measure any surprise he might have shown at my father's unexpected willingness to accept his invitation to step outside. He may have welcomed this response coming as it did from a man ten years his elder, a man a full head shorter, and a man who was likely far less experienced in the local art of the street brawl. And, not knowing that this man had been a collegiate wrestler and had never himself turned down an invitation to fight, Merced may have relished the opportunity to bloody him badly and to show his family, lurking unseen just around the corner, a bit of the fighting tradition for which he and his brother were widely known.

When my father got to the bottom step and reached to open the gate, Merced unloaded an awesome sucker punch across the top of the unopened gate. It was a right cross and it struck my father flush in the temple — the kind of blow that might have been the beginning and end of some fights. That iron gate had a maddening habit of sticking and, for the first time, we had reason to be glad; the blow nearly knocked my father off his feet but one hand had a grip on the gate and the gate held. I don't recall the moment of contact between the two except that it was immediate and that Merced, the boxer, was quickly put at a disadvantage by my father, the wrestler, who swarmed in on him and denied him the necessary distance to make his punches effective. But Merced, tall and scrappy and powerful, was able to use his long-limbed leverage to break holds, to regain punching range and, when my father came in on him again, to gain a hold or two of his own. At one point the two tumbled into the gutter on the far side of the street, a square, waist-deep moat, and disappeared behind a parked car. By now the Merced family had rounded the corner, dismayed I suspect to see the outcome not a foregone conclusion. Seeing them move closer, I asked my mother if I could let Schoern out, Schoern our German Shepherd who was racing back and forth unable to see the struggle but able to hear it, smell it. My mother looked down at me.

"Your father can take care of himself."

The fight raged down Crystal Gade almost to the Dutch Reform Church and then turned and headed back uphill toward the house. It seemed that Merced was no longer pressing for advantage but showing signs of retreat — still fighting fiercely but more to hold the older, shorter combatant at bay. But it could still go either way. At last the two were back in front of the gate, and my father had Merced on the pavement with his thick forearm across his windpipe, swearing to kill him if he ever threatened our family again.

While my father was bringing his forearm to bear on Merced's windpipe, three women of the Merced family were beating him over the head and back with broom sticks and mop handles (Where did these weapons come from I wonder? Had someone run back to the house for them or had they brought them along just in case?) Incredibly, my father ignored these repeated blows until Merced's body went limp and a gurgling sound came from his throat. At this point my father, enraged by the repeated blows the women had been raining down on him, stood and grabbed one woman in each hand, sandwiching the third in between, and threw them against the jeep. For those of us watching helplessly from the landing, nothing could have been more beautiful or more relieving than the sight of those three women crumpling and falling to the pavement.

But the Merced family was not to be denied the final word. As my father turned to see what had become of Merced, a boy appeared out of nowhere and hurled a brick into his ribs. My father went down on one knee. Everyone scattered. The fight was over.

In telling this story over the years, I have been guilty of only one exaggeration, the length of the fight. Considering the fact that my father's life seemed to be in danger, my sense of time may have been distorted. Looking now at the second hand of a clock and playing the events over in my mind, it seems unlikely that the fight could have lasted more than 15 minutes. Still, 15 minutes or so after my father had left the lobster tails I found myself standing in the downstairs bathroom watching my mother pick asphalt grit out of his back, watching my father's blood swirling down the drain, and a tattered piece of Merced's shirt still clenched in his trembling fist.

After a shot of rum, my mother and father headed off to the hospital and two hours later they returned, my father's midsection taped where the brick had cracked two of his ribs. By that time, Pam and I had eaten our share of the over-cooked lobster and were sent to bed. Also during their absence, I'd fetched the remains of Merced's shirt from the bathroom wastebasket. The shirt, originally white with large red polka dots, now sported several islands of pink where the blood had been partially rinsed away, connecting the dots into a newly patterned landscape. I squeezed the scrap of shirt dry and hung it from bedsprings beneath my mattress. This would be my talisman, my banner of proof that our family had been tested, and bloodied, but had stood its ground.

Thirty-five years later at my luncheon with Anton Merced, something happened to clear up — once and for all — an uncertainty about that night. During our initial conversation at his Bunker Hill house, Mr. Merced had claimed not to be the man who fought my father. It was his younger brother, Hugo, he maintained. At the time I'd taken his word for it. But later, certain doubts had begun to creep in. His younger brother, who'd died two years before, could not corroborate this fact and I wondered if Anton Merced, given his physical similarities to his brother Hugo, might have used this to disguise the truth. At the time, the possibility still existed that Anton Merced could still be imagining me to be a Federal Agent interested not in the details of a fight he may or may not have had with my father, but in the whereabouts of his fugitive son. And if he thought this to be the case, could there possibly be some danger in store for me? I was stirring up the Sweet Bottom Massacre after all, so who knew for certain what blind alleys I might be getting myself into.

During our luncheon that day — a very pleasant one, really — I was plying Anton with various questions about the fights he and his brother used to get into when they were serving as Army Medics in Puerto Rico. He seemed to enjoy these tales and the effect they had on me. At one point, he pantomimed a straight left he had thrown, which in his words, caused his victim's teeth to "fall out in his hand." It suddenly occurred to me that the gesture of the thrown punch carried some critical, unspoken information that could help clear something up.

But I would have to be careful, indirect.

I changed the subject to his pitching career. Was he a righty or a lefty, I asked.

"Southpaw," he answered.

That clinched it. He pitched with his left, he ate with his left, and the pantomimed punch he had thrown was also a left. The punch first thrown at my father, the one that traveled across the top of the gate and hit him in the temple — that punch, indelibly imprinted in my memory, was, unquestionably, a right. In that moment I felt safer, felt certain for the first time that Anton Merced could be trusted.

—ɯ—

When I think of Jimmy Merced hurling that brick at my father, it raises certain questions. First, had the tables been reversed, had my father been bettered by Merced and my mother and sister thrown against a jeep, would I have gone to the street myself? Perhaps given a family crisis of that magnitude I would have had to do something. But I doubt I could have done quite so thorough a job, due in part to physical limitations. I was two years younger than Jimmy Merced and a well-thrown brick requires a good purchase and the requisite power. But that is only a part of it.

The other part has to do with the *idea* of throwing that brick, of seeing that possibility. The idea of throwing a brick. I think of the two photos Anton carried in his wallet that show his son cleaning a fish, age 8, and a year later astride a horse. The horse photo was taken on the old Mahogany Road near the Peterson Farm in Rosendahl, where the Merced family had several horses. The children were allowed at an early age to roam freely and adventure over that rolling landscape. He had a pellet rifle and permission to shoot pretty much whatever he wanted. In the photo taken at the Frenchtown boat ramp, Jimmy has a knife in the belly of a snapper he is cleaning and has doubtless just caught off the South Bank in a predawn outing with his father and his Uncle Hugo. It is a fish he will eat for dinner.

My own stateside encounters with nature seem rather tame and circumscribed in comparison. I remember, for instance, a Scout jamboree that took place in a glen out of sight of any structures somewhere 20 minutes north of Rye. In one place the glen slipped into a kind of gully with jutting protrusions of stone and I stopped my running about to stare at the disorder, to revel in it really. I had seen this kind of wildness in the Catskills for one week each summer but I had not expected to find it so close to home, so close to the manicured world of Rye. Also in the Catskills, I had seen my father dive from the top of a 30-foot waterfall, Fawn's Leap, but I swam poorly and shivered greatly and had yet to jump off the club's 10-foot board. My adventures were not of the hunting and fishing and horseback riding variety but more the amusement park kind. The town dump and the graves of Quakers had been the soil of my imagination.

Looking at those two photos of Jimmy Merced, I realize I hardly knew this boy, this boy whose house was just around the corner from my own. Still, having grown up around that corner, I saw him often enough, and, after years living in town, I can say at least that I know the kind of boy Jimmy was. He was a young Virgin Islander.

Certain things can be said about such a boy. First of all, an island boy like Jimmy Merced would know how to throw a stone well. That is, first, to spot the stone, to see its possibilities, to select the right stone for the occasion. His fingers would know at once the best flying contours and whether it will lift or drop, angle, or skip. He would know how to wrap the index finger to give it attitude and how to use thumb and middle finger to balance the load. And an island boy would not throw a rock; he would fire a rockstone.

An island boy would know the taste of fungi and kallaloo, of boiled fish and stewed whelk, and the best neighborhood trees for mangoes and tamarind and genip. He would know which side of what drawer to find candles when the power went out and the various other things one could do with the matches. An island boy would know also how to make a noose from the spine of a palm frond to catch a lizard, or how to draw a hairy ground spider from its hole using the fuzzy-tufted grass that often grows nearby. He would know the wasp-sting of a jackspaniard, the barb of ketch-n-keep, the thorn of the casha, the burn of stinging nettle. From the beaten end of an iguana tail bush, an island boy would know how to plait a wet whip and how to make it crack on the pavement.

An island boy like Jimmy also knew how to climb a coconut tree and how to twist the coconut on its stem to make it fall. He knew how to paddle a batto, a canoe made from wood, bowed sheets of galvanize, and tar. He knew also, as I did, how to cast a sprat net, how to put lead sinkers in each hand and one in the mouth and the folds of the net across the arm and how to throw with a sideways twist. He knew how to fish with a handline, using whelk for bait, and, if the fish weren't biting, how to use a three-pronged hook to "ginge" one from a passing school. He knew how to clean a fish and, if his mother was not there to do it, how to cook his catch over a coal pot or over a three-stone fire.

An island boy like Jimmy did not wonder who was rummaging in the side alley in the wee hours of the night or what truck was idling out on the street. Children all knew it was the honeywagon, gathering the wretched pudding from the neighborhood outhouses. This nightsoil crew were deeply mysterious underworld others who, it was said, could, without provocation, cover you with the neighbor's stool. Another truck familiar to island boys sprayed a cloud of mosquito spray and, running behind the truck, children grew delirious with their ability to vanish like a jumbie into the cloud of poisonous vapor.

Each morning, an island boy would hear roosters ricochet across the valley followed by donkeys followed by bells, the little island waking itself. He would know at night the howlings of cats who had blindsided each other in the gutter and the snarls of dogs who follow in packs the one in heat who accommodates all. He would know the more silent creatures as well: lizard and iguana, mongoose and rat, pelican and boobie, and, swift and silent above, the chicken hawk. He may have seen in the high flight of this hawk, the unexpected wrigglings of a baby mongoose. He would know how the broken iguana hit by a jeep grows more swollen each day and how the thrush in the papaya tree will call you outside only after it has gorged itself, to gloat over the damage it has done your fruit.

In the schoolyard, an island boy would know how to play at the serious business of marbles, how to balance his pitchie on his index finger, leaning on his center finger, his thumb nail used to launch it — not roll it — so that the marble, like a missile, hits its target on the fly. He would know who was a real quacksa and who was just lucky, and he would know how to cuss the fellow who liked to poke or call your hit a dirtshook. He would know how to card off one marble to position himself for the next, and he would take special glee in spalling or otherwise disfiguring the favorite marble of another, by busting it a lash or driving it a shot.

And when marbles or anything else got slightly out of hand, he would know the language of fighting. That it could erupt from the slightest provocation and that even if you had no desire to fight, bystanders were only too glad to give the shove necessary to get things going. A push required a push back, which required a harder push in return. The Merced advice to Hit First was a practical and valiant way of improving the odds. After a few good cuffs, the wrestling usually kicked in where a neck hold was a sure winner unless, of course, someone went for a rock. Young Jimmy Merced, who attended Lincoln School, would have had at least his share of giving and taking blows.

An island child would not be surprised to meet a sister or brother for the first time. A child's father may or may not have lived in the house and there would be no shame if his mother had a child for a next man. In the Merced family, the half-brothers and sisters would have been extensive. In those days other adults on the street would know you by name and report your slightest sins to your father or mother, often resulting in licks being generously administered to your backside. If you were sent to bring water from the corner well, you would hold your tongue and be careful not to show the slightest trace of vexation but save the pout for the street.

Turning on to Main Street at midday, a child like Jimmy Merced would not wonder why the shopkeepers were closing their doors. Up the street would be the black-cloaked funeral procession following on foot the pick-up truck carrying the same coffin he might have seen Hodge, the Backstreet carpenter, hammering together the day before. Jimmy would also know that the procession would end up beneath the mahogany trees in Western Cemetery where the coffin would be lowered into the ground, and nearby, leaning on a shovel or a tree, would be a sallow Anguillan gravedigger known to schoolchildren as Vampire, waiting to finish the job.

If Jimmy Merced knew Vampire, then he probably knew Small Boy, his albino relative who worked in the pharmacy and was known — behind his back — as Vampire Cousin. He surely knew, as well, the other cast of familiar town pariahs: Bang-Bang, a bullet-shaped Mongoloid from Barbuda who had seen too many westerns; Trembling Dick, whose palsied gyrations were acceptable to the general populace; and Sammy and Sylvester Toenail, the swollen-headed twins who drew the cruelest comments from schoolboys; or Bing, the toothless sidewalk artist who copied dimestore comics into copybooks. He would also have seen the cargo loader on the waterfront, a Puerto Rican cut off at the hips who got around on a floor cart, his huge arms shuttling him from place to place. He would know the usher at the Center Theatre and the insults said to him when the lights went out, and he would know the words and when to clap to the Pet Milk jingle that played before each show. In the case of young Jimmy, he would have seen the aunti-man poet who passed the Merced house on his way to his bookstore atop Crystal Gade, and he would have heard how he went to jail because the police catch him budging up a next man.

Because Jimmy Merced and I lived in the same neighborhood, there were certain experiences we shared. I know, for example, that he went on errands for his mother. A certain stop would have been Lockhart's Bakery, deliciously upwind of his house. He would know all the items in their display case and how to scoop his fingers into a 3 cent french bread to pull out the warm dough and savor the crust for last. On his way to the Emporium, he would pass the huge pink pillars of the Dutch Reformed Church where weak-voiced white people sang each week, and stepping down into the cool shadows of the Emporium, he would often have asked Walter Pennyfeather for basic provisions — sugar, flour, Pet Milk. Jimmy may have known, as I did, the advantage of having the old man go behind the curtain for something to allow time to sneak a tootsie roll from the jar and that the dragging sound of the old man's foot gave plenty warning of his return. The walk home from such errands might take young Jimmy to Miss Dahlia's green gate where frozen ices — soursop, cherry, tamarind — sold for a nickel. And he may have known that soursop, because it did not stain your lips, was less likely to excite questions about correct change.

Living across from The Gate, Jimmy knew more than most about steel band. Like any island child, he would know a mile away that someone was tuning a steeldrum by the ping-ping-ping of the hammer and the pang-pang-pang of the sledge. He would know that old bicycle inner-tubes were cut into ribbons and wrapped around a stick to hit the notes. He would know which three nights of the week *The Shooting Stars* played at The Gate, and because the band members took their break under the corner light, he probably knew a few of their names. He would have known the rhythms of the band's favorite tunes and, from the radio, the lyrics of some of those songs. Jimmy Merced most certainly knew, as did I, the words to *Young and Strong*.

> *We young and strong*
> *We ain' 'fraid of a soul in town.*
> *Who t'ink they bad*
> *To meet them we more than glad....*
> *So if you smart*
> *Clear the way,*
> *If you tink you bad*
> *make your play.*

Finally, living in this neighborhood of town, an island boy like Jimmy Merced would be an aficionado of the local cinema where the preferred hero was the desperado — The Cisco Kid, The Durango Kid, Jesse James — no gum-chewing, song-singing, girl-kissing cowboys allowed. A true student of these films studied the swagger, the unshaved cheek, the hand-rolled cigarette lodged in the corner of the mouth, the creased eyes, the speed of the draw, the delicious agony of the victim, the color and quantity of the blood. When an arrow thwacks into the calvary corporal's chest (this was to be his last mission, his young wife and child at home), the audience jeers at him, and when he slumps forward to reveal how the glistening red arrowhead has passed through him, cries of appreciation fill the theatre. It is hard to overestimate the intoxicating effect these Westerns had on an island boy. I felt it myself. And for Jimmy Merced, who lived only two blocks from the Center Theatre where one could see a twin bill for 45 cents, it would have been no different.

I can see him now, young Jimmy, heading home from such a western. Exiting onto Back Street through the side door, the movie follows him home. The echoes of the matinee crowd fade down the darkening street, but the mood of the movie continues to surround him and a block ahead, a man in the street light could be gunning for him. Jimmy checks the roofline looking for snipers. He imagines a six shooter hanging at his waist and his trigger finger tests itself. He doesn't want to gun him down unless he has to. Up ahead, the sound of The Gate's steel band starts up, bends around the street and carries along the walls. The movie starts to slip away as the pulse of the steel band steps into a familiar song. The man in the streetlight has turned away. The band is playing *Young and Strong* and Jimmy ain' 'fraid of a soul in town.

Angel

Raadets Gade was the street that intersected Crystal Gade just above our house. It went from that point downhill to cross Back Street (where it leveled off) then proceeded to cross Main Street and finally, another 100 or so yards south, emptied on to the waterfront. It was never one of the prettier streets in town but, at the time, it constituted a central axis to our world.

On the first block was The Gate and, adjacent to it, the home of the Merceds, small and yellow, a snarling cur always in evidence. At the corner was Joe's Barber Shop and, outside, the well where those without cisterns drew water and where, several nights a week, members of *The Shooting Stars* took their break. On the next block there was, for a short time, an attempt at a delicatessen but little else; this was the service area for many of the Main Street shops with little more than a few huge padlocked doors. The last block of Raadets Gade, the one between Main Street and the waterfront, had quite a lot to offer. There was a gas and appliance store, a couple of bars, a few small tourist shops, a tobacconist, a newsstand, and a small coffeeshop and bakery. The gutters that flanked either side of this street — particularly where it leveled off — were often choked with filth, usually a greenish swill that combined the discharge of restaurant grease traps with the overruns of failed plumbing. It was always a particular relief to enter The Coffee House where the stench of the street was erased by the scent of fresh-baked bread.

I was sent to The Coffee House almost daily to pick up a 22 cent loaf of Besabe Bread. A scattering of tables supported the coffee, elbows and conversations of the few early risers — all of them somewhat familiar faces, most with the unmistakable earmarks of a hangover. My trips there were usually quick in-and-out affairs because I felt young, self-conscious, unwanted. Usually I spent my brief moment there with my back to the customers and my eyes fixed on a tired travel poster of a twirling matador and a charging bull. Only on my way out the door would I allow myself a visual sweep of the customers at their tables.

My curiosity about the place took an unexpected turn one evening when Niles and I were returning from fishing off the Coast Guard dock. Turning onto Raadets Gade, we were surprised to see blinking lights over the door of The Coffee House, which usually would have been closed for hours. There were half a dozen St. Thomians milling around the front door, and, over it, a sign announcing a burlesque show, DIRECT FROM NEW YORK CITY. Though the word burlesque was new to me, the name of the star attraction — Angel — and all the blinking lights sent a racing feeling through me. Unfortunately, our age and our bucket of dead fish caused the older pleasure seekers to send us on our way.

When I went there the next morning to buy bread I was disappointed to find the cashier ready to help me because I'd wanted a minute to survey the insides of this pleasure palace. But I'd come prepared. By pilfering a few cents from my father's penny box I was able to send the cashier to the lowest shelf to cut me a piece of bread pudding, allowing me a good 30 seconds to look things over.

What I saw at first was the disappointing sight of the usual faces, a cart of dirty dishes, a cobweb-encrusted fan spinning in the corner. I turned back to my matador and his bull before catching a glimpse of a freshly painted pallet propped up in the hall. Could this be ... yes, this was probably a small stage and, hidden behind it, the embroidered edge of the sign that had been plastered in the window the night before. The cashier slid my bread pudding into a bag and began to count my pennies. I studied her hands. Was she in on this thing too? I wondered. Was this bland woman whose face I'd hardly noticed in the past, was she actually some kind of fleshpot? Her skin, on closer inspection, looked doughy — like it belonged behind a prayer book or in back with the unbaked bread. She probably had no idea — this suddenly God-fearing woman — that her precious little doughnut shop doubled as a stripjoint after hours!

On my way out, I gave the place my usual once-over and didn't notice until I had one foot out the door a threesome I hadn't seen before, an unfamiliar woman and two men. Could this be Angel? I wondered. I had already committed myself to exiting and could not bring myself to turn and stare. Besides, perhaps this was not Angel at all, but someone's mother. Still, I had to be certain. I walked halfway up the block, turned up a side alley, waited a moment, and then went back — casually slowing as I passed the door.

It was Angel. Someone so pretty would not have previously escaped my notice. She had wavy brown hair and a coffee and cream complexion and where her front touched the edge of the table a hint of cleavage showed. But who were the awful guys with her — one fat, the other mouthing a cigar? I continued down the street furiously debating whether I should pass the door again. To get a good look going the other way would require turning my entire head in the opposite direction my feet were attempting to carry me. No, that wouldn't do. And doing an entire circle around the block just to catch another fleeting glimpse and to possibly be noticed (Is it my imagination, guys, or does that little boy keep walking by the door?) would be acutely embarrassing. Was it really possible to see this goddess dance before me without her clothes on? We needed a plan. If Niles could build a rocket, if he could find treasure in his backyard, surely there was some hope, however small, of feasting our eyes on this woman's naked breasts.

The performances were only on Friday and Saturday nights, so we had plenty of time to come up with a plan. Niles was not optimistic. I must have seen some prison escape movie recently because I was all for tunneling in or hiding in the bathroom during regular hours or disguising ourselves in some way. Secretly hidden in these hare-brained schemes was the sense that this was a mission of rescue and that Angel, seeing me in the middle of her routine — seeing my innocence and my willingness to save her — that Angel would come running from her platform into my arms. I would then tear a curtain from the window to help cover her wildly bouncing bosoms and, together, leaving the stunned onlookers to their gasping, race up Raadets Gade to the safety of my room. This part of the plan I chose not to confide to Niles, particularly when he announced that the best plan was to just go down there and see if we could just steal a peek. Niles didn't seem to grasp the heroic urgency of this particular adventure.

That Friday after dinner, we told our folks we were heading down to the Coast Guard dock for some fishing and left with the usual metal bucket and handlines. Those we immediately stashed in a culvert after we had passed The Gate where my father was tending bar. Down the street we could see a sizeable crowd — Jimmy Merced and his buddy, Bappo Scabriel, among them — milling around outside the Coffee House. Jimmy and Bappo were talking to Anibal, a familiar local bully. Nothing was said as we passed and, moving closer, we could see two kids our age clinging to the gutterspout, their toes wedged into the window sill, peeking between the top of the sign board and the window. Our cool and casual approach quickened.

"Hey!" the bully called out. "All you get from here."

"Man, Anibal, gimme a break, no?" I pleaded.

"You can't read? — no one under 18 admitted."

The two black squirming bodies struggling to maintain a grip on the downspout were definitely no older than we were.

"What about these fellows?" I asked.

We heard sudden music and a thumping drum.

"Ple-e-e-ase."

One of the fellows lost his hold and jumped from the window sill and I scrambled into his spot. At first I couldn't find the peephole but then I saw a sliver of blue light slipping through. By pushing my eyeball up to the windowpane I could see the stage.

But what I saw was not Angel. Instead, I beheld a slender blonde in a G-string, her back arched as if going under a limbo stick, trembling to the saxophone in a frightening and violent manner, her hips slithering like a reptile. Unable to cling any more, I let go and Niles took my place.

"You see what you want?" Anibal asked.

"It wasn't Angel."

"Hey, the blonde's a lot better than Angel. All Angel does is swing her big boobs around."

That was all.

"But that's what I *want* to see," I whimpered.

"Hey, you guys, you hear shit? Little white boy wants to see Angel's jugs."

This got a good laugh. But from the back of the crowd a large black man who had been talking to Bappo and Jimmy stepped forward and hoisted me by the seat of my pants into viewing position. And he didn't then leave me to cling by my fingernails but supported me with his hand in the small of my back. Bless that man, bless him.

Soon enough the music started again, and then came the catcalls. Angel stepped out with a high-cut bikini bottom and a long purple sash wrapped around her torso and neck. She danced as best she could in her high heels, each time unwrapping the sash when she turned her back, and then, at the crucial moment, re-wrapping herself again. Just when the music seemed to be winding down and I had about given up hope that her luscious breasts would ever be completely revealed, she wrapped the sash into a ball around her fist and threw it to one side. Then she turned to the howling audience.

My first feeling was one of disappointment. They were not as pert and impossibly firm as the breasts I had seen in the artist renderings in the basement in Rye. But I quickly overcame this judgment and for the last 20 seconds of the show I studied these, my first, breasts — the mysterious and gelatinous way they obeyed gravity in the way of a dream. She was a nice girl, a pretty girl. And her movements were soft and sweet, not like the frightening and lascivious gyrations of the wanton blonde. I had to rescue her from the cigar-smoking man.

That was the only time I saw Angel in the flesh. Twice I saw her on the street after school, on my way to a milkshake at the Oasis in my green and white uniform. Once our eyes met — miraculous really, considering my eyes were level with her breasts. There they were, those awesome symbols of power, behind a simple white halter-top — the fabric straining under the authority of her flesh as if, at any moment, her brown flesh could burst from the prison of her garments and stun all of Main Street.

After the third weekend — after all the powers that be had seen first hand the menace such a sight could have on the moral fabric of the island — The Coffee Shop's liquor license was revoked and Angel disappeared, ascending, I suspect, to New York. My trips to The Coffee House for our morning bread were not the same after that, and the bread pudding never tasted quite so tart once she was gone.

Good Shepherd

Within a year of our arrival on St. Thomas, it became clear that the boatyard was in serious trouble. Although there were occasional days where the glassbottom went out several times with a full load, this was seldom the case. Engines broke down, captains came and went, and even my father's attempts to teach scuba on a regular basis were unprofitable. Added to this, his partner, Mr. Colsen, had to bail out because his father had died and left him the family business and a ton of dough. My father was not exactly filled with regret.

To make ends meet, Mom continued to work at the Continental, selling to tourists music boxes and cuckoo clocks, and, in her spare time working as the local Fuller Brush saleslady — traveling door-to-door on Saturdays selling her wares. Pop continued part time at the boatyard, part time at The Gate, and part time at the Liquor Locker. This establishment was located two doors up from The Coffee House on Raadets Gade and a good 50 yards off Main Street — not a great location for a store that sold primarily to tourists. To liven the place up a bit the Liquor Locker proprietors set up a small bar in one corner where locals were allowed to keep their own bottle of booze and, for a modest monthly fee, be kept in ice. Tourists who stumbled on the place were usually smitten by its charm.

But the private bottle arrangement was doomed to failure. What started as a clubby affair among friends quickly led to friends of friends, the original rack of half a dozen bottles soon extending to the ceiling — each wrapped in brown paper with the individual's name written in magic marker. Soon there were hangers on, lushes in before noon who were loaded by lunch. "Membership" became increasingly difficult to control. When a certain local was turned away — a boozer from an old island family who was a cousin of the police chief — the owner was accused of discrimination (an accurate charge), and by the end of the week the private bottle was a thing of the past.

One Thursday afternoon, I went there to deliver some end-of-the-year note from my teacher. Pop was chatting with two other parents, each nursing a highball from their bottle. I had come in on the tail end of a familiar conversation about the lack of summer activities for their kids. Then one of them turned to me, my head barely visible at the end of the bar, and informed me I was going to summer camp.

"I am?" I said turning to my father.

"You betcha."

The two bar stools swiveled away from me, and I thought I detected smirks, as if they were privy to some kind of joke.

"In the States?" I inquired with a hopeful note.

"No," he replied shaking his head and drying a tumbler. "You'll hear all about it at dinner."

I left with a vague mixture of hope and apprehension. Summer camp — though I'd never been to a real overnight camp — meant to me lakes, pine trees, horseback riding, canoe trips, archery — all the things I associated with the Catskills. But I didn't know of any camp on St. Thomas, and he'd said it wasn't in the States. At dinner, I learned that this particular camp was on St. John. They couldn't tell me much more about the place except that its finest feature was the cost. For two weeks of camp, the expense was only 20 dollars — they couldn't afford *not* to send me there. Seeing my disappointment, Pop said he was sure that this camp would have many of the things most camps had.

"Horseback riding?" I ventured.

"I doubt they have any horses."

"How about canoeing?"

"I don't know. But for 20 bucks you can't expect Camp Hiawatha, for Christ's sake."

I ate my mashed potatoes.

"It's run by the Baptists," my mother explained cheerily.

Pop glared at her.

"Why do ... the Baptists ...?"

"Don't worry. All you need to know is that they're very big on cheap summer entertainment. You'll have a ball. Now eat your spinach."

"It's where you get religion," my friend David explained.

We were waiting at the Red Hook dock for the St. John ferry. Already there were a couple dozen other campers with their bundles and bags.

I asked him what they meant by "get."

"I don't know. That's what my parents keep saying. They think it's a big joke."

One of the last to show up at the dock are Bappo Scabriel and Cletus Roebuck — known to his chums as Tallboy. They get out of the pickup driven by Bappo's dad. In the back of the truck are Jimmy Merced and two unfamiliar boys. They call out teasing things to Bappo and Cletus. Jimmy tells Bappo behave himself and asks if he remember his Bible and see how he already forget his sleeping bag. Bappo and Cletus are the last to board the ferry, and Bappo is skylarking and muttering curse words at a bag that is coming apart. That Bappo is going to be my fellow camper is taking a bit of getting used to. He is big for his age and attends Commandant Gade School, which would likely qualify him for being none too smart. Both he and Cletus are a tad old for this crowd, but their parents, like mine, are probably cashing in on the cheap food. When the truck pulls away from the dock, Jimmy Merced calls out a parting comment and I see there are two goats in back, and I wonder if, being out on this end of the island, they'll be swinging by the abattoir on the way home.

On the ferry ride over, I sat on the edge of a lively conversation between several boys who had been to the camp the year before. Talk centered on the less appealing aspects of the place. One was a thing called Hard Labor Hill which campers were forced to go up and down when they misbehaved. Then there were the latrines and the wild boars that tried to get into your tent at night, and, finally, various culinary descriptions rendered in excruciating detail of the hideous things one would be expected to eat. There was much laughter and good cheer, each of these veterans trying to outdo the other, the tortures spoken of fondly — even joyously — by the survivors as if the tortures were, themselves, what made the camp so much fun. I heard no talk of religion.

The ferry was met at Cruz Bay by several adult white males, Rev. Snopes chief among them. His black greased-back hair sat on his head like a helmet. After brief introductions, we were trundled off in six waiting jeeps, all of them 4-wheel drive. Though I had grown accustomed to curvy, bumpy, unpaved mountain roads, this was a totally new level of discomfort. All the cheery talk aboard the boat was now replaced by sealed mouths and grimaces as our rear ends absorbed the relentless slams of the metal seats. The bush crowded the road. Dust came up through the floor panels. The exhaust fumes curled back into our canvas compartment.

As Cruz Bay, that last outpost of civilization, receded like a memory, certain worries began to insinuate themselves, and I began to imagine that I was being abducted. All the talk about Hard Labor Hill and bad food brought to mind other kinds of camps I had heard of, labor camps, and I wondered if the 20 dollars for two weeks was just a trick and these people with southern accents not Baptists at all but kidnappers, and the place we were being taken to not a camp but a remote hideout where I would never be found. The fact that others in the jeep had survived the experience the year before did not hold any water with me; they could be in on this thing. The guy across from me whose knees kept banging into mine had a similar look of dismay on his face. He was from St. Croix, and this was his first year, too. While I was seeing my way clear to telling him he was being kidnapped, the jeep cleared Bordeaux Mountain, and I saw Coral Bay a few miles to the east and a thousand or so feet below. There were a few structures, tracings of a road, hope.

Good Shepherd Camp was located (and still is) well beyond Coral Bay, on a blistering-hot scrub and cactus peninsula called Calabash Boom. The final stretch included a serpentine series of switchbacks that looked like a controlled cliff. Our driver, Brother Bob, fiddled with various levers, searching for the lowest gear. Had he ever attempted this thing before, I wondered? After the first switchback, the road became a riverbed where there were seldom more than three wheels on the ground. I hung one foot over the tailgate, ready to bail.

I suspect the Baptists had chosen this God-forsaken outpost to lose money and save souls because some departed convert had willed it to them, and the isolation from the temptations of the real world suited their purposes. The camp was situated on the side of a steep hill (Hard Labor) overlooking the coast. There was, structure-wise, a small mess hall, a screened-in bungalow, two latrines, a storage shed and, of course, the chapel. At the base of the hill, on a mud flat festooned with large crab holes, was our campground. We were all herded into this area and told to leave our gear and then shepherded up to the sweltering mess hall for baloney sandwiches and Kool-Aid.

Our indoctrination speech was administered by the Head Shepherd himself, Rev. Snopes. First he introduced the other members of his flock: Brother Les, Brother Bob, and Brother Jed (all, it turns out, summer conscripts from the Kentucky chapter of this Calvary Baptist mission, all in their late teens or early 20s), and the staff, which included three St. Johnians — two kitchen helpers and a handyman.

Rev. Snopes had a soothing, silky-smooth way about him and certain calming gestures I came to know by heart. One started with both hands

far apart, palms up, dropping in a low, wide arch, and sweeping together — the palms turning into clenched, beseeching fists at his heart. The
other started with hands at his sides, then a half-loop and the palms up
and forward, the blessings spilling forth. I noted with all this raising of
arms that there were no tell-tale rings of perspiration and no hint of heat
in his face. His jet-black hair stayed swept back and perfectly in place,
proof positive, I felt, of the wonders of Brylcream. The meeting ended
— after descriptions of some of the swell activities that awaited us — with
a lengthy prayer filled with much beseeching and vouchsafing.

The prayers were appropriate preparation for the next task — setting
up tents among the crab holes. Many of the holes had been recently
packed with rocks and sand giving our campground the appearance of a
lunar landscape or of a battlefield of recently exploded mines or mortar
shells. The area was located adjacent to a gut which, during heavy rains,
was guaranteed to overflow into our tents. On the fringes of the campground, huge displaced land crabs scuttled about among the snaking
roots of mangrove trees observing our mysterious tent pitching, waiting
to move back into their own quarters. We were cautioned also about wild
nocturnal boars that would try to get at our food. They would even eat
our soap and toothpaste.

My tentmate was Dana, a classmate from All Souls. Our tent was
pitched — with help from Brother Les — on the highest ground we
could find maybe three inches higher than the lowest. We were given two
cots, mended in spots, which were stenciled with the name of some
Baptist church in Kentucky — recycled, no doubt, for the purpose of sav-
ing souls in the Indies. After pitching tents, there was stickball among the
crab holes and a swim at the "beach" — a coral-encrusted, sea urchin-
studded stretch of coast about 100 yards from the campground. Then it
was on to the showers, which were located at the back of the church
(cleanliness being next to Godliness?) and administered from raised 55
gallon drums in two brief doses — one five-second get wet spurt and a
second, generous, ten-second soap-removal stream.

Dinner began and ended in prayer. In between were sloppy joes, pota-
to chips, carrots and celery. For desert there was apple sauce. There were
no seconds and a hard and fast rule about eating everything on your

plate. One West Indian boy, accustomed to much hardier fare, refused the last half of his sloppy joe. Forty-five minutes later he showed up at the campground after having gagged down the last of it.

Before going to bed, there was one dark piece of business I had to attend to: going to the latrine. I had walked past it earlier and caught a whiff and had been focusing my energies in an effort to forestall the inevitable. At that time both doors were closed and several other campers were waiting their turn, and there was a good bit of casual banter between those waiting and those doing. Communal crapping was a new and frightening experience for me. Just shooting the breeze and then letting her rip? I didn't think so. Although I did not judge others because they had to defecate, I may have hoped to instill the belief in others that this particular activity was somewhat below me, that sloppy joes and the like found their way out of me in a more civilized manner.

I waited until moments before lights out to make my move and, with my flashlight extinguished so as not to draw attention, slinked out of the campground and headed for those two dark houses on the hill. Once there, I double-checked to make sure no one was looking, and only then turned on the flashlight to see which of the two would best attend to my needs. The little circle of light searched out each of the odoriferous confines; there was the board, there was the hole. It was excruciatingly simple. Nailed to the wall was a pack of papers, not toilet paper but little squares more akin to butcher paper, something used to wrap a pork chop.

I steeled myself, took a long draught of fresh air and plunged into the chosen cubicle. There I sat listening to the sound of the day's food falling — not easing into the crystal waters of a porcelain bowl — but falling for what seemed a sickening amount of time, and landing — splot — in the amassed stool of a dozen lowlier stools than my own. After the final indignity of applying the little squares of non-absorbent paper, I zipped up and peeked to see if anyone was out there, anyone who might identify me.

(Ah-ha! There he is! I told you, boys!)

Seeing no one, I stepped out and, realizing I had survived the experience with body and reputation intact, I stepped back in to address one unanswered curiosity. Bravely, I flashed my light down into the dark hole.

It was just as it had sounded. Five feet below the seat lay the dark pudding, its surface flecked with white edges of paper, like doomed moths, trying to escape. I returned to the campsite, flashlight extinguished, breathing in the fresh air, feeling unburdened, made new, feeling greatly relieved.

Each morning between nine and twelve o'clock there were three classes and three groups of about ten children each alternating from one class to the other. I don't remember much about the classes. Art and sports were mostly stringing beads and hitting a tired tennis ball with a stick. What I remember most vividly are the religion classes which were much more interesting than those offered at All Souls. The music was stirring and fun, not like the lugubrious Anglo Saxon convolutions I was familiar with. Here we sang of little lights and running rivers, of arching bridges and burning bushes, songs with catchy refrains and foot-stomping rhythms. Each morning, the class started with one of these songs to get our blood going which, after an hour of stringing beads, was not always easy. Then there was a bit of scripture — John 3:16 chief among them — and some discussion. Brother Bob and Brother Les alternated as our teacher except on Friday when Rev. Snopes, the heavy hitter, lent a hand.

Brother Les was very good at the religious metaphor, often using the words of a song to explain the song's meaning. Hence, *This Little Light of Mine* (I'm gonna make it shine, shine, shine) was not any old light but an invisible light we all carried inside — *if* we loved Jesus. *May the Circle Be Unbroken* was not a circle like one might draw to make a marble ring but a different kind of circle, an invisible one that was there all the same. I had never heard this kind of talk before, and I liked the idea of this coded world where one thing was actually the other.

In class, Brother Les spoke of a dusty hermit crab he had seen by the side of the road. He told us that he saw himself in this crab and asked us if we knew why. We didn't have a clue. Finally, Bappo, from the back pew wondered if it was because Brother Les looked something like a crab. Brother Les fielded this and some stifled laughter graciously but, seeing his control slipping, decided to help us along. He saw himself in the hermit crab because he and the crab were on the road of life. Already I began to see. In this world, the shell of the crab was the faith that he carried with him, he explained, and this faith was a house that protected him so that, no matter how difficult and dusty — or sinful — the road of life became, in the end he would be safe. There were other similarities as well. I looked around to see if other campers appreciated the way this hermit crab business worked and was appalled to see Bappo and two other boys actually giggling and skylarking. I knew that Bappo, in addition to being Jimmy Merced's pal, was someone I had once suspected of ambushing me with stones on the way from school. Bappo had no respect for anything. Brother Les was a pretty cool guy, I decided then and there, and he deserved more attentive listeners.

But Brother Les has not finished. He goes on to tell us — and this is the cruncher — that, like the hermit crab, we too must die. He allows a few heartbeats to let this sink in. How many of us have ever received a burn on our skin? He wants to know. He folds his arms and leans back to listen. It is our turn to talk, and we talk confidently of irons and of stoves, of matches and exhaust pipes. Brother Les listens attentively, and you realize he's a pretty good guy, all and all, and probably pretty popular with the girls back in Kentucky. Soon he tells of such a girl — nice girl, real pretty — who died in a fire. The neighbors heard her screams but could do nothing. Her skin actually came off in the hand of the firefighter who went in to save her.

I look back to see if Bappo and company have heard this.

The good news, Brother Les tells us with a smile, is that she was a Christian. Her suffering would have been less than that of a hot coal falling into the ocean depths as she entered into the glorious Kingdom of Heaven. But other people, people who are not Christians — here, his eye passed over us — who are sinners in the eyes of the Lord, for these people death will be no more than a starting bell, a bell that sends them plummeting into the flaming oven of eternity. Then, to make the point, he asks if we still remember the burns we have just recalled, and we do, and he says all of them combined can not *begin* to describe the flames of Hell. Then there is the horrible matter of eternity. This he will not even attempt to describe.

We closed out with a stirring round of *This Little Light of Mine* followed by a brief prayer followed by stickball among the crab holes. It surprised me to see most of the campers fall immediately into a stickball frame of mind, careening and screaming down the hill. I lingered a bit trying to disassociate myself from the mayhem, trying to think of something to say. But Brother Les was busy closing the chapel, so I trotted off behind the others.

Down on the mud flats stickball was quickly in session and each day the sides stayed the same. Bappo was captain of our team, and Rodney Peet, the undertaker's son, was the other. The ball was a battered tennis ball and the sticks lengths of dead mangrove root. The trick was to run the bases without spraining an ankle in a crab hole. The first day when it was my turn to hit, I kept fouling it off which delayed things while fielders tried to retrieve the ball by extracting it from the tangled mangrove roots. Bappo cussed me and came over. What happen? I can't hit straight? To show me how he wrapped himself around me, twisting my torso, lifting my right elbow, and choking me up on the mangrove root. He was big and solid, Bappo was, and he smelled like soap.

On the very next pitch, I sent a rocket into the left field cactus patch and as I rounded first I heard Bappo yelling.

"Go all the way, m'son. Go all the way!"

On alternate days, Brother Bob was in charge of giving us our religion. He was younger than Les and chunkier and not as given to literary allusions. His great strength, as I saw it, was his ability to crack the door of Heaven and Hell to show us campers just what these opposing kingdoms looked like. Even then I think he borrowed a couple pointers from Brother Les.

For instance, to describe the pleasures of Heaven we were each asked to give an example of something we *really* enjoyed, something we really liked to do. We heard about milkshakes and baseball and rollercoasters and candy. There was climbing trees. Bappo's friend, Cletus, even said girls. All of these were acceptable answers and to them Brother Bob added his own idea of a good time which was reading the Bible. Now, he informed us, all of these earthly pleasures rolled into one would weigh less than a feather compared to the mountain of joy contained in one second of Heavenly bliss.

Then (and hadn't we all been waiting for this?), we turned our attention to the horrible business of Hell. Pain was called for and greedily we delivered. Boiling tar, poison arrows, tooth extractions, parental beatings, having the Empire State Building fall on your toe, being consumed by a shark, tied to an anthill, being cut into eentsy-weensy bits by a razor blade, fried and eaten by blood-thirsty cannibals, having the Atom Bomb fall on your head. Brother Bob put an end to it and required us to combine these multiple horrors into a single gruel of eternal torment. This, he then revealed to us, was itself only fractionally as excruciating as the manifold sufferings of Hell.

And Brother Bob was not reluctant — as Brother Les had been — to delve into the matter of eternity. If he didn't discuss this kind of thing with us, who would? We heard of the little bird moving an entire mountain, grain by painstaking grain, from one side of the Earth to the other. He described the hurricanes and typhoons this bird had to endure as it circled the globe over and over.

A hand went up.

"Yes, Bappo?"

"That bird go dead before it get the mountain move."

This was only an example, he explained, that this bird moving the mountain was not something that could actually happen. We were relieved to hear this. Brother Bob went on to say that the example was designed to show how long eternity is. It was meant to show that the amount of time it took that bird to move and reassemble the mountain on the other side of the world would be equal to only one *second* of eternity.

"What about Purgatory?" Dana asked.

This landed on Brother Bob like something thrown from afar, from the far side of the moon, something unexpected but welcome all the same.

"Well Dana, why don't you tell us what you know about Purgatory."

"It's a place where you go between Heaven and Hell," Dana ventured. "If you behave well when you're suffering in Hell, you get to go there and after a while you can even get to Heaven, I think."

Brother Bob shook his head slowly to show us how sad it was that another church would cruelly lead a child with such vain and pathetic hopes.

"Dana, is the Bible the Lord's Word?"

"Yes."

Brother Bob nodded slowly.

"Does the Lord tell lies?" he asked.

"No."

"Well, Dana, nowhere in the Bible is there a single mention of Purgatory. Purgatory, Dana, is a place dreamed up by people who want to think there is a way out, a way not to accept Christ and still be saved."

That is what Purgatory was.

When the lights went out that night I lay awake in the tent with certain wonderings, mostly about sin. With the Baptists there were no frocks, no gory crucifixes, no bread or wine. Sermons were delivered in shirtsleeves and the bottom line was Damnation. Now at All Souls there was incense and genuflecting, more serious than Christ Church in Rye. But this was a whole new level of Godliness. And Sal, the boatyard handyman, was a Seventh Day Adventist. They really took sin seriously. No chore was beyond Sal's ability, but he wouldn't carry a wicker basket containing the rum for the Harbor Cruise. At Kingdom Hall the month before, Sal and Lucy had presided like Nubian potentates over their marriage reception. Zinc tubs filled with Fanta and Malta and bottles of stout were provided for all, but there was no alcohol (my parents made do with a flask) and dancing, being sinful, was not allowed. We learned too late — my mother was wearing pearls — that Adventists also viewed jewelry as sinful. Neither bride nor groom wore jewelry but a Pepsi-cola pen and pencil set adorned Sal's breast pocket. Why in one religion was wine part of the ceremony and in the other a sin? And what could be said of the idea that a single sin could seal one's fate?

These silent tent wonderings were not unfamiliar ground after a year living on St. Thomas, but they were brought into particularly tight focus with all the talk of Hell. Pam, after a year in Catholic School, was big on her Rosaries and Hail Marys and, having turned 15, had taken it upon herself to coach me on the subject of retribution. According to her, all it took was one Mortal Sin. A guy could be a saint his entire life, have a single impure thought and bang, get hit by a truck. Did this guy get a crack at Purgatory? I wondered. Or was there such a thing?

The way I saw it, Pam, despite her sudden religiosity, had her own possible Mortal Sins lurking — in impure thoughts if nothing else. After Sal's wedding reception at Kingdom Hall, Pam made light of the sly grin on Lucy's face and of the thoughts she might have entertained of the nuptials that awaited her with that mighty stallion of righteousness. She slipped out of her velvet dress.

"Lucy's going to have her arms full tonight," she said squeezing into a pair of cut-offs.

"When Sal climb on to that," I said echoing words I'd heard in the schoolyard.

"Horse go buck up," Pam added, her eyes narrowing, her teeth biting her lip just a bit. It was hard to imagine Sal as Pam did, buck naked, departing from his daily devotions — his chest, the smooth muscled arms, the taut belly, the mighty loins all called upon to create more Adventists.

Pam was also the one who had pointed out Sister Margaret sunning herself in a blue two-piece at the end of Lindbergh Bay. On the pretense of looking for sea grapes I had admired her slender defrocked limbs and the way she anointed herself with suntan oil, her fingers making circles on her tummy. Would the Baptists or Adventists view this kind of sunbathing as sinful? I wondered. With eternal agony at stake, there seemed to be a dangerous degree of uncertainty about what was and wasn't a sin. There was, for instance, the matter of Father Nibbs who, it was said, had a fondness for Bourbon. Very little talk of Hell from him. But I was certainly as sinful as Father Nibbs, I figured. I tried to imagine Father Nibbs tumbling, dumbfounded, into the flaming pit.

"Goddam fucking bo'hog," Dana cursed sitting bolt upright in his cot.

"You're dreaming," I informed him.

"You *think* I dreaming."

He shined his flashlight at the tent flap and reached under his cot for the stick he'd sharpened earlier with his Swiss Army knife. Sure enough, a bristly-haired snout parted the flap. Dana drove the spear home and the beast ran squealing into the night.

—✸—

Hidden in the forests of Reef Bay Valley, several hours hike from the nearest road, are the ruins of a sugar plantation from the 1700s and, further along, up several turns of the tumbling gut, a boulder pool with ancient inscriptions of uncertain origin. I don't recall much of the hike there except the unexplained coffin in the basement of the estate house. But knowing what I do now, we probably drove to the end of the road in the Estate Carolina valley west of Coral Bay, and hiked in from there. That would have taken us across Bordeaux Mountain, past the turn-off for Lameshur, and into the valley. A good six miles on Kool-Aid and bologna sandwiches.

I do remember Mr. Samuels being our guide, though I doubt I knew his name at the time. He was a forest ranger of sorts and an old time St. Johnian who knew the botany and history of the place. At the estate house and at the sugar factory — or what remained of them — he helped us see the past. He asked us to imagine the walls of the valley stripped of trees, sugar cane as far as the eye could see. He put a roof on the estate house for us and, where a termite nest grew, hung portraits on the walls and spoke of the mahogany dresser, the canopied bed, the candlelight of a modest chandelier, the lady of the house drawing a comb through her hair. He explained the walls, the corners cut from heads of brain coral, the yellow ballast bricks brought from Copenhagen, the sea sand and molasses in the mortar, and the volcanic blue bit stone. He hinted, also, at the folly of the adventure, its collapse triggered by a needed gear for the mill that sank aboard the ship trying six months later to deliver it.

Mr. Samuel spoke also about the 1733 slave rebellion that had occurred on St. John. I doubt I remembered much of what he said beyond, perhaps, the whites who were macheted to death, and the mass suicide of the cornered rebels six months later. I certainly remember the petroglyphs and the gut running, the water clear. At the falls above the petroglyphs, Mr. Samuels asked us to try to imagine the forest as it had once been, but we were all too relieved to get wet and eat our bologna sandwiches to pay much attention. We lounged about on the hot boulders, going in and out of the cool stream, the water we carried onto the stones bringing the carvings to life. We were sitting where others had sat, leaving our wet footprints where stone carvers had left theirs.

The final day of camp, Rev. Snopes took the helm of the closing religion class. Mysteriously, to one side of him was an easel and a board draped with a piece of cloth. He said nothing about it, deepening our curiosity. He just wanted to have a short word with us, is the way he put it, just a chance to go over a few things we had learned in camp. We were asked to recite John 3:16 and then reminded of the passage's meaning. Of course, implicit in the promise of everlasting life was the other possibility. He talked about sin and about Jesus but spoke little about the torments of Hell, something I'd come to depend on.

Then, after telling us he had something he wanted to share, he pulled the cloth away to reveal a chalkboard drawing that took a bit of staring at to properly decipher. In the upper right a broad swath appeared which headed toward the bottom of the board; this was the Road of Life. At the bottom of the board, in orange and red chalk, were the leaping Flames of Hell. One could easily see how the Road of Life went nowhere except to the precipice. But departing from that road and turning at the brink in a very satisfactory manner is a much smaller, narrower and windy road which turns away, labors to the upper left of the board to a tidy little rainbow of many colors. Rev. Snopes' hair was mesmerizing, the way it shined and stayed perfectly in place as he clenched beseeching fists and allowed blessings to fall from his outstretched palms. It was not enough for us to accept Jesus into our heart quietly, he informed us; we must each be prepared to make a more public commitment, a time when one surrenders entirely to Jesus. It was a thing each of us must decide for ourselves. The time was fast approaching, we were told, and I could feel it coming.

That afternoon we gathered wood for the big bonfire that night. The pile grew on a downwind projection of the coast to carry the sparks out to sea. After about an hour, the pile was about 15 feet in diameter and five feet high. Still we went further afield collecting driftwood and debris swept into the mouth of the bay and, shortly, three jeeps backed up with loads gathered somewhere else. I wondered about the wind. The mangrove swamp was over 20 yards upwind from the heap but a wind shift could send cinders right into it.

After dinner, as twilight began to gather, we all headed down to the coast. There was a prayer and a few rounds of *This Little Light* and *Deep and Wide,* and then rags soaked in kerosene were wedged into the heap and lighted. Seated in a circle around the pile, we all watched our little section of fire grow. Brother Les got up to talk a little about how sweet Jesus was and all and about the temptations we must fight. And then Brother Bob, calling our attention to the fire, reminded us about how hot Hell was. It occurred to him that this festive bonfire could serve as just such a reminder, and he noted how the increasing heat had caused us to widen our circle.

When Rev. Snopes rose behind the flames like a mighty wizard and in a booming voice announced that "The Time Had Come," I was relieved. I was certain I wanted to surrender myself, to leave my wicked ways, and to serve God — but I hadn't been sure just how to do it. Here was my chance to publicly come clean, to take up the sword. I rose to my feet as did a sprinkling of others. Then the rest, seeing what was expected of them, rose also — all, that is, but Bappo and Cletus who turned away from the fire and started throwing stones at the sea. Then Rev. Snopes offered a powerful prayer that told how we were God's soldiers who would, for a lifetime, serve him and I knew, tearfully, that I had been accepted. That I had been saved, and the weight lifted. We sang a few happy songs after that and watched the flames leap far above our heads and the sparks sail into the night, and the cinders fall out to sea.

Purgatory

W hen my mother met me at Red Hook I was full of glad tidings. I couldn't wait to tell her but managed at first to talk instead about camp things: hikes, tentmate, latrines, arts and crafts.

"What did they feed you?" she asked as we pulled out of the Red Hook area and headed east toward town. She was probably interested to see how the Baptists spread 20 dollars over 42 meals. I told her the food wasn't great but chose not to elaborate.

"We learned some good songs," I said finally.

"Camp songs?"

"Kinda. You want to hear one?"

"Sure."

I sang a lively rendition of *This Little Light of Mine,* adding a hint of two-part harmony on the shine shine shine part. At the end of it, I explained that the little light was not really a light like a flashlight or anything.

"I see," she said, her eyes straight ahead on the road. She didn't ask just what kind of light it was, and I pondered this watching the familiar East End scrub slide by the window.

"It's kind of a light you have inside you," I explained.

"Uh-huh."

"It lights up the darkness," I added repeating the words I'd heard spoken time and again.

"Your birthday present from Uncle Sam arrived while you were away," she said switching subjects. "Your father opened it by mistake."

"Oh, good."

"You want to know what it is?"

"Sure."

"A sling shot!" she said with wide eyes.

"A sling shot?"

"A very fancy one," she added. "A Wham-O."

I'd gotten a weapon for my eleventh birthday and my mother was happy about it? I'd already had a homemade one taken from me only a few months before.

"Of course you're not to shoot dogs and cats. Maybe you and Niles can set up a target."

"Yeah. Shoot at a can or something."

"Uh-huh."

I started whistling *This Little Light* as we passed the Nadir gut and drove along shady Brookman Road toward Fort Mylner. Her car, an old gray Volks with a cut-away top of white canvas with surrey fringe, drew a few stunned looks from locals standing at the bus stop.

"And guess what?" I said.

"What?"

"We had religion classes, too, and we learned all about Heaven and Hell and the Bible."

She said nothing to this, downshifting at the intersection and looking both ways, as if, possibly, she'd been too busy concentrating to hear what I said.

"And I got saved."

She heard that all right. I told her all about the bonfire and how I'd been the first to stand. And I told her all about the chalkboard drawing with the broad and narrow roads of life. She seemed to be concentrating too hard on the potholes to hear everything that I was saying. Her ears perked right up when I mentioned something about Rev. Snopes.

"Is he the man I met," she asked, "the man with the greasy hair?"

"Uh-huh." That was the guy. I told her about the big bonfire and how Rev. Snopes had gotten almost everyone to stand up for the Lord.

Though my parents had some strong feelings about the kind of religion being dispensed at Good Shepherd, they were tight-lipped. I suspect my father objected to the thought of his Episcopalian son quaking in the isles with crackers as much as having Hell scared into me, but what could he say? He'd figured 20 dollars was a small price to pay and now he had begun to see the bill of goods more clearly. And he was being continually reminded of it by my whistling *This Little Light*.

"I'm getting a little tired of that tune," he said at the dinner table the day after I got back. It was Sunday, and I had whistled it in the back of the jeep coming and going from the beach. I guess I was trying to hold on to the feelings that were already beginning to slip away.

"Sorry," I said rising to clear the dishes.

"How about something a little more varied," he said trying to take the edge off, "something like *Night and Day*."

"Now *there's* a good song," Mom chimed in.

My father started to whistle and Mom threw in a few words.

"Night and day, you are the one..." Mom swooned.

I wasn't in the mood to laugh, even at this miserable performance. With great seriousness I continued clearing the dishes. God was watching me, testing me, I felt.

Later, upstairs, I was humming *This Little Light*.

"Don't let you-know-who hear you," Pam said from her room. I stopped what I was doing and went to the door. I stared at her and my eyes started to go teary.

"Geez, I'm sorry. Don't be so touchy."

"How would you feel?" I started.

"So Pop doesn't like you to whistle a tune. You're going to cry about that?"

"I'm not crying," I said brushing a tear from my cheek.

Pam closed the book she had been reading.

"It's not just a song," I explained. "It's about God."

"Duh, Willie, " she said with wide eyes. "Don't you think we know? Don't you think we can *see* those Baptists scared God into you?"

"They did not."

Then she told me what had happened the day before at lunch. Mom had reported things I'd told her about Heaven and Hell and about the broad and narrow roads of life and about the big bonfire. Pop was so mad he brought his hand down on the table and sent the aspic hopping out of the serving dish.

"He almost went down to give Reverend what's-his-name some real fire," Pam added.

"He did?"

"Mom talked him out of it."

What was it in me (Satan perhaps?) that welcomed this news? That painted a quick, forbidden picture of my father at the door of the Baptist Church in Frenchtown raking Rev. Snopes over the coals? Yet all this had been kept from me. The business of singing *Night and Day* had been their way of keeping their feelings from me, of humoring me, of weaning me away from the obsession.

"If I was there I wouldn't have listened to all that crap from Brother Bob, I'll tell you that," Pam added.

"What do you mean?"

"All that crap about Heaven and Hell."

"You listen to the nuns about Purgatory."

Pam gave me a blank look.

"So what's wrong with that?"

"Purgatory doesn't exist," I said with total certainty.

"Oh *really?*" Pam said swinging her feet onto the floor. "You think a bunch of hicks know more than nuns and priests who have spent years..."

"It's not in The Bible."

"So *what?*"

"So plenty. If it's in The Bible it's God's Word."

"So you believe Adam and Eve really existed and that a snake spoke to Eve? The Bible is full of things that aren't true; they're tell-me-why stories, Willie, stories with messages in them."

"So the Bible is full of lies?"

"Not lies, stories."

"So you don't think The Bible is God's Word?"

Pam just looked at me.

"You're really thick. That's why the Baptists have you around their little finger. They told you about eternal damnation and you swallowed it — hook, line and sinker. The Baptists are famous for that."

"The Catholics aren't too bad at it either."

"Bullshit."

"Sinner."

Now she was mad and if I didn't watch out she'd give me a good punch.

"You're the sinner," she said. "You kill lizards."

She had taken off the gloves.

"Well as long as you have your rosaries and say your Hail Marys and go to confession, I suppose you can be forgiven for walking up and down

Main Street with Chelsea Moolenaar trying to get boys to look at you."

I had *just* exceeded the limits.

"Get out of here!" she said advancing on me. "Get out or I'll punch your arms black and blue!"

"Sinner!" I screamed, slamming the door.

"Wait till Judgment Day, buddy," she yelled after me. "We'll see who's the sinner then!"

I had a hard time getting to sleep that night and the alley cats didn't help. There was a small stash of throwing rocks for such occasions, and I even went to the window a couple of times. But I thought about the neighbors and lizards and about being a sinner and decided not to throw any rocks just then.

Shooting Pool

That summer, shortly after Good Shepherd, I ran into Bappo Scabriel fishing off the Coast Guard dock one night. He was there with Jimmy Merced and Jimmy's little sister, Eliza. Niles and I had been fishing for over an hour without noticing them when they came up from the rocks by the Legislature and moved into the light on the south side of the dock. Niles and I had caught only a karang and a small one at that, and I could sense Niles getting a bit desperate with competitors nearby. Then Bappo sauntered over to us and asked Niles if he had an extra hook, which Niles reluctantly surrendered. Bappo did this without acknowledging me, even though we had recently spent two weeks at camp together. He went back to the other side of the wharf. From where we sat casting handlines, they appeared as silhouettes. Soon there was a commotion, the little girl squealing. Jimmy Merced had something on the line.

"They catch a congo," Niles said.

Eels were serious business. I had seen Niles shoot an eel with a spear-gun and watched how the eel, with a hole straight through it, worked its way up the spear like a sidewinder trying to get at him. Usually eels stole your bait or you hooked one and it knotted itself into a fissure. They weren't worth the lost hooks.

Niles went over and stood with Bappo looking into a bucket, Jimmy and Eliza a few feet to one side. I debated the matter. It had been over a year since Jimmy Merced had thrown the brick at my father. I wasn't sure if he still harbored a grudge of some sort, but Niles seemed to be having a lively conversation so I tied my line off and walked over.

Bappo looked up at me and smirked giving little tugs on his line. Off to the side, Jimmy muttered something to himself and started to pull his line in. Then Bappo thought of something to say.

"So them preacher-man put some fear in your ass, eh?"

"Not so much," I replied.

Bappo looked over at Merced who glanced at me and let slide a chance to be unkind. Jimmy said something to Eliza and they moved away from the light. She had a thumb in her mouth and the fingers of her other hand hooked into a loop of his belt causing his pants to slip a bit over his hip. I looked into their bucket. A snapper, two redman and a grunt. The congo lay on the dock beside a single edged razor, a clean rectangular notch of flesh gone. The eel's flesh was already back on Jimmy's hook, out there in that dark water looking for a bigger fish.

—⚍—

The fact that Bappo Scabriel had gone to Good Shepherd Camp made me wonder if, perhaps, Jimmy Merced had attended the camp a year or two before. My memory of him taunting Bappo from the back of the truck at the ferry dock further fed that curiosity. When I mentioned Good Shepherd to Anton, Jimmy's father, and told him that Bappo had gone there, he seemed to remember a St. John camp but couldn't recall if Jimmy had been sent there. But he doubted Esther, his wife at the time, would have sent Jimmy to get "brainwashed by a bunch of holy rollers." Summertime would have more likely been spent in Rosendahl, he explained, where the family had horses, and where Jimmy could use a pellet rifle to hunt for thrush and mountain dove and sometimes duck or even quail — birds that could be cooked into a stew. That got Anton talking about hunting — spots out in Fortuna that were good for duck, or a place out in Bovoni, near the salt flats, where he used to go deer hunting with Hugo. But at the time I was more interested in the subject of religion. When I asked him if Jimmy had attended any church, Anton, having to shift from firing shots to worshipping God, seemed momentarily lost. He recovered to assure me that, as a youngster, Jimmy had regularly gone to the Dutch Reform Church with his mother. He had made his Confirmation. His moral development was thoroughly taken care of. I did not press the subject.

But his words made me wonder. The Dutch Reform Church was generally considered the white people's church. If his mother hated white people as Anton has suggested, why would she attend that church, or, for that matter, choose to marry a white man? Although it is not my responsibility to speculate on the origins of Jimmy Merced's racial antipathies, I can't help but wonder, all these years later, if racial feelings arose as a result of her marriage to Anton? Jimmy's first cat scunt comment to me would have been at age twelve. At that age, my own mind could have echoed similar sentiments about certain St. Thomians. But not sentiments I would ever have spoken aloud. Perhaps these feelings were inherited from Anton and Hugo. Both men claim to be "white" (though one grandparent was Anguillian), but I wonder if those two brothers, in light of their family's diminished circumstances, had taken a kind of junkyard dog approach to those more fortunate than themselves? As a boy Jimmy Merced may have overheard tales about cinematic brawls his father and uncle had around town with the Navy and U.D.T. Still, Anton would likely be the first to deny any hard feelings toward white people. I am white, he might say.

There is another speculation I have allowed myself. Perhaps Anton's characterization of things is a bit self-serving and his relationship with his son darker than he cares to reveal. One could reasonably ask whether Anton's self-described violent and unpredictable behavior carried over to his family life. A person operating on this speculation might wonder whether the real source of Jimmy Merced's racial hatred was his own father.

A couple of weeks after our conversation about Jimmy's moral development, Anton and I arranged to play pool down at the Normandie, a well-known watering hole in Frenchtown. I picked him up at the base of Bunker Hill. He had on a pair of Bermudas and a polo shirt and had trouble getting his legs into the car. Walking from the parking lot beside the Frenchtown ballfield I was struck by the number of nods and waves he received from passersby. Although some of these acquaintances were his age or older or probably knew him from his wild days, a good share were in their 20s and 30s and I wondered if they knew him more as the postal clerk of their youth or for his son's role at Sweet Bottom.

When we played pool, Anton shuffled around with the cue, often trailing a supporting hand along the edge of the table. He seldom made a shot with more force than required and usually left the cue ball where it could continue to do its damage. Although I occasionally won, the afternoon usually ended with me down in total games. And when I won two in a row he would softly accuse me of practicing on the sly. Slowly we were developing a way of joking with each other, even of making fun of each other and we each seemed to enjoy this tentative testing of the waters, this lowering of our guards.

One afternoon on the way back from playing pool, Anton extended an invitation to dinner.

"You and your better half," he said.

"That's very generous of you, Anton. I promise to be on my best behavior."

"You may have to do a little better than that."

My wife and I showed up with a bottle of wine the following Sunday night. His wife, Elizabeth, was working in the kitchen, so Anton played the host introducing my wife to his assorted children and grandchildren. We also looked through a couple of family albums. The photos were mostly of his more recent family and only one photo showed him more-or-less as I had remembered him, taken perhaps in the early sixties.

As we paged through the album I kept hoping for a photo or two of Jimmy, but I was disappointed. The two photos I had seen — the one astride the horse and the other cleaning the fish — Anton kept in his wallet. And when I asked if there were any photos of Jimmy, he said no, that these albums didn't go back that far.

But in the back of one album among some loose papers was one photo of a man's head in profile. It was a color photo, but it looked black and white, stark and joyless and very unlike the other cluttered and colorful photos in the album. This was a prison photo taken of Jimmy Merced, a few years after the Sweet Bottom Massacre, a photo Anton had forgotten about. Jimmy's head is shaved and his Adam's apple juts out, and there is a lifeless look in his eye. The image is corpse-like, something from a wax museum.

Alongside this photo was a birthday greeting card from Jimmy to his father, something he may have picked up at the prison commissary. Inside was this note:

Dear Daddy,

As always it was a pleasure getting your letter. I appreciate your words on the importance of having a strong mind and body and I can assure you I am making all efforts in that direction as I work to achieve my redemption from this bondage. I saw Ayesha and our two sons only last week — but just for a short while. When I am with my sons I feel strong and through them I can feel in a small way free.

In answer to your question, yes, I am still working on my book and have two possible publishers. I am waiting to hear from a third.

I thank Allah for the blessing of still being alive and being able to call you Father. I love, honor and respect you. Please cherish your health and stay alive for a good long while, for we will meet again.

Love,
Your Son — Jimmy

The handwriting on the card is script, fairly neat and controlled. The business of cherishing life and of thanking Allah and of honoring his father do not sound like words of a wanton murderer (or an abused son, for that matter) but they may have been intended for the prison officials who read his mail. I wondered then as I do now what kind of book the author of this letter was working on. The title, *Coming of Age in Paradise,* was mentioned by his mother at the trial. What became of that book? I wonder if Jimmy Merced carried the manuscript with him when he left the penitentiary to come to St. Thomas for his date in court. If so, did the book travel with him on the fateful journey back to jail when he hijacked the jetliner to Cuba? Perhaps the book was wishful thinking and the possible publishers only that, or perhaps the manuscript, left in his penitentiary cell, was perused by federal authorities looking for hints to his whereabouts and it still sits in a sheaf of papers in an FBI file. The book, like the man, has disappeared.

One afternoon driving past Western Cemetery on our way to play pool at the Normandie Bar, I asked Anton if I could one day see where his parents were buried.

"No time like the present," he answered.

We pulled in the shady road that runs through the cemetery and walked in from there. I was struck by the number of new graves and concrete vaults in unexpected places, wedged between the roots of mahogany trees and the buckled pavement, placed atop the concrete box of a cousin or in-law. I wonder who planted the mahogany trees and when, and what lay on this ground before, and whether it's still possible for the gravedigger's shovel to hit pure dirt, a foot or two down, undisturbed since Indian days or earlier. There is a funeral in progress not far from the entrance. I look for gravediggers leaning on their shovels, but in this case, no gravedigger will be required; a steel-blue casket is being slid into an empty slot, and it is a mason who stands by with a bucket of mortar. Further along on a mound of fresh dirt festooned with wilted flowers I recognized the name of a high school student recently knifed in the cafeteria. Silence carries through the flickering tree light. Anton draws my attention to the grave of a cousin, Peterson, and we see the grave of Captain Vanterpool, Nile's grandfather. Some dates go back two hundred years. Anton leads me east and tells me that each year at Carnival, he brings a glass of brandy to pour into the soil of his father's grave and then, a moment later, confesses he's failed to do it for years. The grave of his grandparents surprises me. It is elegant and understated, carefully composed of flecked pieces of blue bit stone. It is low to the ground with a tapered crest and a beveled edge around a plaque that says simply "Merced," no dates. The grandparents' grave confirms Anton's claim of wealthy ancestors. He steps over to a nearby grave to pilfer a small vase of wilting flowers.

"And this is my mother, here," Anton said putting the flowers on a low unpainted concrete grave. "And my father beside her."

These two lower, less distinguished graves call to mind that his family and mine share more than a few similarities and I think, there in the graveyard, that if my father were to have met Anton in a different context and later in life, they would have felt easy with each other and had, over a couple of drinks, plenty to talk about. I imagine my father here with us, walking, and try to picture him alongside Anton. There is another person missing from this picture and I imagine him, Jimmy Merced, walking toward us. Because I have never seen him in person as a man, my mind sees him as a boy, years before the misfortunes of his life. But this boy carries a machine gun, and suddenly I feel his presence beneath those mahogany trees and wonder whether Anton has secretly spoken to him, and whether I may, unknowingly, be in danger.

It is the job of graveyards to give rise to fears and to wonders that probe the nearness of one's own mortality. Walking back to the truck that day with Anton, I notice a termite nest in a mahogany tree and, descending its trunk, a patient trail that meanders through the roots and into a crack in a nearby crypt. I feel leaving the graveyard that I am pulling against its current. The earth wants my bones, feels them walking across it. When I pass out of the gate I am carrying my mother and my father with me. And their mothers and fathers and all the generations.

—∭—

The summer of Good Shepherd Camp my father saw to it that my religious convictions were fortified with lessons on the importance of hard work. Hard work, I had been told at camp, was a sure defense against wickedness and, truth be told, I had begun to slip. Try as I might, the Flames of Hell were hard to keep foremost in mind.

That summer, Niles was something of a regular down at the boatyard where, in exchange for helping out, we could get ourselves into various forms of mischief. Mostly we'd fish, though, or sail or clown around on the Love Junk, or, occasionally, launch a rocket, or slap something together with driftwood. Recently, a gutted seaplane had been towed into the yard and when we got tired of playing Sky King, we severed the pontoons and made a raft. We also that summer gained access to the yard's eight-foot pram with its five-horsepower engine. The pram was supposed to be for fishing and diving purposes, but it was also a huge escalation of trouble-making potential. We cruised over to the main harbor and out to Water Island to look for Navy ammo dumps or to throw eggs at evening diners on the hotel's terrace. Recent troubles with Cuba had resulted in a large Navy build-up. We tooled alongside the subs and destroyers tied up at the Sub Base piers and pretended we were in on an operation, or used the pram to fish off the wreck in Krum Bay, or to go over to Lindbergh Bay to build sand traps for unsuspecting beachgoers, or to the end of the runway at twilight to watch aircraft swoop over our heads.

At times we actually helped around the boatyard, sweeping up or sanding a hull. And sometimes we were sent along on the glassbottom trips to help point things out and liven things up a bit — particularly on the afternoon runs when Captain Dan was into his second mayo jar of Cruzan and apt to get a bit surly if asked too many questions. In return for our efforts, Pop might give us a free coke or a couple of bucks, and sometimes he treated us to lunch across the street at Labb's Rib Cage where one could gorge on barbecued ribs.

At Labb's, a largely galvanized structure behind the family's home, the pigs and chickens in the yard and near your table were tomorrow's menu, and some you knew by name. Mr. Labb was from Guyana and claimed to have Carib Indian in his blood (he knew how to roast and season iguana) and his girth gave you every confidence that he knew a thing or two about pork. While Mr. Labb oversaw the operation he allowed his nephew, Raffie, to turn the spit. I knew Raffie because he sometimes came to fish off the boatyard dock and also because he was one of Jimmy Merced's hunting pals. In addition to feeding the pigs and chickens and helping with the barbecue, Raffie raised fighting cocks. On the few occasions I saw Jimmy Merced out back, the two were sitting by the cages under the flamboyant trees where Raffie also had a captive chicken hawk in a large walk-in cage. This was a beautiful, proud creature. Raffie liked to tell folks how he'd saved the wounded hawk, but he failed to mention who'd shot it. He had. Raffie and Jimmy did most of their hunting around the Brewer's Bay gut or by the water catchment above the old Navy barracks where Niles and I sometimes hunted thrush or tested his balsa gliders.

Once Raffie helped us get such a glider out of a very high and dangerous tamarind tree limb, with the deal that he could get to throw it. The glider was a beautiful Niles' creation, 6-feet wide, its ribs thin balsa slivers covered drum-tight with rice paper. It floated like a gull. Raffie took a moment to appreciate the glider's finer features, its delicate construction. Then he carried it to the top of the Bournefield water catchment (Niles in hot pursuit with various instructions and words of caution), and, with a soft, knowing touch threw it southwest in such a way that it caught an updraft, held its course, and soared west over the bush above Brewer's Bay. That was the last we ever saw of that glider.

We camped out several times that summer, our first overnight effort at Perseverance Point ending poorly with ground spiders — large and hairy — chasing us from our blankets and on to the last bus back to town. After this embarrassment Niles saw to it that future outings — usually to Hassel Island — were perfectly executed. He had all the gear — a tent, canteens, Army issue tarps, ammo belts, flack jackets, guns, the works. He had a beautiful pump-action pellet rifle he'd ordered from a *Field and Stream* catalogue that could put a pellet through one side of a can and out the other. On our expeditions this left me with his old BB pistol, which was basically worthless but felt impressive hanging on my hip. Hell, I was packing some heat and I had a shitload of BBs.

Hassel Island had not always been an island. It had once been a peninsula and an active part of the harbor until it was lopped off at the base less than a century ago to create a boat channel and improve the harbor's circulation. The act of severing the island had the effect of freezing it in time and leaving it with various ruins and an old coaling settlement that had become a ghost town. Few people had access to the island but because Nile's grandfather, Captain Vanterpool, was the Harbor Master, we were allowed to catch the Pilot Boat at dawn when it ferried the change of watch to the signal station located on a hill above the harbor's mouth.

Most of our time on Hassel was spent exploring the island's forgotten places. Usually we hiked a mile or so to a small beach on the southeast end of the island to set up our camp and then went up to the signal station at the top of the hill and to Fort Frederik on the point. We looked for iguanas in the shadows of the old stone garrison that once housed the fort's militia and the cannon ball supplies, and we scavenged about in the gutted remains of two stone warehouses washed over by the 1867 tidal wave. We also explored Prince Rupert, the ghost settlement that had been a coaling station and ship repair yard. Sometimes in the late afternoons, we went there to draw water from the cistern and it was easy to fall under the spell of its silence for there was always, on the walkway beneath the mahoganies and between buildings that had once bustled with life, a sense of being watched. Maybe by something that no longer was. Niles, after the water was drawn, might put a finger to his lips and we would listen. Listen for something we could fear. Around sundown, we made a point of being clear of the place.

Other locations on Hassel were invisible, reclaimed by the bush. On one hill above Prince Rupert are the rusted remains of huge fuel tanks and, on another, a WWII gun emplacement. On old maps drawn before the island was an island, the road out there is very clear. It crosses from what is now Frenchtown and goes across a narrow bar just west of Creque's Shipyard and curves up and southward along the island's spine. On those same old maps there are several structures visible along that

narrow hilltop road. One, we were to find out, was an old isolation infirmary for infectious diseases — small pox, yellow fever, the occasional
leper. And beside it, a small graveyard.

We would have known nothing about the graveyard except for an
evening conversation overheard on Nile's porch between his grandfather
and his uncle. They claimed there was such a place — a graveyard just
west of the island's spine and next to the old infirmary — that had been
looted by sailors in 1917. Tombs broken into, graves unearthed. These
porch conversations were not always to be trusted and, at times, designed
to be overheard. When we walked inside from the porch that evening,
Niles quickly dismissed the graveyard talk as untrue. Foolishness. But we
would have to be sure. The sensible thing to do, we agreed, would be to
have his uncle draw us a map.

The morning we set out to find the graveyard, it was before dawn and
the water was like ink and the throaty inboard rumble of the pilot boat
the harbor's only sound. On the way across the harbor we were surprised
to see Jimmy Merced, Cletus Clendenin and Raffie Joseph heading out
from the jetty by Villa Olga in Hugo's boat, rowing toward the slip at
Creque's Shipyard. Niles wondered if it had something to do with some
wild goats Cletus' dad was said to have out there. I wondered if they
weren't going to hunt or fish.

Niles and I were all geared up with packs, sleeping bags, hefty provisions (including ammo), water, Army-issue shovel and pick, various
archeological implements. In Nile's talk on the way there, he began to
refer to the graveyard as the Lost Graveyard so that our efforts to locate
it began to sound a bit heroic. The archeological theme quickly surrendered to century plants, casha, ketch n' keep, ping wing, monkey puzzle,
wild tamarind and ground cactus. There was also in that bush a world of
iguanas underfoot and overhead and, in hidden places, the painfully present jackspaniard nests. Almost at once we shed our packs and excess
equipment and got down to shirtsleeves and machetes. The map, because
of our zigs and zags, was no more than a reference point on the two
occasions we could see beyond the bush back to the harbor to get a bearing. Niles was better than I with a machete, but before long he began to

curse the bush and his uncle. I stood back, held things, did a bit of cursing myself, trampled fresh cut and used my own machete to take the occasional swipe at offending vegetation.

The graveyard and what remained of the infirmary, when we finally found it, was situated on a mid-island hilltop. Hacking our way through the graveyard gate, the first thing to catch our attention was a broken masonry crucifx. To the left of the gate was a shattered crypt. Then two partially unearthed graves and, also on the left, a row of four tombs, all broken into. At first we saw only a scattering of bone — a section of hip here, a rib, a femur, a piece of jaw, teeth — and, in one place, part of a metal casket liner. We were in the center of the little cemetery, which was almost covered with tree limbs and vines, when we saw four more looted tombs and, straight ahead, two unearthed graves and a final crypt, apparently intact. In one of the graves was our first skull and it gave us a good start. It seemed unassociated with anything, as if it had been thrown there. Where are all of the other skulls? Niles wondered. One of them, we see, is set back in one of the looted tombs, a healthy swatch of brown hair still rooted to one side.

Niles cut a length of wild tamarind and trimmed it to a long stick. This he lodged in the hole at the base of the skull and lifted it toward us, placing it on the unlooted tomb. As he moved it across the crusted marble slab it made a hollow corky sound. Together with sticks we rolled the other skull out of the pit (though it slipped twice and rolled horribly back) and maneuvered it beside the one with hair. It was then we discovered the skull had a major gash above the temple.

The work of the looter's shovel? Niles asked. Or some near-death blow to put an end to someone's suffering? This is a delicious subject for speculation, and we sit about eating fruit cocktail as if it is an entirely normal thing to be jawing in the company of open graves. Niles fished his Brownie out and prepared to take a snapshot. He had to use the stick to nudge the one with the hair a bit closer to the other to make it picture perfect. As he framed up the shot I imagined the two skulls, the two faces reappearing tomorrow in the bottom of a tray of fixative bathed in his red darkroom light.

The slab we were atop belongs to a man from Liverpool, England, though I doubt we paid much attention to it or to the beautiful lines of verse written there. The dates on the slab are 1828-1872. Young, maybe a yellow fever fatality. Probably brought to this hilltop infirmary beside the graveyard and kept in isolation for weeks before his death. Although this tomb appeared at first to be intact, the grave robbers had tunneled in from the side. What kind of person, Niles wants to know, would by lamp or candle light, grope about among the moldering remains of a corpse dead over 50 years? We agreed that anyone who would do such a thing would have to be particularly uncouth.

Later, back at the campsite, Niles announced that someone had been there because certain things are not as he left them. At first I think he is only trying to spook me, but later we find fresh broken whelk shells where someone has used them for bait. We remember seeing Jimmy Merced and his chums Cletus and Raffie that morning and wonder if, perhaps, they have been poking about. We inventory our cookies and find them intact.

That night, camped out on the beach, Niles kept raising the specter of the undead, pondering the macabre by firelight. What would I do, for instance, if looking up at the moonlit hill toward the graveyard, I was to see a line of candles coming down the hill in our direction.

"I would swim out into the harbor," I said.

"They could still get you."

He had been giving the matter some thought. He would use the sticks of the fire to fend them off. Better to take a stand than swim for it with all that dark water out there. The bush back from the shore began to appear abnormally black and it wasn't hard for me to imagine those candles, to imagine offended spirits, jumbies perhaps. Before we went to sleep we cut some long wild tamarind and put the ends into the coals just in case.

I had difficulty getting to sleep because the sand beneath the tent was slanted and lumpy. I was also, at the time (only a month after Good Shepherd), in the habit of saying my prayers. But that night the part about delivering us from evil stopped me. I wondered what Brother Les or Brother Bob might have had to say about the day's activities. Wasn't rooting around in graveyards, actually moving the bones of the dead, the very *essence* of evil? If Pam had it right, that would put me in line for some major retribution.

Boy, 11, Hit by Truck.

Mysterious Ailment Cripples Child.

My prayers that night doubtless included a promise of renewed devotion and future good deeds, possibly even a promise to go to confession. And this would have been accompanied by a solemn oath to never go back to that graveyard again, so help me God.

Never lasted a month or two. When we returned, Niles made a map of the hilltop and inventoried the place: 27 grave sites in all, some china and old bottles from the infirmary, a couple of horseshoes, a bed pan, some pieces of coal. We went to the graveyard maybe half a dozen times after that until the day we discovered, on the corner of one vault, fresh candle wax of unknown origin. Who else could possibly have been there, we wondered, and did the candle wax mean they'd been there at night? We stopped going to the graveyard after that. But I still wonder about that wax.

Pilar

Returning to All Souls for my first day of sixth grade, I was shocked to discover that the seventh grade had been moved to another building and with them had gone Pilar Bermudez. I had only seen her twice over the summer, once at a church beach picnic and the other time walking in the funeral procession with Jimmy Merced, and I had been looking forward to seeing her daily. The year before I could at least catch glimpses of her between classes and at recess. But now she was to be largely out of sight, and she even had a different schedule than me. Only on Friday afternoons when she came over for sewing class could I see her several times in one period by leaving study hall on repeated trips to the water fountain across the hall from her open classroom door.

But seeing Pilar like this began to wear on me for it relegated my hope of one day being her boyfriend to the realm of sheer fantasy. I had begun to wonder if I would ever cross the frightening frontier of sex. Already, two of my classmates — both of them West Indian — had ventured across, one of them, Delbert, with his cousin Shantelle in a rain barrel. Though I knew this girl — she was only twelve with small budding breasts — I now viewed her with heightened appreciation. But Delbert was black and had muscles, a much more desirable prospect than me.

The fact is, I had begun to view myself in unflattering terms. Unlike almost everyone else in the schoolyard, I had no muscles to speak of and I imagined myself to be frightfully skinny. I also lacked the prerequisite West Indian attribute of a prominent rear end. When a new white girl in my class was one day dubbed "bumless" and the name stuck, I started to take stock of my own rear view. What could be done about this embarrassing lack of contour? To compensate I began adopting an arched pose which helped, but I wondered if there wasn't some way to further enhance my rear end, perhaps something I could wear beneath my regular pants. Toward this end I made shorts by cutting off the legs of an old pair of khakis. The khakis had rear pockets with flaps, which, with the added bulk of my regular rear pockets, gave me a rump worthy of envy.

Was it my imagination or did this transformation help to elevate me socially? With a more pronounced rear end, my calypso seemed to flow more naturally and even my marble game improved. This was the time to think seriously about Pilar Bermudez. To that end, I decided to confide in Lionel. If there was anyone who could help me in the ways of romance, it was Lionel. Lionel was the dark Latin type, very suave, the model of sixth grade sophistication and, of no small note, the nephew of the Governor.

When I confided that I was hopelessly in love with Pilar, Lionel generously consented to take me under his wing. The first thing I needed was cologne — a small bottle of Canoe would do — and this was available at his aunt's store for a modest price. I had seen the effect this magical liquid had on girls who invariably swooned at the mere scent of Lionel. After that, there was the matter of my shoes. All the cologne in the world could not add luster to my nondescript loafers. Lionel had black shoes with buckles and taps so that you could smell and hear him before he even came into view. I was overdue for a new pair so my father said to go ahead and get some. Fortunately, he didn't come along to Bata to assist in the selection process. The model Lionel had with the buckles to the side were unavailable, but another model with the buckles front and center were.

When my father saw my purchase, restraint failed him.

"You look like you just stepped off the Mayflower."

My father had fallen to wearing flip-flops so I wasn't about to trust his opinion. One unfortunate and unexpected side effect of the blackness of the new shoes was to further highlight my white socks. This would not have been too bad except that my pants were a bit short — the result of a growth spurt — and had begun to "pick whelks," the expression around the school yard. To remedy this I let out the hem which left a band of unfaded green at the bottom of my legs. Still — what with the cologne, the shoes, the improved rear end — I felt I was about ready to make my move.

Lionel, however, felt something was still lacking. What was needed was a gold chain and a little gold-plated cross that I could also buy at his aunt's store for the low-low price of five dollars. I cringe to imagine where I might have come up with that much. I wasn't, myself, that wild about wearing a crucifix, but lying on Lionel's coffee and cream-colored skin, it gave a girl something to rest her eyes on. Hadn't I seen someone — maybe Pilar herself — touching it seductively? This was when Lionel would devilishly arch a dark eyebrow and follow it with a wink or a grin or a witty word. Girls often touched Lionel when they talked to him. He could even whisper Spanish things to them.

Once I had my gold-plated cross, only two items remained to complete the picture. The first was to get taps put on the heels of my shoes. Getting the taps installed was easy enough, but hearing myself clicking down the street and echoing through the halls took some getting used to. Lionel assured me I sounded cool (it sure sounded cool when *he* walked with them) so after a couple of days I stopped walking on my toes and outstep and just gave into it. The final touch had to do with my hair. Leaving nothing to chance, I decided to switch from Wild Root, Niles' brand, to Brylcream, Lionel's. As luck would have it, his aunt's store had just gotten in a new supply.

To be honest, the changes did not produce the desired result and I did not, deep down, feel greatly enhanced. Only Lionel's repeated assurances that his coaching had achieved a positive effect sustained me. He pointed out that I hadn't yet been close enough to Pilar; with me at the water fountain and her in a classroom across the hall, how could I expect her to go wild with desire? She hadn't even smelled the cologne much less seen the gold chain. About the only thing she had seen (and only I knew this) was my improved bum which I had made a sure show of by bending over in a major way to drink from the water fountain.

"Look, Pilar could be sitting in there wishing you would talk to her."

Could that be *possible*?

"But what do I say?"

Lionel looked at me and sighed.

"I don't know. Ask her to the movies."

Ask her to the *movies*! This was an outrageous escalation of expectations. It was well and good for Lionel to go around asking girls to the movies because his father owned the movie theater and he was well-versed in movie-going etiquette. I only wanted Pilar to like me and, perhaps, to one day love me. I wasn't expecting her to want to go to the movies with me!

Lionel was losing his patience. He had a plan. That afternoon we would time our movement through the hall to coincide with the bell. He would be the one to bump into her and I would ease into the conversation and, after a few words, just casually ask her to the movies. Didn't other people, people I actually knew by name, ask girls to the movies? I asked myself. And suppose Lionel was right and Pilar's blood was seething beneath the surface like mine and only her ability to disguise her lust was preventing a veritable volcano of fulfillment?

During study hall we went over the plan one more time in excruciating detail (what he'll say, what she'll say, how I will just drift into the conversation) as the clock on the wall closed in on 2:45. When the bell rang I sauntered into the hall, my insides aflutter, and lingered with Lionel near the water fountain waiting for Pilar to leave class. By now I was fairly confident I could at least say hello without acute social embarrassment. One by one the sewing students filtered out of the class and into the white afternoon light.

Last to leave the classroom, her arms wrapped around her school books, was Pilar. So beautiful, even in her school uniform. Lionel eased over to her, and I nodded my hello. I stood just behind him, letting him set the mood, the casual friendly mood we had talked about, had prepared for.

"I think I'll leave you two alone," Lionel said abruptly, giving Pilar a gentle nudge my way.

We both looked at him.

"I think Willie has something he wants to say," he said backing away. "Gotta go."

Pilar turned her eyes on me. They did not seem to be yearning windows to an inflamed heart. The sound of Lionel's taps echoed out the hall. This was not the plan at all. What about the casual conversation? He was abandoning me, leaving me to twist in the wind.

"Well, I..." I began.

"Yes?"

She shifted the books in her arms. They were heavy. She didn't have all day. It was now or never.

"I was wondering if you want to go to the movies?" I heard myself say.

"With *you?*" she said with mild shock. Her eyes traveled down the length of me and she seemed to be counting the stitches where I had let out my pants, or sizing up the Mayflower buckles on my shoes. I touched my cross hoping to draw her eyes to it. Was she possibly being coy?

"Yes, with me."

Her tone and look quickly shifted to one of true pity. I was, after all, a mere sixth grader and she in seventh.

"No. Not today. I really have to go home."

Not today. Did I detect a loophole?

"How about tomorrow?" I ventured in a final, heroic effort.

"I don't think so."

She had pulled the plug on the pity. She was walking away. I said something brave like, "Oh well, maybe some other time." A breeze entered the hallway and cooled my sweat-drenched back. I turned down the hall in the opposite direction Pilar had gone, walking on the balls of my feet and on my outstep, not wanting to hear the taps, not wanting to remind myself of who I was.

—◊—

STEAL YOU BLIND

—⚬⚬⚬—

Tropical Picnic

During our second full tourist season on the island, it became clear that the glassbottom boat would never keep enough food on the table. My father had, by that time, worked as assistant manager at The Gate, part-time clerk at the Liquor Locker and, most recently, as evening bartender at the Bamboo Bar, a well-known watering hole beneath the Grand Hotel. Mom had supplemented her regular work selling china at the Continental with Saturday door-to-door sales of Fuller Brushes. The sight of my mother dressed in a moo-moo and flip-flops heading off with her catalogue and her bag of brushes seemed to confirm in the worst way our new-found island status. Who would buy these brushes? Pam and I wondered. In fact, a number of people did put in orders. The problem came six weeks later when Mom brought the desired items to the person who had ordered them only to find out they didn't have the money. Soon our downstairs closet was cluttered with shoe brushes, lint brushes, vacuum and waxing attachments, special brooms and dusters.

The final straw came one day when Mom was hawking her wares at the base of Bunker Hill, not far from where the Mercedes now live. When she called "inside," a West Indian voice said to come up. On the gallery a louvered door, slightly ajar, led to a darkened room. As my mother was about to knock, a scraggly cat teetered down the gallery, one eye clouded over, the other gone.

"Oh you poor dear," my mother said. "You're blind."

"Yes I am," shot from the dark room. "What do you want?"

Whose idea was it, I wonder now, to travel house-to-house in a West Indian neighborhood selling Fuller Brushes? My father was very sensitive to remarks about his business acumen, but was this his idea? He had a money-making scheme for me too. One day he presented me with two aerosol cans of shoe polish he had gotten in the mail. It was the newest thing. His idea was to go down to the Center Theatre on Saturday and Sunday afternoons to make a killing. There, between the wall of the St. Thomas Apothecary Hall and the gutter, were a hardened cadre of shoeshine boys, Bappo Scabriel among them, with their Kiwi-coated boxes, their fast hands, their strap and tap routine with the buffing cloth. For a quarter these guys could put a killer shine on rawhide. The idea of my hitting the corner with a can of flit held little appeal. At best, I would be the brunt of jests and stifled laughter, and, in the unlikely event that I was able to steal any of the business, I'd probably get beaten up for my efforts. My father graciously allowed me to decline this invitation to corner the local shoeshine market, but my lack of initiative may have dismayed him. Perhaps the shoeshine business was a calculated message from my father that our fortunes had diminished and that nothing could any longer be taken for granted. Or perhaps he simply saw in those black shoeshine boys a dignity he didn't see in me.

My father was not, himself, immune to judgment on the subject of work. Around this time he came up with the Hack Wilson's Tropical Picnic idea. This was how the Tropical Picnic was to work: A couple is picked up at their hotel in the morning and taken to beautiful Magens Bay, where they are taught to snorkel and treated to a cocktail and charcoal burger. After lunch, the couple is whisked off to Coki Point, where they snorkel over a coral reef before being returned to their hotel. All this — food, cocktails, snorkeling, gear, two beaches, transportation — for only $12.50 per person. Once the details were fine-tuned — including a mile-long checklist with everything from fins to potholder to planter's punch mix — a nice brochure was made. Then several small photo albums showing the day's events were set up at various hotel desks. Problem was, the Tropical Picnic was under-priced, and the jeep could only carry four paying customers.

I went along on the first outing with a young couple from somewhere. They were amazed at the great deal they'd gotten and thrilled to learn they had actually christened the event. I could see Pop beginning to grow weary of the happy talk about the bargain they'd gotten. But when the jeep overheated on Donkey Hill and steam started to billow from the hood, he managed to keep a stiff upper lip. This was no problem, he assured his passengers, for he had planned for just such an event. There was a jerry jug of water stowed beneath the rear seat. It was on the checklist.

The Tropical Picnic idea withered in a few months after the jeep broke down and the tourist season started to pick up. I didn't mind hanging out at the boatyard, and by that time, I was useful enough not to feel in the way. I could serve sodas, sweep the dock, cast off, answer the phone, clean the glass, chop bush, take money, and rest in the equipment shed with Harold or Sal. From Sal I heard all about Tortola and Jesus and about the wages of sin, and if I listened long enough I might get a helping of his wife's West Indian cooking. Harold, the other yard hand, was from Anguilla and more interested in small sloops than Jesus. His tall thermos could be found in a burlap bag on a hook below the hand cleaner and in it were the wonders of red bean soup with dumplings or boiled fish and fungi or a pungent mix of goat and kalalloo. Harold was not Herculean like Sal but veins snaked across his sinewy forearms like fire hoses on pavement. I felt hopeful that occasional infusions of this hearty fare would lead to a similar muscularity. One thing was certain: The Velveeta or tunafish sandwich in the paper bag on the bottom shelf of the refrigerator was not going to do the trick.

When a new captain was hired I was sent along on glassbottom cruises to help out. Pop made like it was to help cast off and dock but I was sent because I had the bearings to line the boat up with particularly shallow coral heads or guide her over the wreck from stem to stern. I knew the fish names and even came to know certain fish by heart — a barracuda by the wreck, a snapper in the canyon. I had grown familiar with the same lines of navigation traveling over the same stretch of shoals. Once in a while we'd see something unusual but most often not. I often had the sense that the sea bottom was playing cat and mouse with the glass, as if something hidden or unexpected was just to one side or the other of our vision, as if the reef consciously concealed its secrets when we passed over and went back to business as usual once we were gone. Sometimes I preferred it when the bottom fell away and the light tunneled and twisted into the darkest trenches where there was nothing to see at all.

One day at the boatyard a wailing police squad car flew up the rutted drive and scrunched to a stop sending up billows of dust. A minute later it went flying out with my father and his diving gear in it. I was told to mind the fort but from the roof I could see the police car speed over to the Sub Base. I tucked the cash box in the safe and ran along the shoreline past the first of several piers just in time to see my father, geared up, descend the ladder of the pier and slip into the water. There was an ambulance, a crowd on the pier and two lifeguards from Lindbergh Bay.

Someone was a goner.

My father's air bubbles moved toward the pilings. One of the lifeguards began to shout. I could see Pop's yellow tank just beneath the surface and something being towed. I am about to see my first dead man. He is black. His arm, well-muscled, is lifted to the rescue workers at the base of the pier. They try to pull him from the water but the arm slips free. He is heavy. He has, himself, turned to water. Two men use a towel to get a purchase on his arm and begin to pull him up the side of the pier. His head and neck roll unthinkably from his shoulders, muscles and bones have turned to a shiny, black gelatin.

Just beneath the belfry of the Anglican Church was my All Souls' class-room. Once in a while, there was a bell that rang when someone died. It was the same bell that also called people to Sunday services, in the same belfry. But the sound of this bell, this funeral bell, was very different. First, it came when one least expected it, in math class, say. It did not, like the noontime Angelus, proclaim in ding-dongy notes the joy of God, but sent, instead, a single unexpected bong straight to the heart, a note held until the last echo had been rung out of it. Then the bell would be allowed to rock back in its cradle with a dull thud. Ten seconds of silence followed before the next bong, the next thud. Nine times the class read-ied itself. Nine times the bell rocked back. It was the sound of the bell rocking back that made the bell so horrible, that carried the message. Since arriving on the island I had seen first hand and for the first time proof that people actually died. There was the coffin-maker on Back Street, funeral processions down Main Street, and the graveyard itself. Added to these, the bell rocking back in its cradle gave me the sound of death, and my father lifting the body from the Sub Base water gave me the look of it.

While it was one thing to see a dog dead on the road or a bird fallen from a tree, it was quite another to see that quality of lifelessness in a man. Death presented its mysteries to me, and so too did life. In the schoolyard there was talk of obeah and jumbies, vengeance and hexes. There was also the Cow-Foot Woman, half-man, half-beast, half-living, half-dead. Was it true that Eldridge Schulterbrandt's cousin, a fellow who sold candles in the market, was an Obeah Man? How much truth was there to the rumor that the Police Commissioner's heart attack had to do with his beating the dog of a root woman we often saw just above the schoolyard who was said to live in a tree? I began to view my surround-ings with a degree of suspicion. I began to see it even in religion class with Father Nibb's fondness for Revelations and the Book of Numbers. As a part of our Confirmation process, we were made to say our confes-sion on six separate occasions, to confess not in an anonymous box like the Catholics but to Father Nibbs himself sitting with his back to us in a chair. Revealing my deepest sins to Father Nibbs was out of the question. I fell back on the only sensible recourse and lied.

On the wall of the sacristy just above Father Nibb's head was a plaque inscribed with a quotation about the hidden power of God, saying the universe was linked in such a way that "thou canst not stir a flower without troubling a star." The words added fuel to certain wonders I had about the secret relatedness of things. Might the man placed in the tomb last month or a century ago be the stranger in the marketplace, out for the day? Might a woman, through no design of her own, round the corner and turn into a dog, the result of some cosmic trickery? What was I doing one year ago at this very instant, by the way, and what bearing might that have on matters? Was there a number, perhaps, that had some meaning, some bearing on my life — the page of a book, a telephone number, a license plate, a blood count? I cast about for my number and after much indecision settled on 254. Did that number have something in store for me? Or was it deeper? Might a man sipping bush tea in Savan in conjunction with a cock crowing in the market and a cat knocking over a sugar bowl in Polyberg, might these things combine in some unseen way to cause, say, a man swimming in Sub Base to inhale sea water or strike his head on a piling?

Occasionally on Sunday night, our family would go to Mountain Top Hotel for their sumptuous buffet. The top of St. Peter Mountain was a world apart from town, cool, breezy and misty wild in the way the island might have been a thousand years ago. At the door leading on to the terrace was a mural-sized painting. The mural places the viewer beside a tethered green iguana and an earthen pot and just below a hammock looking seaward. In the foreground is a young Carib warrior yelling at you, pointing toward the horizon. There, just rounding the point, are square sails entering the harbor. The mural depicts an extraordinary instant in time, the point of contact, when Columbus landed at Salt River on St. Croix in 1493. After dinner I would rise from dessert ahead of the others to go stand in front of it. The damp foresty smell that surrounds Mountain Top is there at the door and with the mural. A thousand feet below, echoing from the blackness like distant cannon shots, is the relentless sound of surf pounding the coast.

I began to have an eerie feeling about Mountain Top and noticed something peculiar about the place. I noticed driving there that our jeep did a number of switchbacks as we worked up Mafolie or Solberg hill to the point where the road enters the estate. During this time town is always below you, receding further and further from sight. At the gate of the estate one enters a shadowy thicket, a long and winding corridor of bamboo and flamboyant trees. Then, mysteriously, you emerge from this tunnel and town has disappeared. Instead, you are on the other side of the mountain and, far below, is Magens Bay, and beyond it a sprawling chain of islands. I did not understand this topographical sleight of hand, the trickery of rounding a ridge with a blind twist of road (but had I gotten out of the car and walked those 200 yards I would easily have seen how the transition was accomplished). So I wondered, might the top of St. Peter Mountain be in some sort of a spell, bewitched in some strange Sacred Indian Ground kind of way?

This was pure foolishness of course, and for a time I kept these thoughts to myself. But suppose, just suppose, I had miraculously stumbled upon some mysterious crack in reality, something others had noticed but not thought to comment on. Should this be left to chance? After a couple more trips up there, I remained convinced. It was time to play it out. I had already told Pam about my special number and she hadn't flinched. Instead she had tried the tree falling in the forest business on me. She was, I decided, fair game for talk about Mountain Top being bewitched.

One evening after supper I found her ironing the pleats to her school uniform. She seemed quite intent on it. The business-like way she was going about this mindless task gave me courage. It was just this kind of matter-of-fact atmosphere that the subject required.

After warming her up with a little small talk about Mountain Top, I slipped in a kind of by-the-way remark about something strange.

"What?"

"Well, have you ever noticed on your way up there you see town below but when you get there you see Magens and Tortola and all the islands?"

"Yes, I've noticed it."

"Don't you think it's a little strange?"

"What?"

I was already wishing I hadn't started this.

"Well," I explained, "that all of a sudden you look and see something that wasn't there before."

She looked at me blankly, then narrowed her eyes..

"It's the other side of the mountain, Willie. That's why they call it Mountain Top. And by the way, are you feeling a bit touched?"

I was already into this thing.

"But you never go *over* the mountain. You keep going up and town is back there. The road goes past the gate and through the woods. But when the trees clear, where's town?

"Just vanished into thin air, I guess."

"OK, just promise me that the next time you go up there, pay close attention when the car goes through the bamboo."

She pulled the plug on the iron and wrapped the cord around the handle.

"Fine, if it will make you feel any better." She slipped the skirt on a hanger. "And you can close the door on your way out. But beware. On the very other side of that door you may find yourself in another room."

I thought about this a second longer than it should have taken me.

"Very funny."

Though I couldn't have put a finger on it at the time, these thoughts, while strange, were not off the chart. On St. Thomas a slightly different threshold existed on the subject of what was normal. My parents over cocktails with friends spoke often and fondly of the strange individuals who made up their cast of friends and acquaintances. Pam was of the belief that the island itself was to blame, that it somehow attracted odd types and affected them in strange ways. There were few taboos. It was not a social dilemma, for instance, for the homosexual who owned the antiquarian novelty shop to dress from time to time as a woman, or for Nueshia, the Haitian Madame, to talk casually of her string of Port-O-Prince whore houses. When *The Daily News* photographer hanged herself in the closet across from The Gate and a month later the trombonist was stabbed to death a few doors down, the subject was given little more weight than the arrival of Stateside meat at the market or news of someone's termite problems. When Lesmore Joseph, a quiet, likeable All Souls student, stabbed his grandmother to death, it created quite a stir but a week later talk of the crime fell off.

For hundreds of years St. Thomas' well-protected harbor has attracted all sorts. The original name of the town in the late 1600s was Tappus, meaning beer hall, the first place a sailor could get a decent drink after crossing the Atlantic. When the Danes declared the island a free port, there were a few hard and fast rules about getting along; boats beyond the mouth of the harbor were permitted to pursue their European grudges and scuttle each other, but while in the harbor foes were required to get along and drink the same grog. To some, the harbor that draws people in and protects them combines with the tumbling landscape and stunning vistas to lend an air of frivolity and madness. Carnival seems to embody the spirit of the island and, to some degree, to be permanently in session. The island could do things to a person. The geography, the climate, the strange mix of cultures all contributed to this intoxicating smorgasbord of island life. No one was entirely immune.

Take Uncle Harlen. Here was a guy who in most instances conducted himself like the Chairman of the Board. In Rye, he had been a pillar of the community and an elder of Christ's Church in Rye — very civilized, tremendously likeable, and not unfamiliar with the pleasures of good Scotch whiskey. But like my mother's other brother, Sandy, Uncle Harlen was said to have a screw or two loose. At one point, Harlen and my Aunt Ellen had been on the island for several months after having bought a vacation home of their own. No problem.

Then word arrives that Harlen is on a roll of some sort, up at all hours at one or the other of the island's seedier night spots. Soon Mom is visiting him in the mental ward of Knud Hansen Hospital. Uncle Harlen. Chairman of the Board. Two months on St. Thomas and the guy's a nut case. Then we learn Uncle Harlen has escaped from the ward and, ass to the wind in his hospital smock, run through Polyberg toward Yacht Haven, the ambulance sirens in hot pursuit. Cornered, Harlen ran out onto the dock where the guys in white tried to con him into coming with them. He jumped into the water, swam to a large drainage pipe and crawled up it a block or two into the Pearson Gardens housing project

where he surfaced through a storm drain. The Chairman of the Board
had given them the slip. There was a donkey tied to a tamarind tree.
Harlen, in excellent spirits by now, commandeered the beast and rode
him — still in his hospital smock — all the way up to Skyline Drive, a difficult three miles. He arrived home in time to watch his wife receive the
call from the hospital informing her of what she has just discovered.
Harlen gets on the line — much subdued after the long donkey ride —
and tells the authorities that he just needed to pick up some personal
items and will head right back to the hospital. They commend him for
his civic-mindedness. A couple of weeks later, Harlen is out and about
playing backgammon and talking stocks and bonds.

—◆◆◆—

One day my father sent me to the post office to pick up a parcel that
turned out to be the baseball stuff he'd ordered from the States. Mr.
Merced was the one on duty. He took the notice from our box, frowned
at it and went in back to retrieve the parcels. At that time I still imagined
him to be the man who'd fought my father, so I was not fooled by his
light-hearted display of banter with the Postmaster, Mr. Testamark, about
a local horse race. He handed over three packages and then surprised me
by tieing two of them together so it would all be easier to carry home.

Inside were three bases, a home plate, a catcher's mask and mit, and a
set of shinguards. My father had tried to get a ball team together at All
Souls a month before, but he and Father Nibbs had quarreled. Now Pop
was doing a Saturday morning practice with a few of us at the Sub Base
ballfield, a weedy lot between the Navy repair hanger and the U.D.T.
quonset hut. Most of the kids were from All Souls except for Niles and
another high schooler, Aubrey. We'd shag some flies, get some fielding
tips from Pop, then choose up and play a couple of innings. Plans were
afoot to put together a team to play Antilles, the island's only private
school, and I was getting myself pretty worked up about it.

We lost that game, 9-1. The Antilles kids were sharper than we were,
and they knew all the pepper talk. They were also a bit snooty and, with
one exception, all white. After the game we complained that their team

included two players from Catholic School, one of them a hot shot with a smooth glove and a big mouth who had a habit of hitting long balls and saying things to the pitcher (that would be me) like "Oh, baby. Give me another like the one I blasted out of here last inning!" They told us we could have anyone on our team we wanted. At least that way, they explained, we'd be more worthy competition and the game might last more than three innings.

On the porch that night, Niles, who had been stewing about the game, wondered if he might be able to deliver some players from the Charlotte Amalie High School team. Serious ballplayers. He mentions several including Jimmy Merced and Willis Chesterfield, both pitchers. Also a guy named Hodge who plays short. Niles reminds me that Jimmy Merced is a half-cousin related by marriage, and while they aren't that friendly, he might be willing to do us a favor. The next day Niles informs me that Jimmy Merced has declined, offering no reason, but that Chesterfield has agreed to play as long as we can give him a ride so he can get to an afternoon church service. Hodge will also play, and Niles says maybe he'll ask Bappo or Cletus Clendenin.

The day of the game our people show up at 8:30 for a little warm up. By nine o'clock there was still no Chesterfield. No Hodge. The Antilles kids arrive in three cars, one of them a Thunderbird convertible, and we look agog while the parent makes a big show of lowering the top with a push of a button. We then manage to bobble a few easy grounders while our foes unload their gear and there are a few smirks and stifled laughs. Shortly, they take the field for their warm ups and, truth be told, they are looking sharp. A lot of talk, and the big mouth from Catholic really pouring it on. It is getting late, and I am beginning to get that sinking feeling when a pick-up truck arrives to drop off Chesterfield and Hodge. Chesterfield, after a few hellos, starts to warm up on the sidelines and immediately the smart Antilles infield chatter tails off. Chesterfield is lanky and coal black. His wind up is smooth and the delivery fast and unpredictable. The Antilles kids leave the field in silence and prepare to face him.

That day Chesterfield's dominance was complete, and the Antilles kids reasonably gracious about the 11-0 defeat. At one point between innings, Niles drew my attention to the genip tree beyond left center, where two kids were picking genips. Jimmy Merced is one of them, out on a limb throwing bunches of genip to Bappo who was catching them. By the next inning, both were sitting at the base of the tree eating genips and watching the game. In the later innings when a parent came and took one of our players away, Webster called into the outfield for either Bappo or Jimmy to come play. At first Bappo waved him off but then he and Jimmy exchanged words, and Bappo came loping in and with a borrowed glove played second. The next inning he got his ups and sent the Antilles' pitcher's new Official Major League baseball over the barracks in left and down a ravine. The towering blast had Jimmy Merced on his feet shouting, and Harold, the Antilles' pitcher, heading over to the T-bird for a bit of parental consolation.

After the game, my father gave several guys a ride home in the jeep. Chesterfield was a Seventh Day Adventist, and he'd promised his mother he'd go to afternoon services because he'd missed the morning one. On the way into town, we stopped at a fraco cart for some shaved ice with syrup. Niles had cherry. Hodge got guava. I waited to see what flavor Chesterfield chose. He asked for soursop, and I watched him pour condensed milk over his. Then he said good-bye and headed toward Savan. I noticed his baggy cream-colored sweatshirt with the hole in the elbow was still perfectly clean. Chesterfield flowed the way he walked. He was long and lanky, strong with beautiful black skin. I ordered a soursop from the fraco man and then, for the first time, had him top it off with a bit of condensed milk. Seventh Day Adventist or not, I decided, Willis Chesterfield was a pretty cool guy. A person might not even mind being struck out by a guy like that.

—〰—

When Ingemar Johannson knocked out the invincible Floyd Patterson in June of 1960, I was quietly relieved. Increasingly, there was evidence that white men could not stand up to the blows of a black man. This was certainly true in the schoolyard and the muscular bodies that filled our island landscape left little hope for change in the adult world. I had come to believe that such a fight could easily lead to death and that my fragile white skull would likely collapse if a Delbert or an Estril or a Tyronne were to find any reason to take offense. Playing marbles, I tried to steer clear of situations that might lead to my public humiliation or possibly, I reasoned, to accidental death. A piece of Bazooka or a Mary Jane was often on hand if it was necessary to stave off bullies, and if someone raised their palm at me and told me to "wait" (until after school) I never hesitated to linger a bit after the final bell. I avoided certain streets on the way home, and if a rock caromed of a wall I was passing I might figure it was a Jimmy Merced or Bappo Scabriel ambush, or any one of a number of imagined tormentors taking aim.

One recent event had brought the situation into particularly tight focus. It was just another schoolyard fight, the kind that usually ended in some dirty shirts and a neckhold. This time it was between Hal, a friend of mine, and Tallboy, a big-boned wharf child, and it erupted over a senseless argument about a cowboy movie both combatants had seen the day before. Then something was said about someone's mother, and the playground came to a halt. Further insults were exchanged and the poking started, and Tallboy began to circle Hal, his fists up. This was *just* the kind of schoolyard entertainment we gloried in and so it was this day with much cheering and encouragement. But then Tallboy hits Hal a roundhouse clout in his nose that sends a geyser of blood spurting out his nose and down his shirt. Soon there is blood on his hands and arms and all over his face. Immediately onlookers are uttering their sympathies and running for the teacher and handing Hal a handkerchief. Now everyone likes Hal and pats him on the back and talks about how worthless Tallboy is. But minutes later, after Hal has been taken away, there is delirious talk of the blood — did you see this and did you see that and how the blood sploosh all over the place. I contribute my own bams and oh Gods but I am shaken. Hal and I are buddies, and it could just as easily have been me. It is only a matter of time, I figure, before my white skin will be similarly humiliated by a battering of black fists.

So when news arrived that a Swede named Ingemar Johansson had knocked out Floyd Patterson, I was given hope. And when *Sports*

Illustrated showed up at school with a photo of Floyd out cold and the Swede towering over him, little was said but there was much private gloating. I wondered about the photo myself. What had the Swede eaten to make him so strong? I imagined him to be a nice fellow, this Swede, sweet but deadly, the kind of guy who doesn't object to reminding the world that white guys can be tough, too. I liked the photo with him in a business suit more than the ones in his trunks because, truth be told, his skin looked a bit flabby. But this defect I was determined to overlook.

When word of the rematch reached the schoolyard there was talk of little else. I kept my Swedish sympathies to myself, but managed to chortle privately with the appropriate parties. By the time the rematch actually rolled around I had gotten myself pretty worked up. Ingemar had single-handedly laid to rest the notions that black was necessarily stronger and now, with this next fight, he would lay forever to rest any lingering doubt. This was my prayer.

Some nights, after I'd turned out my bedroom lights with no one to see me, I would shadowbox in the dark. I become Ingemar bobbing and weaving with Floyd, a helpless feather pillow in my clutches. Pow! The pillow flies across the room. I follow it bobbing and weaving. I pull it again from the canvas and serve up another devastating blow. At times Ingemar becomes me and it is Wayne or Tyronne or Tallboy who is receiving the unexpected walloping. I am in training. I am getting ready for the Big Fight.

On the way to school one day I brought up the subject of the big fight. My father slowed the jeep at the Sub Base intersection.

"Should be some fight," he agreed.

I waited for him to say who he wanted to win, but he didn't. He pulled away and turned through the cemetery toward Frenchtown.

"Who do you want to win?" I asked.

"Patterson," my father answered.

Patterson! I looked for some hint of jest. Had all those blows I'd dealt my pillow landed on the wrong man?

"I think Johansson is pretty good," I led.

"Good fighter."

I had been patient long enough.

"Why do you want Patterson to win?"

"He's American."

Though I knew Floyd Patterson was an American, it had not occurred to me that it made a difference. And my father had said it with just a hint of the quiver that came to his lip when he was either mad or irrationally proud about something. In this case the word American had brought it on. I wonder now if there wasn't an aspect of the Lewis-Schmmeling fight he saw in this fight. I decided by the time he let me off at the post office that he was entitled to his reasons and I was entitled to mine. There were too many wrongs riding on this fight, too many schoolyard grievances to be righted. This was a black and white thing. It was very well that Floyd Patterson was an American, but in the schoolyard that wasn't the issue. If Johansson had been an American and Patterson from Nigeria, sympathies would not have gone to the lumbering white American. If I wanted Johansson to settle some racial score, it could also be said that Patterson was helping settle for the local population, in a symbolic way, something far deeper.

The night of the fight I went to bed feeling confused. On my bureau was a three-foot long model of the U.S.S. Enterprise, which I had laboriously pieced together. It was an archangel of American might, its deck bristling with jets, their wings folded watching over me. And yet, in my heart I was still siding with a foreigner just because he was white. I got out of bed and went to the carrier and knelt besides its dark silhouette as if to ask its forbearance for my wanting the American to lose. The carrier was particularly silent. I was asking not only that the American lose but that he be punched in the nose for the entire world to see. That was a lot to ask of an aircraft carrier.

I went back to bed feeling conflicted and lay wondering if, perhaps, at that moment the two men, the two countries, the two races were slugging it out. I am suddenly ringside and Floyd is flat on the canvas, the titanic Swede above him. Floyd, the American, comes up off one knee and is flattened again, his head on the canvas, the blood splattering the red white and blue bunting. The red white and blue. The red white and blue. The towering Swede is salivating now, looking just a bit dog-like.

Four. Five. Six. Floyd propping himself up. Seven. Eight. Somewhere Old Glory waving and Patterson now on one knee, the evil Swede licking his slobbering lips, nine, Floyd on both feet now, ten and I am out of my bed staggering but still conscious. Suddenly I am Patterson, and the Swede, both pillows bunched together, looms above me coming in for the kill. Out of a bottomless well of black strength comes the fist no one believed possible, and the blow collides with the Swede's temple and the tower of white flab collapses on the canvas.

"What's going on in there?" my father called from the hall.

"I was getting something... tripped...going to sleep now."

I heard him move back toward the porch. I was on the floor, the pillows dimpled with my punches, holding my breath, hearing my heart in my ears. In the window the first moonlight cleared the trees and it shined down on the carrier deck, the jets glowing like saints. I held the pillow up to the aircraft carrier as if to say we won and at the same time to say, see what you made me do. The carrier glowed and said nothing and I buried my face in the pillow and wept.

The next day the schoolyard was ahum with it: Patterson in the first round. He had undone the Swede in a fraction of the time it had taken the Swede to defeat him. To share the schoolyard joy, to surrender to it really, opened me up to the full-scale hero worship of Emile Griffith, the local boy who would that same year capture the World Welterweight title. Griffith could be seen walking in town like anyone else and schoolboys clustered around him. I was one of those boys, and before long he knew my face and would hail me up. Once at Lindbergh Bay I had seen him at the beach in a pair of shorts and had been awestruck by his perfect physique. This was, I decided, the ultimate actualization of my theory of fungi and fish, *this* was the end product. When Griffith fought the Cuban boxer (who had said unkind things to him at the weigh-in) and killed him, the boxing world expressed its dismay. But schoolboys feasted on the photos of the Cuban, hung up in the ropes, battered senseless. The X-ray photo showing the four holes drilled in the skull in an attempt to relieve the pressure was of special interest. We learned that the Cuban had called Griffith a *maricon,* or aunti-man, at the weigh-in. It was the kind of thing that would not be tolerated in the schoolyard, we reasoned, and the Cuban had paid the price.

—ᘯᘯ—

I had a recurring dream around this time. In it I could hear the sounds of a tennis match nearby, the familiar echoey pock-a, pock-a, pock-a, I had known in Rye. In the dream, however, the sound is in an island landscape. More than once I dreamed I heard it as I was climbing the steps to Niles' house and, unlocking the gate, I stopped to listen. I seemed to know in the dream that there were no courts in his backyard, yet when I got there the large retaining wall was replaced by the green canvas and at the base of the fence I could see the familiar gray-green clay surface of the court. When I climbed the steps to that upper terrace expecting to see players in white stroking at the baseline, I see instead Niles's grandmother pulling sugar apples from the tree and putting them in a zinc tub.

Who can say what dreams mean? Looking back at that dream, I see myself still longing for a world I imagined had been lost. How different might life have been if I were still living in Rye? Although I knew how to play a calypso on the steeldrum and how to skin-dive and waterski, and though I could catch a fish and shoot a gun, and tell an artful lie — there were pieces missing. On the one hand, I imagined I was lucky; on the other that I was not. In some respects I was happy but in others I was sad. How different is that from any child growing up? Not much, I suppose. Like many children, I sought to assign blame; if it were not for this, if it were not for that.

But I managed to keep up my guard, to maintain a facade of contentment. If a child from the island's private school said something derogatory about All Souls or called me a "native," I would give no satisfaction but curse that child in my most virulent calypso, affirming rather than denying my native status. At the same time, if an All Souls classmate (an unthreatening one, that is) said anything derogatory about white people or indirectly about America, I would mount the opposite defense. I was slowly becoming a whole composed of conflicting halves. I did not, at this age, see this in myself, really, and though I may have sensed there was part of me that was unhappy, I refused to allow others to see it.

Erect Class

In the seventh grade at All Souls, the attainment of a classroom erection became a prominent feature of our studies. Often a look of mirth or the stifled laughter that rippled across the classroom would find its origins in Kiethroy or Delvin or Rodwell's trousers. On occasion boys would place books on their laps and make them move for the others. The boy who could make several textbooks move was to be particularly admired. One fellow, Dalton, though the class pariah in other matters, was particularly fond of impressing the girls with his massive book-moving feats. Most of these accomplishments occurred during first period English when the morning's dusting of baby powder was still fresh upon Clarise Lockhart's chocolate cleavage.

Things took a bit of an odd turn one day when a new boy, Craig Older, followed me home to trade some comic books. Craig was white. His father was Coast Guard, and his family was from the Gulf Coast and Craig had a bit of a twang. More than a bit. We were not exactly friends yet, but we had recently discovered one thing we had in common, a powerful interest in Pilar Bermudez.

That afternoon we were on the upstairs landing fooling around with some Dinky Toys, a few cool military vehicles and race cars, when a pretty girl passed by on the street. We commented on her breasts, and Craig's hand went conspicuously into his pocket. Talk turned at once to Pilar Bermudez, each of us extolling her virtues. Craig announced that if Pilar passed at that moment he would not be responsible for his actions, and he would likely "throw her down" in the gutter beside our house. I allowed as how I could imagine doing something of that sort myself at which point Craig unzipped his trousers and pulled out his erection.

"Come on, Pilar," Craig grimaced. "Come and get it, girl."

Before I could react, Craig pulled a wine carafe off the hall shelf and plunged himself into the wide mouth. I stood there speechless as this family heirloom of blown blue glass enveloped him.

"Come on, take yours out, man," Craig twanged.

No way was I going to expose myself in this sexual camaraderie. Any encouragement was apt to bring out even deeper hillbilly tendencies, I figured, and I did not care to have my own flaccid quarters unfavorably compared to the engorged erection of this redneck. Disaster was averted by the sound of the gate: my sister home from school.

Craig was having some difficulty dislodging himself from the carafe so I ran down to intercept Pam. She had picked up the mail at the post office and was thumbing through it in the living room. A moment later Craig walked down the stairs with a sheepish grin with no untoward bulge noticeable. He exchanged greetings with Pam, acting the southern gentleman to the hilt, then headed home with only an arched eyebrow of understanding between us.

Later, Pam asked me what the wine carafe was doing on the window sill. I looked at it, dumbfounded.

"I don't know," I stumbled. "I think Craig was looking at it."

"Well, if the wind blew the curtain and this thing went crashing down, Pop would skin you alive." She picked up the carafe, her fingers around the thick blue neck, and placed it back on the shelf.

Quite a few other white kids started to wash up around this time, often bringing with them trappings of their former life. Not all were healthy influences. The same year that Craig arrived at All Souls so did another white kid, this one from Pennsylvania. He showed up in the middle of the year and word was he'd gotten kicked out of a boarding school. I sat behind him and a little to the left so I could get a good look at him. This new kid was different. He was alarmingly at ease for a first day in a new situation, bantering with the locals, utterly lacking in subservience or, for that matter, the blessings of the other white kids in the class. In fact, at recess it became clear he already knew some of them and, worse, he was bigger and possibly stronger than me.

His name was Rusty. Rusty had a short, blonde flattop and a greasy D.A. He was a fairly handsome guy, really, and quick to smile. I hated that. Within a matter of days Rusty was moving more smoothly with some locals than I had been after a year, and his arrival was definitely going to affect the pecking order. What was needed, I decided, was a critical misstep and a fight to bloody his nose. I lay in wait trying to see my way to a plan where he would offend someone like Tallboy.

But before that happened I started, despite myself, to like the guy. One day I discovered him drawing a hot rod. This machine was low to the ground, had huge wheels on the back and flames painted along the side, and the hood was open revealing an engine with all its mysterious parts drawn in considerable detail. The realization that Rusty, in addition to everything else, was artistic and mechanical made me a bit wary. At first I'd tried to dismiss him as a hick, too dumb to be anything but nice. Now I began to comprehend the sickening truth — he was, by all available yardsticks, cooler than me and, if anything, it was I who was the hick.

One day, admiring one of Rusty's dragster drawings (which all seemed remarkably similar) he turned to me.

"It's easy to draw," he said.

"But I don't know anything about engines," I revealed.

"You don't have to, man. Just trace this."

He put a piece of loose-leaf over the drawing and quickly outlined the contours. Then he roughed in the rest.

"See? Now you can take this and trace it a couple of times and then you'll be able to do it without tracing."

Rusty was an OK guy, really.

"You mean you don't know anything about engines either?"

Rusty hesitated.

"Oh yeah, I know about them. You just don't *have* to. You just have to *copy* it."

"What is this?" I asked eager to name a mysterious tube coming out of the top of the engine.

"That's the — ahh — crankshank," he answered.

"And this?" I asked.

"That's the piston, I think."

Piston. Crankshank.

"How about these? I asked of two scoop-shaped contraptions on the sides.

"Combustion chambers," he confided.

We talked a little more about dragsters. This was the kind of thing that cool guys in the States knew all about, I reasoned. Some of the movies that had come to town of late had scenes where guys raced hot rods at the drag strip while shapely babes watched from the sidelines. With all our potholes and scarcely a single stretch of straight road on the island, few people were interested in racing cars and even fewer were really hip to the kind of talk Rusty was laying down.

Rusty, it turned out, was more than willing to let some of his coolness rub off on me. One day when we ran into each other out at Emerald Beach, he showed me a thing or two about inhaling. Now, I was an old hand at smoking but Niles and I had always avoided inhaling. Rusty made it clear that it was senseless to smoke if you didn't inhale.

"What's the point?" he asked taking a drag and sucking it into his chest.

We were up the beach and downwind from the beach bar. Rusty smoked Luckies (Newports and Salems, the kind Niles and I preferred, were for sissies, he explained) and he kept them rolled up in the sleeve of his T-shirt — when he was out of sight of adults. He also had a WWII Zippo lighter that he could open with a snap of his fingers. I studied his technique. There was nothing to it, he explained. He showed me how he could also say a few words without any of the smoke escaping or, on occasion, pop out a few smoke rings just for style. And not to worry about coughing, it just took practice.

On the way back from our smoke we stopped into the bathhouse where I had left my snorkel and mask. Rusty pulled a wallet out of a pair of pants and pocketed some bills. Out of a second pair of trousers he came up with a watch. It was only when his hand went into a third pair of pants that I realized what was going on.

"Hey, what are you *doing*?"

"Just getting a little spending money," Rusty explained. "My Mom cut my allowance. Can you believe these jerks? Just leaving this stuff hanging here?"

I shook my head. "Just asking for it," I managed to say.

Well, I had stolen small sums from my father's change tray on his dresser, but this was different. Rusty didn't even *know* these people.

On the way out to the road to hitchhike to town, he counted the loot.

"Thirty-one bucks," he said with a whistle, "and a Bulova watch. That's more than I figured. Not bad for about two minutes work. Here, take this."

He handed me a ten.

We got a ride back to town with a tourist couple in a rental jeep. We climbed in at the end of a conversation about a lost watch.

"It probably fell out of the towel and got buried in the sand," the young and pretty wife said.

"I could have sworn I left it in the bathhouse."

Even though town was out of their way, they agreed to drop us there if we didn't mind pointing out a few sights along the way. They were from Massachusetts, and on their honeymoon, they told Rusty when he asked, and they were staying at Mafolie. They asked us the usual do-you-live-here questions and what-did-your-father-do-before-he-moved-down-here kind of stuff. Rusty did most of the talking even though he'd only been on the island about a month. He laid on a crock about how his Mom and Dad were killed in a plane crash and how he was forced to live with a cruel step aunt who owned the local funeral parlor. All this was said with utter sincerity with not even the slightest giggle or smirk. At one point my new friend took out the guy's watch and fiddled with it right behind his back. Only when he saw my face constrict in horror did old Rusty get off a good chuckle.

Robbery was new to me and I didn't like the way it made my heart race. Still, it sure was a handy way to pick up a few bucks. That summer, 1962, we hit the Emerald Beach on a fairly regular basis and, on occasion, we worked the bathhouse at Bluebeard's Beach as well. Sometimes these hits were with Rusty, more often with other summer friends. When we worked the bathhouses we were usually careful not to take too much except when the Navy was in town. Niles would have nothing to do with it. Of course, he had a permanent and safe source of funds in his Grandmother's bureau drawer.

It was not until later that summer that I met Rusty's mom and was invited to their house for the first time. I was surprised to find he lived in an elegant stone house located on High Road, a house with tall French doors, a sweeping terrace and a commanding view of the harbor. His mother was slender and youngish, pretty but with tired eyes. His stepfather, whom he called Jeff, owned the local gravel business and drank pretty much all day long. The gravel business was not, it turned out, what kept them in style.

In Rusty's room I discovered a desk plaque that had fallen behind his stack of hot-rod mags. It was teak with a bronze plate engraved with the name, Russell Winthrop Olendorph IV. I looked up at Rusty who was checking himself out in the mirror, dragging a comb through his hair.

"Is this you?" I asked.

He looked at the plaque with a pained expression and tucked the comb in his back pocket. His real dad had given it to him a couple of years before and he couldn't bring himself to throw it away. I later learned that Rusty's grandfather had owned a railroad and a steel mill and that his real father had died the year before in a hunting accident, the particulars of which, Rusty later confided, were not entirely accidental.

One night I was awoken by loud voices. Someone was arguing. It seemed to be coming from my parent's room across the hall but at first that seemed unlikely. I had never heard them shout at each other. I sat up in bed and tried to make out what the argument was about. Then I got out of bed and cracked the door to Pam's room. She was sitting bolt upright and she raised a finger to her lips. The door, if opened much more than a crack, had a loud creak to it so I stood in the narrow opening and listened. We could pick up only fragments.

Then my mother's voice came in loud and clear. She was sick and tired of him screwing around with other women.

The voices were lowered. I stepped back and eased the door closed and stood, not breathing, in the darkened doorway, not wanting the floorboards to creak or the springs in my bed to make a sound.

I lay in bed remembering things Pam had said months before about a certain woman friend of Pop's. But she was Mom's friend, too — wasn't she? Pam had asked whether it wasn't strange that this woman, Ginger, was often at the Liquor Locker when Pop was working there in the afternoons and at The Gate later or at the Bamboo Bar when Pop was on call. She was a bit heavy with red hair and a deep voice. But Ginger had a boyfriend, didn't she? I asked. Wasn't Harvey, the magazine guy...? But Pam had been impatient with me. Harvey spent half his time in Puerto Rico, and they didn't even share the same apartment when he was on St. Thomas. Besides, Pam remarked, it wasn't that simple. She was getting the feeling that Pop had more than one girlfriend because he spent all this time working in bars. Mom, who seldom chose to leave us alone, went only to The Gate and only because we wanted to go there to listen to the steel band. Up until that point, the night we heard them argue, I would argue with Pam. Sure Pop got home late, because these places were open late. He couldn't very well leave work before closing time. Besides, the thought of my father lying naked with one or another woman was not something I could comfortably visualize. But after that night, the night we stood speechless in the dark, after that night I could imagine all kinds of things.

One morning around this time I was on my way over to Niles' house to see a rocket he was developing when I ducked into the Emporium to stock up on bubble gum and Mary Janes. There was a customer at the counter with his back to me. Mr. Pennyfeather was scooping flour into a paper bag with his usual delicious precision, hands tapping and patting and finishing with a special fold and tuck. He then filled the customer's tin with Kerosene. When the customer paid for his order — soap, flour, kerosene — he turned around and I saw it was Jimmy Merced.

He was taller, older, and I realized I hadn't seen him in some time. I seem to remember catching his eye but I don't entirely trust that memory. What I do remember is his seeming older. I think, looking back and having talked to Anton, that this must have been shortly after his return from the States where he had been living with his mother, Esther, who had gotten a job working in the Manhattan tourism office shortly after her divorce from Anton. The apartment Jimmy shared with her was in the Bronx. He would have been 15 or 16 at the time.

Anton likes to blame Jimmy's problems on the time he spent there, particularly the Bronx because, he claims, Jimmy came under the spell of Malcolm X who spoke regularly nearby. This is, perhaps, a comfortable excuse for Anton because he was not there to share any of the blame. Still, he may have a point about New York. Though Jimmy Merced's hot-headedness pre-dates his trip north, the Bronx could easily have seasoned it further. When Anton talks of this time in Jimmy's life he prefers to talk about the boy who came back from New York, the handsome boy who went to Charlotte Amalie High School, who got decent grades, who was a star pitcher of the Chickenhawks baseball team. Anton describes a boy who was popular, who fished and hunted and rode horses, a boy who liked girls.

It isn't hard to imagine Jimmy Merced living in New York, inhabiting a world not distant from the one I'd left (and a place I lived later in life), not hard for the imagination to fill in where memory is lacking, to imagine his experiences as my own. I remember returning to New York one summer when I was 16 and trying to avoid looking up at the glass and steel towers, trying not to do anything to call attention to myself. On my first outing I was supposed to take the cross-town bus. When I got to the bus stop, I saw a sign that said No Standing. I thought it odd that people should not be allowed to stand at a bus stop, but figured it was to prevent people from loitering. So, while I waited, I walked back and forth along the block always staying within running distance of the bus, but feeling foolish. When several other people stood up at the stop, I stopped walking around. Later I learned the No Standing sign was referring to cars. It was all right to stand at a bus stop.

I can imagine minor embarrassments of this sort for Jimmy, minor dislocations. I see him holding the subway strap and measuring himself against others in this city of the world. I can imagine a tenth grade field trip to The Statue of Liberty and Jimmy up there in the crown or with visiting cousins on the 86th floor observation deck of the Empire State Building. I can see summer outings to Ferry Point Park and certainly a trip or two to Yankee Stadium only two subway stops from home. I can see certain lessons, subtle and unspoken, about race and place.

A subway ride from Van Courtland in the Bronx to his mother's job at Rockefeller Center would have provided a regular reminder of that geography. Certain stops, certain times of the day, certain types of people. I can imagine him getting off at 72nd and walking the last 20 blocks through the park. Softball game, carousel, duck pond, lovers, kites. I can imagine him glancing at the fancy Fifth Avenue windows or being told to move along by certain doormen. Perhaps Jimmy knew as I do that St. Patrick's Cathedral just across from his mother's work was a place one could go and sit, and when the huge oak doors whoosh shut behind you, the sounds of Manhattan fall silent. I can imagine such things. I can picture Jimmy waiting for his mother around Christmas time, the smell of pretzels and chestnuts roasting on a curbside cart. I see him turning away from shopping bags heaped with presents to stare down at the ice rink beneath the big gold statue. I imagine him watching a certain skater do spins when out of nowhere a pretty girl says something to him and they fall into talking. She has light brown hair and flashing blue eyes and she asks if he likes to skate and he says he's never tried and she says she just loves his accent and where is he from and how cool is that and then she is swept up in a group of schoolgirls going to some place in the suburbs and he feels that he could love this girl and that she had maybe felt just for a second that she could love him. This girl. This white girl. And for a moment Jimmy is touched by that glowing yuletide feeling. Just for that moment.

I can imagine such things and imagine as well a yearning to return to the islands. Jimmy was in New York for about a year. I don't know what truth there might be to Anton's claim that he was influenced by Malcom X. What I do know is that a year or so after he left St. Thomas he was back again trying to pick up where he had left off. And that's probably when I saw him walking out of the Emporium that day.

Contant 99

T he land on which my father chose to build our Contant home seems strange to me now, given all the land available at that time. We moved there from town in 1961. Its finest feature was that it was on a hill near the boatyard and that it was flat and easy to build on. It could also be said that from the house one could see islands on the horizon and sunsets every day of the year. What this also meant was that the same sun beat in upon the house from ten in the morning until sundown with no help from the trees which were casting shadows the wrong way.

The other unusual feature of Contant 99 was its proximity to the airport, not far from the line of flight where engines are always maxed out. In the windows of low flying take-offs one could clearly see with binoculars the silhouetted heads of passengers, many of whom were probably white-knuckled until they cleared the hill. I wonder if my father, vaguely nostalgic for his bomber pilot war years, found something soothing in the distant starting of engines, the faint taxiing, and the throttling up. My mother, in the middle of dinner conversation, sensing a low plane, would palms upward "help" the pilot. One could yell over smaller aircraft but conversations had to stop for DC-3s, the plentiful workhorses of Caribair. Whatever might have been quaint about our home's location would perish in the years ahead when the first 727s started scorching the sky over our heads.

The best thing about our new Contant house was that it was ours, not the landlord's, and no chained mongrel snarled in the yard at all hours. Our nearest neighbor could not be seen and, unlike town, the location did not offer immediate access to bars and nightclubs. I think my father stopped making sandwiches at the Bamboo Bar around this time but there were still nights when he was out late. Pam had gone away that fall to school in the States, and though we still ate together at our old table, the same chairs, same plates, same silver, it was different without Pam. After dinner, my parents would lapse into long and terrifying silences.

In still another respect our new house in Contant was proving to be an improvement. This would be in the realm of making mischief. There were several other mischief-makers in the area and no end to possible activities. There was, for instance, the dead body trick — always good for a few chuckles. Stuff some overalls and a workshirt, maybe put a thick stick up the pant leg to snap like a bone. Add a little ketch-up. Leave the body on a blind corner on a moonless night with the head — the hardest thing to fake — hidden in the weeds. Then watch what happens when each driver rounds the corner and hits the body, which the headlights have picked up only at the last second. On that curve, hit-and-run drivers were the rule not the exception.

A further entertainment was to rain stones down on the galvanized roofs in the valley, always around midnight. One huge warehouse had a particularly resonant sound, but required a strong throw. The stone would freefall 100 feet before calam-bam-de-lee-bam-bam-bam, which started the dogs and roosters. We'd retreat into the bush, wait a half hour smoking a cigarette or two until things had quieted down and folks were *just* slipping off to sleep before returning to the road for the grande finale. With six or eight stones apiece, two or three guys could keep the whole valley up just as long as it took to wear our arms out.

One night I was exposed to the art of using an icepick to puncture a tire. We were in town and Raul, another new kid from the States and a friend of Rusty, was the expert here. Fact is, all it took was one good stab. He sank the ice pick into a tire and, sure enough, the air started hissing out. Rusty tried his hand at this new, unthought of form of entertainment with equal success. A friend, Egbert, was with us but declined. I wanted to be one of the guys but I feared the ice pick and was certain the tire would explode in my face, blinding me or rendering me deaf. I'd heard jamming a twig in the valve worked well but Rusty promptly pointed out that this required more effort and increased the risk of getting caught. Raul grunted something that I translated as meaning it was also for sissies. There were only two ice picks anyway, and Raul and Rusty were just too busy stabbing tires to pay Egbert and me much attention. Within minutes, every car from the Grand Hotel to the market was sinking. If a spare was visible it too got the pick. At the marketplace, we hooked around to Back Street, hungry for a few final stabbings. The narrow corridors echoed our happy cries and brought a man onto his balcony to yell at us. Egbert and I ran. But Raul sauntered around the corner. Hey, what could the guy do? Raul pointed out. He couldn't very well leap from the balcony now, could he?

The next day on the way to the beach, Pop stopped at the post office to check our box. Two cars sat on their rims, but no one noticed. Through the back of the jeep I could see the dozen or so cars in the Emancipation Garden parking lot in a similarly lowered state. I hungered to reveal this delicious crime to someone. Opposite the Lutheran Church, a man in his Sunday best was getting his jack out. Soon others would be discovering their predicament. A dull surge of contentment coursed through me. I had been a part of this mess. In a way, I had helped out.

The following Monday bright and early and in the middle of religion class, a messenger came into our ninth grade classroom: Someone was wanted in the office. The person who is wanted turns out to be me. It is me they want.

Me? The *office?*

Is it something to do with my report card that I'd returned late? I wonder leaving the class. But in the *middle* of classes? That doesn't make sense. I am just beginning to have a sinking, freefalling feeling when I see Egbert coming out of Spanish and then, crossing from the Parish Hall, is Rusty. This is all very familiar. Less familiar are the two police officers standing in front of the office, waiting.

We are heading to the station for questioning in the squad car, and my heart is doing somersaults in my chest. It wasn't *me*, I tell myself. *I* hadn't been the one to actually puncture the tires. We are driven straight to Fort Christian — where the jail is and where Raul, brought in from

Catholic School, is waiting. We are placed in separate rooms and told to write a narrative of our activities the previous Saturday night. With no opportunity to corroborate each other's stories, we are forced into the nightmare of actually telling the truth.

We were all placed on probation. This required us to report to our probation officer once a week. We were also required to pay back the cost of the tires we had punctured. By luck, the police went with our numbers and by further good fortune all of us had gambled on similar figures — eight to ten, ten to twelve, the highest estimate a fifteen, a fraction of the real total. All in all, we were pretty relieved and not particularly contrite. If he did it again, Rusty said, he'd limit himself to a few choice vehicles belonging to people he particularly disliked. This seemed a sensible approach, and we quickly served up the names of a few deserving candidates.

Before I had much time to slip into further troubles, my father informed me that he was going to try to put me in a school in Puerto Rico.

Puerto *Rico?*

"I can't even speak Spanish," I protested.

"That's the idea."

The next weekend we flew over and found our way to Colegio San Justo in the rolling hills of Trujuillo Alto, 30 miles east of San Juan. There we met the Headmaster, Father Cunard, a roly-poly cleric with a cherubic face. After a short chat in his office, I was taken to an empty classroom, given a test of some kind and allowed 45 minutes to complete it. Outside the louvered jalousies, I could see a vast expanse of green grass, playing fields, hedges, eucalyptus trees, a chapel, a dorm or two. I turned the first few pages of the test, not seeing it, and looked back out the window. At this moment my father was probably giving Father Cunard the low down on my recent activities. I looked again at the test, this time seeing it. In the pit of my stomach, I knew this school would never ever take me. But, already, I wished they would. I pushed into the test my mind treading water, peddling but going nowhere, my eyes continually straying out the window. When the clock on the wall said 15 minutes to go, I had barely started. I flipped through the test looking for something easier than comprehension paragraphs. Numbers, graphs, fractions. Out the window the beckoning grass was wildly green. And the mountains in the distance a kind of blue. The classroom was on the second floor, breezy. The seats were in tight rows, the blackboard deadly serious. Very little scribblings on the desktop, either. This was what a real school looked like. This school would not be wanting to have anything to do with me. I flipped back to the comprehension section and searched anew for something with a quick answer. By the time Father Cunard came to pick up the exam, I'd answered less than a third of it. A miserable performance. Humiliating, really. And my father right here to witness, first hand, just how pathetic, how *ignorant* his son really is.

Father Cunard leads me down the hall flipping through the test booklet as we walk along, concealing his contempt beneath talk of Christmas and how quiet things are with the students gone. Outside the office he gestures to the bench and gives my shoulder a little pat. I know what that pat is. It is the pat of death. And now he is walking back into his office, his black smock like the executioner's, brushing the ground. The door closes, and I imagine him handing the test to Pop, shaking his head regretfully. I imagine also that he will show my test to the office staff when we are gone, and everyone will get a good chuckle.

My father comes out first and I see Father Cunard behind him, just getting off the phone. I look up at my father.

"You're in," he says.

"I'm....?"

Father Canard appears behind him looking owlish and smiling. I am in. But how could that *be*? Now Father Cunard's hand is on my shoulder, assuring me in tender tones about how much he looks forward to my becoming a member of the San Justo family. He is sure I will have no difficulties adjusting to campus life. We continue out the building. The walkway is etched perfectly into the manicured grass and bordered on one side by a neatly trimmed hedge. I feel a sudden sub-current, a tremor, something unanticipated in all that order, something to fear in all that green.

The remainder of Christmas vacation before returning to San Justo I was kept on a very short leash. On weekends, I was allowed to hitch out to the beach with my friends (always handy when one is short on cash), but during the week I was to work at the boatyard where there was always, my father reminded me, a machete and a couple of acres of shoulder-high guinea grass in case I had difficulty keeping myself busy. I helped out — sweeping, sanding hulls, landing the boat, answering the phone. The phone calls brought me to the office and, hence, to the cash box. There was fifty bucks at the start of each day. A twenty, two tens, a five and five ones. By three in the afternoon, on a decent day, there was twice that and, what with the bar and making change, I could usually slip myself a five, sometimes less. Other days, when business was slow, taking anything was a bit reckless. But I'd often do it anyway.

That fall a new guy, Juan, had been doing most of the yard and dock work. He was from the Dominican Republic, the most recent replacement for Sal who had taken his marital problems with Lucy back to Tortola. Sal, we knew, had spoiled us, and Harold, with his stewed goat and red bean soup, was available now only on Saturdays. Juan couldn't speak English, but he compensated with zeal. Still, explaining the pump or the compressor or how to answer the phone was a problem. Mom liked Juan because he seemed so earnest, but Pop didn't seem to hold out much hope for him. Language was part of it, but I sensed my father didn't entirely trust him.

One afternoon around closing I was out back topping off the fuel tanks when yelling erupted on the far side of the building. I ran there to find my father standing in the shallows holding a speargun — both bands cocked — on Juan who is fully clothed and up to his waist in water. Juan is screaming "No No No" and my father is yelling son-of-a-bitch this and that, the gun, unsteady in his hand, pointed at Juan's chest. Juan is now beseeching *me*, and I think I must have yelled something. Soon the yelling stops and things begin to cool down. My father tells Juan to get his clothes and to never show his blankety-blank face around again, and I wondered what Juan could *possibly* have done to deserve this kind of treatment.

On the drive home, Pop spelled it out.

"He'd been stealing."

"*Juan?*"

"From the cash box for the past week or two."

I think to say how Juan didn't seem the stealing type, and Pop says that was the way it had looked to him too. He'd been hopeful. But when it comes to hiring people, my father tells me, you can never be completely sure which guy will end up being a good worker and which one will steal you blind.

—◊—

Boys don't need much of an excuse to get into trouble and, in those early St. Thomas years, trouble had a way of getting out of hand. The ice pick business had been such a case. The Juan misunderstanding was another. On a smaller scale, friends passing the garage window of an absent neighbor might challenge each other to see who could come closest to it with a rock. There were two ways to lose at this game. A classmate who worked at Sears used to steal rolls of quarters then started taking bills. Eventually he got caught and placed on probation. Others in Bournefield stretched giant mail-order rubber bands across the road at night to see the effect they had on car antennas and motorcycle drivers. Someone could get hurt. That was the idea.

Around the same time I was falling into trouble with tire slashers, several friends had things get out of hand. One got caught throwing matches from the back of the truck his grandfather was driving. He had already created two brushfires along roads further east and had waved at the fire trucks heading out. He ended up in a military school in Florida. Alice, another friend, took her brother's motor scooter for a spin and split her head open on a utility pole and died a week later. Another acquaintance, forbidden to jump out of planes until he got his grades back up, one weekend sneaked over to St. John to do a jump he figured his parents wouldn't catch wind of. But he missed his drop and landed 40 yards offshore and his lines tangled and his boots and jumpsuit filled up with water and he drowned. Trouble had a way of catching up to you.

It would be later that same year (the year I first went to San Justo) that Jimmy Merced, then 17, would get himself into a real pickle. Like other local kids his age, a bit of trouble would get way out of hand.

It was a Saturday about mid-morning when Jimmy got off a Manassah bus in Bournefield with Bappo Scabriel and another guy, Elmo Hendricks, who lived nearby. They were going to cut through the golf course that morning and ride their horses over to Brewer's Bay for a swim. Two of the horses belonged to the Merced family. The third belonged to Elmo. At first, they could not find one of Merced's horses, Butterscotch, a palomino that had been allowed to roam free.

When they spot her, Butterscotch is in a clearing below the water catchment with a man, a white man, riding her. When Jimmy runs up and confronts the man, the man asks what proof Jimmy has of the horse's ownership. The horse has been loose for three days, the man complains, and the owner should have more of a sense of responsibility. But Jimmy hears none of this because it is his horse and he has been yelling for the man to get off and now he is looking at the ground for a good rockstone.

When the fist-sized rock connects, it strikes the man flush in the temple and topples him from the horse. Jimmy gets on Butterscotch and rides her up the fairway to where a trail leads to the water catchment. This is not at all the day he woke up to. It is, when one looks at the sweep of someone's life, a very bad day. The kind of day that ricochets in unpredictable ways, that causes, two months later, a trial and the choice of jail or the Army.

Jimmy Merced would have reported for induction that spring. First there would be the trip over to Fort Buchanan in Puerto Rico for the physical. Then, a month later, Basic Training. That means he left St. Thomas that April, which would put the horse incident a few months after his return from New York and not long after I saw him walking out of the Emporium that morning, with his soap and his flour and his kerosene.

San Justo

When I think of our return to San Justo after Christmas vacation, our rented car probing the hills of Carolina, Pop and me trying to remember the landmarks — this cantina, that crossing, the little bridge, the stand of bamboo — it brings to mind a needle making a pattern in cloth. The needle knows the cloth only lengthwise but it pushes on, knowing the pattern it must follow, knowing that in the end there will be a knot to tie and a thread to cut.

We got there a bit early and ate at a roadside lechoneria. The food looked suspicious, foreign. I looked to my father for some sign of the food's strangeness, some indirect acknowledgment that I was entering an unknown world. He gave me none. I expected him to have some important thing to say to me other than to keep my nose clean, but he didn't. It seemed impossible that, within the hour, he would actually leave me. We ate, making busy with our forks and knives, covering our silence until our plates of beans, rice, lechon and tanya were scraped clean.

We drove over to the campus, still green, none of the students yet back. The buildings are Puerto Rican in style, which is to say of concrete and of a utilitarian design. I am to be in Room Three a list informs us. We drive around the cafeteria to the main dorm and unload my bags. We discover the door to my room has been nailed shut.

"Not very inviting," my father says.

We peer through the screen window and metal louvers. There are four beds in a line, a row of wooden cabinets along one wall and, dimly in the back, the tiled surface of a bathroom.

"Could be worse," my father says more to himself.

My father tells me to wait around until someone with a hammer or crowbar shows up. The rest of the students will be arriving soon. He has to get back for the five o'clock plane. There will not be anymore that needs to be said, apparently. And soon I am shaking my father's hand and then the car is backing away. He has one last opportunity to get off a little wave but he chooses not to, and the rental car turns through a stand of eucalyptus trees and disappears. I look about me and hear voices. I slip to one side of the stairwell. Two sets of feet start up the steps and I am relieved not to have been discovered, a new boy, lurking in the shadows. I return to the door of Room Three to see if something can be done about those nails. I will not wait for a hammer, I decide. I will go find one.

That evening at six, students are gathered on the stairs of the cafeteria waiting for the bell. Everyone is dressed in the school uniform but me. I linger about trying not to be too far on the edge of things but my khaki pants, in a sea of blue, draws people's eyes. A few heads turn my way, a few nods, a whisper or two. I am trying to make a mouth that looks like it is politely interested in something new. I am wanting my face to show I am a threat to no one, but that I am also unafraid. A loud boy at the top of the stairs says something and gestures for me to come up. I go. Many of the older boys are up there at the top of the stairs.

The boy asks me, in Spanish, if I speak Spanish. I say something weak like no mucho. This seems to tell the boy all he needs to know. Next he asks me if I am something.

"No entiendo," I reply, trying to look earnest.

"Tu eres un *maricon?*" he repeats more slowly and with a smile.

Tu eres, I know. The other word I have heard before. Somewhere. He repeats it again and I think I hear an accented version of American. Is he asking me if I am an American? Is that it? He is smiling, waiting for my answer.

"Si," I answer.

The stairwell explodes with laughter.

"Maricon! Maricon! Maricon! Maricon! Maricon!"

My three roommates were Hector, Gato, and Umberto. Hector was the Room Leader, a senior. He was handsome and compact with the build of a boxer and sultry curve to his lips. He had served time — I found out later — for marijuana. Hector had little to say and it was in one's best interest not to give him any reason. Gato and Umberto were fellow ninth graders. Gato (cat) was the name used only by his friends. Teachers and others knew him as Ernesto. Gato's hair crowded down upon his eyebrows giving him a truly simian appearance, and one that was supported by six toes on each foot. Umberto, on the other hand, was small, with a round flat face and pasty skin. He took tight little steps and wore his pants exceptionally high and was religious in his devotions. He was at church in the morning when we awoke and there when it was lights out. Much of his time was spent up at the chapel and in the parsonage helping Father Cunard with religious matters. He and Father Cunard had a special relationship. He was the only acolyte allowed to sweep the vestry and clean the chalice, the only one entrusted to laying out Father Cunard's garments. Soon, during a freshman class barbecue at the rectory, I would notice how Umberto was familiar with the contents of every one of Father Cunard's kitchen cabinets.

That first night there is talk after lights out. I ask if the room had only three people in it before vacation and am told by Umberto that each room always has four. Who was the guy in the room before me? I wonder aloud. There is a silence in the room and Hector, the boxer, answers. His name was Sigefredo, a real nice guy. He'd died the first day of vacation when his motor scooter slid under a truck.

Took his head off, Gato says.

That is why, Hector explains, there happened to be an empty bed in Room Three.

My education at San Justo — the year and a half I was there — consisted of fits and starts in the classroom during the week followed by frequent outings to San Juan on the weekends. San Juan in the 60s was already a large city by island standards, with all the qualities fine and not so fine to keep a boy my age occupied.

To get there one was required to catch a publico to Rio Piedras and from there a bus into San Juan. To catch a publico one stands by the side of a country road looking for a sedan that is full of people. There is always room for one or two more. Most passengers are campesinos, all have parcels. Sometimes a passenger will disembark before arriving in Rio Piedras which is always a relief, first, because it gets someone off of someone's lap and, second, because it forces the driver to come to a complete stop, a pause from the reckless careening and passing on blind curves, and a reprieve of a hundred or so yards at more moderate speeds as the driver works back through the gears.

The publico comes to a rest at the start of Avenida Commercial, perhaps the single highest concentration of zapaterias, joyerias and pasterias on the planet. Usually we would walk its length hoping in the jostling crowd to be brought into contact with a breast or two. Toward the end of the Avenida was a movie theater with some racy Spanish title and on either side a display window of a calconceria where girdles, bras and panties adorned curvaceous manikins in red and black lace. By purchasing a bocadillo from a curbside cart one could linger legitimately and ogle the merchandise. Then it was on to the bus stop and the real reason we had left school — to go to Old San Juan.

Over time I managed to become friends with classmates who had homes in Isla Verde and Condado and who would allow me to ingratiate myself for the weekend. Some of these friends were veterans of various bordellos. When I first heard this, it frightened me. I longed to be reassured that most children my age were incapable of this kind of sexual knowledge. I was dismayed therefore when Bebo Serano produced two photos showing actual couplings — one a staged chain of four people and another, more distinct, of a man screwing a woman. In this one the penis was actually visible disappearing into the darkened forest of the woman's nether region. The woman had her hand covering her face. The man was swarthy and fat, a real scuzball. I had difficulty sleeping that night fretting about this image.

One weekend several friends invited me to join them on a trip into Old San Juan to go to a whorehouse and I was fresh out of lame excuses. To avoid being deemed hopelessly uncool, I accepted this invitation. During the days leading up to this outing I was torn on one hand by the desire engendered by repeated descriptions of sex from those more knowledgeable than myself, and, on the other, by the photo of the scuzball and the way his thing was swallowed by this, this *hole* between the woman's legs. I had at times longed to have my own private parts similarly engulfed but seeing first hand and for the first time in graphic detail what such a thing looked like took the mystery out of it and replaced it with something worrisome and forbidding.

Only the week before I had stood beside beautiful Lola Belmonte at the beach. We had gone there for the sole purpose of seeing this creature, the one Bebo Serano had done it to — in her parent's beach house, on the lawn out back, once by moonlight standing against a sloping palm tree near the catamaran rentals. I had talked to Lola only a few feet from this very tree and it had made my heart trip. She wore a bikini. The bottom was cream-colored and very tight and the top was coral-toned and faded so that it appeared to be from an older swim suit, one she wore, possibly, a year or two before. Now she was 15 and her coffee-colored breasts had run out of room and this is probably why she chose to wear it, to see the effect it had on someone like me. At one point she spread some coco butter into her cleavage and, complaining of the sun's heat, muttered, "Aye, me quema."

She was burning. Was there a possible double meaning here, a coded message she was sending to me?

"Si, hace mucho calor," I replied with pathetic longing. She smiled but turned away to whisper something to Bebo who chuckled.

She was drop dead beautiful this Lola was, and she was also rich. When her mother called her, she left and a half hour later reappeared in a dress to go with her parents to her cousin's birthday party. The dress was yellow, flared at mid thigh, cut low front and behind, the top held in check by the thinnest of spaghetti straps and I would have given anything for a world without laws and even imagined such a world where I could be a savage and forgiven for ripping that yellow dress right off her.

But those feelings were very different from the feelings evoked by the photo of the scuzball and what I imagined to be a whore. Offered the opportunity to do what that scuzball was doing, I was certain I would have a major equipment failure or, worse, catch some horrible disease. But maybe the prostitutes Bebo and Jorge and Frankie went to were more of the Lola Belmonte design, young smoldering sexpots yearning for a young, skinny blond kid like me.

After several days of my imagining various scenarios and worrying about each of them, we were taking the very bus down the very road that would lead, I imagined, to the end of my innocence. It was a road I had taken before — to visit the El Moro Fortress, to buy socks, to go on a Spanish

class outing to a Mexican restaurant, to see a movie. Now this same road
was taking me to a new place, a place I feared more and more the closer I
got. Now we were getting off the bus and Bebo and Frankie were leading
the way. When we turned down one side street my eyes traveled ahead of
us looking for something hopeful. When we turned up the next street my
eyes did the same. One thing seemed certain: We were getting further and
further from a place where a Lola Belmonte might suddenly appear, nearer and nearer to where dark hairy forbidding places might lurk. But as we
passed doorways — barbershop, bar, seamstress, bodega, pool hall — I
held out hope. Then at the next turn the street changed to cobblestone
and Bebo slowed. He gestured at a place two doorways down.

It was early evening and there was not much life on the street and even
less in the bar as we entered. The decor was checkerboard — black and
white linoleum on floors, walls and ceiling. There was a bar to one side
that was bathed in red light. There were no patrons that I recall although
I was too seized with fear to have seen much of anything. We ordered
our rum and cokes from the bartender and sat at a table where they were
delivered by a waitress who could easily have been one of our mothers.
She collected the money and asked if there was anything else she could
get us. Bebo looked slyly from one to the other of us and then looked up
at her and said, "Si, hay."

She smiled and said something in Spanish I couldn't follow, then disappeared. I pretended to sip on my drink hating what the rum did to the
coke and wondered if it was too late to back out of this. My mind scrambled looking for an excuse — sudden sickness perhaps? Appendicitis?
Two women appeared from behind a partition — both probably twice
my age and neither even remotely appealing — and I am relieved when
they turn their attention to Bebo and Jorge and make little cooing noises. The one with her hand on Jorge's shoulder is better looking than the
one blowing in Bebo's ear although I notice she has very hairy legs mat-
ted down with red stockings. I look to Frankie for some sign that he
shares my revulsion but he is into it. When a third appears I gesture no
and she pats me on the head as one might pat a sad puppy and moves
over to try her charms on Frankie. I take the opportunity to escape.

Across the street is a chicken joint with a pinball machine by the door.

I get a coke and stand there — one eye on the flashing lights, the other on the door of the bordello. I am not nearly as ashamed as I am relieved. I love this pinball game. I have never loved pinball until just now. I notice that unlike other pinball games I have played, this one involves romance. The object of the ball's desire, apparently, is this Jenny Mae girl in cut-off jeans and a sleeveless shirt tied off at the waist. When the ball hits the bumpers old Jenny May lights right up. If the flippers send the ball all the way up to the seat of her pants little red hearts go blinking all over the place and you get 500 points in one shot. After a few quarters I get the hang of just how easy it is to make Jenny Mae go wild.

Twenty or so minutes later Bebo and the boys appear, and I leave Jenny Mae to hear complaints about how this one had these weird bones down there and how the other was more interested in reading a comic book. Frankie says his wasn't so bad except she scrubbed his thing so hard with soap and a washcloth before she did anything that it kind of took the fun out of it. No one made fun of me, which was a relief, and I sensed we were all pretty glad that part of our evening was over and we could now go watch the Abbott and Costello movie down at the Teatro Bolivar.

That June after my ninth grade commencement exercises I joined up with a couple other kids from St. Thomas for the plane home. One was Fitzroy Lewis, who I remembered from All Souls as someone who lived in my neighborhood but he was a junior so we didn't see much of each other at San Justo. The other one on the plane was Sedrick Ross, a senior. Sedrick was really from St. Croix, but he was taking the same St. Thomas flight to spend a week there with his aunt. I liked Sedrick but a couple of months before we'd had a serious run in when he caught wind from someone that I was bad-mouthing St. Croix. I was cooling out on the second floor porch of the dorm with a couple of chums when out of nowhere Sedrick comes up and says, "So what this shit is I hear you talking about St. Croix?"

I am trying to cough up some sort of excuse but before I can I am being hustled down the porch, one hand on my collar and the other on the seat of my pants. Next thing, I am being held by my ankles from the second floor balcony my head and arms dangling about ten feet over a concrete walkway. After extracting various oaths of how I love St. Croix and how St. Thomas is a piece of shit, old Sedrick reels me back in and tells me I am forgiven. From that point forward I managed to keep any ill feeling about St. Croix to myself, and Sedrick and I became friendly if not exactly friends.

When our Caribair DC-3 landed on St. Thomas, we got our bags and went to stand by the hangar door. Sedrick's aunt was already there in a pretty fancy car, and I was relieved he hadn't seen our ratty old jeep pull up. While I was standing there with Fitzroy, a small grey-green bus pulls up and about 20 military guys get out and start lugging their duffel bags over to this loading dock. It's 1963 and these guys, all locals, are look-ing pretty cool, some with little berets and epaulets and this gold cord that looped under their arms and some of them with ascots and most with what I imagined to be paratrooper boots with their pants tucked into them. Then Fitzroy goes over to talk with one of them and they're laughing and soon the troops start to move toward the chain link fence and I can see the tail of one of those military transport planes with a ramp going up into its fuselage.

"Friend of yours?" I ask Fitzroy

"Yeah," he answers smiling. He starts telling me about the guy in uni-form, then stops himself. Come to think of it I should know the guy because he used to live in our neighborhood.

"What's his name? I ask.

"Jimmy Merced."

I look again at the group and pick out the tallest of them and sure enough its Jimmy — though my eye could easily have passed over him — haircut, beret, shades, fatigues tucked into his boots. They are being drawn into the belly of the transport. A blue Chevy Impala pulls up and it's Fitzroy's turn to head home and again I am glad the jeep hasn't rat-tled into view. I watch the Impala pull away and at the same time I hear the military plane revving to taxi and I feel suddenly small and alone in the great yawning mouth of the hangar door.

—〰—

Had it not been for the man riding Butterscotch that day and the stone thrown at his skull, Jimmy Merced would have been finishing his senior year at Charlotte Amalie High School. Instead, he'd been forced to enlist in the Army by court order. It is hard to imagine that transition in his life, the loss of his freedom, his childhood brought to so abrupt an end, but I can imagine his first introduction to military life. Like other Virgin Islands conscripts, Merced would have reported to duty in San Juan and been met at the Munoz Marin Airport by an N.C.O. and then taken to a large room filled mostly with Puerto Ricans and given the oath. If he was like most Virgin Islanders, Jimmy Merced took his cue from the Puerto Rican conscripts who were attentive and subservient. Later during the physical, one learns not to ask about the injections but just to take them like the guy in front of you. And when a man tells you to bend over for a digital exam of your rectum, you bend. You spread your legs. You get over it. I imagine Jimmy Merced followed the example of the guy in front of him, but having a white man stick a finger up his ass might have been testing Jimmy's limits.

Merced would have stayed at Fort Buchanan for the three-week pre-Basic Training orientation. Activities included marching, guard duty, physical conditioning, kitchen duty and target practice. For the Puerto Ricans, there were English classes, and for English speakers, a chance to pick up a bit of Spanish. Jimmy Merced would quickly have learned that Puerto Ricans came in all shades and sizes, and that skin color was not much of an issue. Everyone had the same shaved head and wore the same baggy clothes and ate the same beans and rice. When the conscripts got an afternoon off, they were only a short ride from Old San Juan. It occurred to me only recently that Jimmy Merced and I were in Puerto Rico at the same time. That would mean we rode the same bus line, went to the same movie theaters, and likely bought fresh coconut water from the same vendor set up at Fort Buchanan's gate. We may also have admired the same school girls in their grey and white uniforms walking home from Salgrado de Corazon. And we could easily have crossed paths during the three weeks he was there, though I suppose it doesn't much matter, and I might just as easily have not recognized him.

After Puerto Rico, Merced shipped out to Fort Benning, Georgia, for two months of Basic Training. There, he would distinguish himself in marksmanship, encounter his first real taste of big league racism, and make a few good friends. It is also here that he would later decide to be a paratrooper and be sent off to Fort Cambell, Kentucky, for Advanced Individual Training. There, he would survive a tough paratrooper program that offered jump school, training in map orientation and radio operation, first aid, martial arts, counter insurgency techniques, staging ambushes, escape and evasion. They were skills Jimmy Merced would use on more than one occasion.

—◊◊◊—

That same summer Jimmy Merced was learning to take orders and jump out of planes, I caught up with Niles who was putting his design skills and chemistry classes to good work. Niles was into space flight these days, and preparing to launch a three-stage rocket (one stage, a shot gun shell) with a lizard in the nose cone. I had moved to Contant by then and I had a job as a stockboy at the same store where my Mom worked, and on Saturdays I helped out at the boatyard. When I wasn't working I was often up to no good — smoking, throwing rocks, diving in caves, stealing from bathhouses, ogling bikini tops. The Sunday trampoline at Emerald Beach was an excellent spot for this particular kind of summer activity because if you were serving as a spotter you were supposed to keep an eye on things and with all the upping and downing who could be entirely sure exactly what part of the bouncer you were staring at most intently. When Margo Jeltrup or Ashley Creque bounced, there was no end of available spotters.

That fall I returned to San Justo and there was talk from my father of possibly going to St. George's the following year. This quickly turned out to be a bit of wishful thinking because I wasn't academically up to their curriculum. After casting about unsuccessfully for another boarding school that would accept me, my father put in a call to my Uncle Rutledge to see if he had any notions. This would be the same Uncle Rut who had, some years before, come up with the glassbottom business venture. Some fathers might have taken that as fair warning.

As luck would have it, Rutledge had just the ticket. His younger brother Sam had recently become Headmaster of a small boarding school in northern Vermont. It wasn't exactly an old school having been established only three or four years before, but the academics, while good, were not overly rigorous. The school had some unusual features one of which was an Outward Bound emphasis. This would give me some hands-on experience on how to build a lean-to and sleep in a snowdrift. One of the graduation requirements of this institution would be to spend three days and nights in timber wilderness, alone and without food, something called a Senior Solo. I was not encouraged.

One day a package arrived with an elaborate brochure. On one panel were pictures of a soothing nature — the spire of a New England church, colonial-style white clapboard houses, a snow-clad common surrounded by a split rail fence, students playing soccer, listening to a lecture in coat and tie, sitting around a dining table. On the back panel were photos of a different kind. Here were students in gloves and scarves and hats huddled around a campfire and surrounded by snow banks. Another showed the Headmaster, beard caked with snow, exhorting his legions upward. A third featured a phalanx of those troops, weighted down with gear trudging upward in a long line through waist-deep snow toward a distant fire tower.

There was something suspiciously military about all this hearty marching and camping and from the little I'd seen of military schools in Puerto Rico, I didn't want any part of it. But the students wore coats and ties. I studied the brochure with a magnifying glass, examining each face of each student, searching for the haunted look of the captive. I saw none. Clearly these photos had been screened for frowns, for any sign of discontent. The one showing the column slogging through snowdrifts was shot from behind I noticed. I doubted there were many smiles on the other side of those huge backpacks. The photo reminded me of ones I'd seen of troops in Vietnam wading through rice paddies, their M-16s held over their heads.

When I spoke to my father over the phone, he seemed very upbeat about the whole thing. I expressed a concern or two making sure at first to avoid mention of my Outward Bound reservations, not wanting to sound the wimp and give him further reason to send me off. But my other reservations were sounding particularly lacking.

There was a long silence.

"I thought you wanted to go to school in the States."

"I do."

And it was true.

"So what's the problem?"

I couldn't say that it was because I had wanted something more like St. George's because we had already been over that ground. And I couldn't say I was beginning to like the idea of staying a third year at San Justo because that wasn't true. In the end I just went with my gut and told the truth, that it seemed like a military school.

"It is *not* a military school for Christsake."

"Those photos on the brochure looked like something out of Vietnam," I pressed.

This got me the dead silence I had bargained for, and I braced myself.

"There's one rather major difference," he said.

"Which is?"

"Those guys are getting shot at."

He was right about that of course, and I knew right away that I was going to this school whether I liked it or not. That summer, the differences between camping and killing were brought home to me when Sam West, the older brother of a friend stepped on a land mine and bought the farm and this other guy, Rodwell Peterson — who played third base for the Clippers and used to fish from the Coast Guard dock — got booby-trapped and lost a leg. Almost every week the name of some Virgin Islander was in the paper. Once in a while it was because someone had been elevated in rank or received a special assignment, but often the news wasn't good and the announcement was accompanied by a list of kin. Adding to this poison, there was also around town word from returning troops of a kind of institutionalized racism encountered in the service that was alien to the experiences of most Virgin Islanders.

One of those who would have appeared in the paper was Jimmy

Merced. There may have been no mention of his having to enlist by court order, probably nothing of the rock-throwing incident. There would have been a later notice about his completing Basic Training in Georgia and specialist school in Kentucky. Shipping out to Southeast Asia. And, later, being decorated for valor. But there would be no public record of how Jimmy Merced responded to routine hazing or to any racial incidents he experienced. Certain things came with the territory. Some inductees were startled by the racial double standard, but new Virgin Islands recruits were usually compliant and, in some cases, quick to use the service to their advantage.

Merced was designated platoon machine gunner, assigned to the 101st Screaming Eagles and shipped out to the Central Highlands to help stem enemy infiltration and the flow of war material down the Ho Chi Min Trail. Nothing in Basic could have prepared him for the Southeast Asian jungle, but Merced noticed — as did others from the islands — that he was better adapted to the tropical environment than many of his stateside counterparts. His unit was involved in search and rescue missions and sometimes dropped behind enemy lines to stage ambushes, track troop movements and give coordinates for artillery and air strikes.

Like most troops in that kind of situation, there were bad days. On one bad day, napalm landed wide of the mark and roasted three of his platoon's men. On several other occasions, the unit had to be choppered out of tight situations. Merced's luck ran out one day when his patrol was ambushed by snipers with AK-47s and grenades. He was one of few to survive and last to be hauled aboard the chopper, wounded in the hip. He was medi-vacced to Japan for surgery and later sent to the States for two months of physical therapy. It was during this stateside recovery that he was informed that he was being sent back to Vietnam. Merced's refusal to comply with that order led to his assaulting an officer, which led in turn to a court-martial, to doing time at Levenworth, and to a less-than-honorable discharge.

Years later at the Sweet Bottom Massacre trial, his mother, when asked about her son's unwillingness to return to combat, would offer the following account to explain her son's emotional make-up at the time: One afternoon following an ambush, they entered a village and Merced returned fire on a thatch compound. The young and pregnant Vietnamese woman he had inadvertently put a 60 caliber machine gun bullet through was not yet dead when Jimmy got to her. His mother told how Jimmy saw the baby kick just before the mother died in his arms, and how she looked so much like his little sister, Eliza. Same dark hair and dark skin. Same dark eyes.

—⟋⟋⟍—

Boys growing up on the island have common experiences and lead roughly parallel lives. It is in the departures from the island that paths most often diverge. Usually, a departure was a hopeful thing. First, the act of leaving confirmed there was such a place as Somewhere Else. You were going to a destination. To a new place. Leaving the island meant something big was happening, you were turning a corner. In most cases the departure was cause for celebration. Or relief. But sometimes the departure was the end of some trouble you'd gotten into — like the tire slashing business that sent me packing to Puerto Rico, or the rock throwing incident that sent Jimmy to the judge.

I went to school. Jimmy went to war. Because he went off to Basic Training 18 months before I headed north, it's safe to say that by the time I got into any serious winter camping in Vermont, Jimmy Merced had been jumping out of planes behind enemy lines, lugging a machine gun through the jungle. Killing people on a pretty regular basis.

It shouldn't come as a surprise to me that our lives are often governed by chance, ruled often by the most random or arbitrary circumstances. But it interests me. When I trace the origins of events in my own life, I find the most unlikely deflections. I think, for instance, of a certain dream I had one evening at my uncle's house in Rye when I was 20. I was there alone on an Easter vacation and the dream woke me in a good sweat. A year later, casting about for the subject of a poem, I settled on that Easter dream and it earned me a word or two of encouragement. A few months after that, on a miserable and rainy night hitchhiking west through

Buffalo, New York, a long wet wait forced me to find my way to the Buffalo Bus Station, which resulted, months later, in a poem by the same name. And further encouragement. Today I wonder how different life might have been had I not had a certain Easter dream. Had the motorists of Buffalo been more generous. Had it not been raining that night. Had the eyes of a man at the bus station luncheonette been less vacant and his ankles less white. I wonder also about a chance decision years later to hitchhike to a Nantucket beach one afternoon, a decision that would lead directly to a play in Charlottesville, Virginia, six months later and to an usher who would one day be my wife.

Searching at the lost connections that govern chance brings to mind a pool shot seen in slow motion and reverse, so that the initial impact becomes, instead, the end result of subtle or unseen deflections. In the same way, I wonder how different Jimmy Merced's life might have been had that white man not ridden Butterscotch that day. If maybe Jimmy had missed the bus to Bournefield that morning, or gone fishing instead, or the man chosen to ride the horse an hour earlier. Or not at all. Who was that man, I wonder now, and what circumstances combined to put him on Jimmy Merced's horse that day, that hour? A white man in that neck of the woods probably lived in the adjoining housing built by the Navy in the 40s. I imagine a Coast Guard recruit, maybe, recently arrived from the Gulf Coast with his wife and two kids living in one of those small square bungalows with a patch of lawn and a swing set out back. Or maybe an FAA guy here on a two-year stint involving an airport upgrade, someone like that. Maybe he'd seen the horse a number of times before roaming the golf course, and maybe he'd befriended it with sugar and maybe moments before the incident this man was thinking how wonderful it was to be riding up the fairway this Virgin Islands' morning and how maybe he'd like to teach his oldest to ride and maybe there was even a thought or two about getting back for pancakes or watering his patch of lawn when this boy came running at him from across the fairway yelling at him to get off his horse. And what might have happened with Jimmy Merced's life if the man had simply gotten off the horse instead of lecturing the boy on being more responsible. Or had he ducked and the rock not struck him in the head, but missed.

Things look different through the opposite end of the telescope. When I see in my own life how two hitchhiking experiences, a dream and a bus station have, by the remotest chance, governed events in my life, it reminds me of that pool shot — seen in reverse and in slow motion. In the case of Jimmy Merced, the cause and effect are not the result of unnoticed deflections. In the case of Butterscotch and Vietnam it is like the cue ball slamming into the rack, hopping off the table and rolling across the barroom floor. And if, in a corner of that same barroom, Fate were a kind of poker game where each card was the face of happenstance, I imagine my having been dealt a pair of hitchhikes, a dream, a poem and a bus station. Jimmy is showing two rocks (the earlier one a brick), two golf courses and a horse named Butterscotch. He is about to trade in the horse and draw from the deck of happenstance an Army-issue machine gun.

Looking back at those early years on St. Thomas, there has been an unavoidable tendency to come back to the fight, the street fight my father had with Mr. Merced on Crystal Gade, and to wonder anew at the cause of it. For years that fight stood as a kind of turning point in my childhood and an event that marked the end of an imagined innocence. It was also an event that would one day lead to a conversation with Anton Merced, a man I had, for 35 years, wrongly assumed to have been the man who came to our gate. And that conversation would lead to further conversations over meals and around pool tables, conversations that had a way of coming back at me, of altering an assumption, of seeing the fight in an unfamiliar light.

There is a certain bush common to Virgin Islands hillsides called ketch 'n' keep. The tendrils are barbed and springy and this causes them to behave in painfully unpredictable ways. The bush is both detested and revered and, in the minds of some islanders, a metaphor for our more resilient, tenacious selves. Hit me and see what happen. Strike at the root with a machete and satisfy yourself with the gash you have made at the same instant an errant tendril takes a compensatory wrap of your ear and neck. And so it is when one starts rooting around in the past and something surprising and very much present springs up. And anyone who has been in the clutches of ketch 'n' keep knows the best way to extricat oneself from the hooked barbs is not to pull away from it but to reverse direction. To get away, in other words, you have to push further into it.

And so it is with the memory of the fight my father had with Mr. Merced and the fight's origins and getting to the root of certain lingering questions. What has sprung up before me causes me to redirect. I am backing into the ketch 'n' keep, seeing things in reverse. Seeing, for instance, not what caused the fight my father had with Mr. Merced, but what that fight might have helped to cause. I am looking back and seeing Jimmy Merced. Seven years have gone by. He is back from the war with a less-than-honorable-discharge, out of jail and out of a job. It is St. Croix, summertime, 1972. Just a few months before the Sweet Bottom Massacre.

—ᴍ—

SWEET BOTTOM

—ɯɯ—

The Unreported Call

At the time of the Sweet Bottom Massacre, I was living in Peru. I don't recall any word of Sweet Bottom though my mother may have mentioned it in a letter or spoken of it when she came to Lima for a visit in December of 1972, three months after the crime. If she did mention it, which seems likely, the seriousness of the crime did not sink in. I had been in Peru for almost a year having completed a five-month overland trip there the year before with my old friend Niles. I'd lost contact with Niles shortly after his lizard launching efforts when I went off to school in the States, but we'd reconnected in Boston years later when we were university students there. After graduation Niles and his wife Anne and I outfitted a VW bus and headed south, four months overland through Central and South America. At the time of Sweet Bottom, I was teaching at the American School in Lima, Peru, and Niles was working in San Isidro as an architect. Much of our free time was spent visiting pre-Columbian ruins in places like Cuzco and Machu Picchu, Cajamarca and Chavin. We also surfed up and down the coast — la Isla, Punta Rocas, La Herradura, Chicama.

Even as I write of not having heard about Sweet Bottom in a letter, I begin to doubt myself. I can imagine such a memory, a letter slid under the door of my Miraflores apartment, which I would have put on the side table while I went to boil water for tea. If I chose to open it right then I might have glanced at its contents on the kitchen counter while tea was steeping. It is the memory thing. What is real and what is remembered? I can imagine my mother's letters small and neat very like her writing as a girl in her scrapbook. I imagine word of the hottest September, the cat having kittens, a five cruise ship day, something with an exclamation mark about murders on St. Croix and the word MERCED!! capitalized. Two days off with Hurricane Supplication Day and word of Uncle Harlen off his rocker. Again. Enjoyed letter from the jungle butterfly place. Love.

Mom had had a bit of a breakdown the year before, a year after my parents divorced, so Pam and I scanned her letters for irregularities. The separation had been a long time in the making. I'd been back to St. Thomas for a brief stay the year before shortly after her breakdown and her release from the hospital, which would have put me on St. Thomas the summer of 72, about three months before the Sweet Bottom Massacre. Now Mom was working at House and Home selling blenders to locals instead of cuckoo clocks to tourists and half the island seemed to know her. That's your mother? I was asked time and again. With the Contant house now empty (and my father living on Vieques) Mom rented out the main part and lived in the casita, an attached bedroom and bath with an open kitchen on the porch. I remember that vacation from teaching in Peru, and sitting on the little porch watching her ancient 10-inch Sony. First, *Love of Life* and feeding the animals. Then dinner and *Gunsmoke* or *All in the Family*. We watched and talked surrounded by crickets, the occasional plane passing overhead, Mom nursing a scotch, both of us throwing bread crumbs to lizards.

As it turned out, 1972, the year of the Sweet Bottom Massacre, was to be a big year for madness. First, Mom's breakdown in January. Then Uncle Harlan that spring during Carnival. It was also the year when the sleeping gene for schizophrenia that Niles had inherited from his mother 24 years before, would, like some fairy tale ogre, awaken for the first time.

The onset of Niles' problem was slow to develop, though in hindsight there were early indicators. At the time, Niles and two other architects were in charge of the design of several new government buildings in downtown Lima, including the PIP building. The PIP is the Peruvian equivalent of the combined CIA, FBI, and Secret Police. On two occasions when I was visiting Niles and Anne at their apartment, I sensed an unspoken tension either between them or in some way related to me. Then early one morning a person from the American embassy came into my classroom to report that Niles had shown up at the Ambassador's residence, pounding on the door at two o'clock in the morning. The embassy had pulled impossible strings and gotten Niles and Anne booked on the first flight out that morning. In time we learned that his schizophrenic crash into unreality had been hastened by his work on the PIP building. He literally had the plans essential to State Security and had become increasingly (and perhaps not irrationally) paranoid that something might happen to him when his talents were no longer needed. In a situation like this, particularly in a place like Peru, the lines between fantasy and reality can be exceedingly thin and Niles slipped into that other place.

Even if I had received a letter in Peru mentioning the Sweet Bottom Massacre, I doubt I would have given it much thought at that time. Mention of the Merced family might have caused me to recall the fight on Crystal Gade, to recall the particulars (including the mistaken notion that Anton was the Merced who came to our door) that had come to be The Fight. But I doubt, given my age at the time and my distance from events, that mention of the name Merced would have caused me to dwell on those memories much less ponder the mystery of the fight's origins. And even if I had shown a degree of curiosity and known the facts of Sweet Bottom, I'm still not at all sure that certain connections would have occurred to me.

—ᴍ—

In the new St. Croix District Court Complex there is a 5,000-page file
on the Sweet Bottom Massacre trial. A few years ago, at a time I was visiting a friend on St. Croix, I went to the court on several occasions to
look the file over. It includes details of the crime, the escape and capture,
legal maneuverings, and the lengthy text of the trial itself. The file also
includes correspondence between Jimmy Merced and Judge Atheniel
Stout years after his imprisonment, correspondence that would lead to
the eventual hijacking of the airliner. While I was on St. Croix I also took
the time to visit Sweet Bottom — a place I'd never been — to visit the
actual scene of the crime.

Flying into St. Croix, the plane crosses the mountains just west of the
Sweet Bottom Resort. The fairways run in and through meadows and valleys. Beyond, the vegetation is broken by outcroppings of sugar plantation
ruins bleached white by the sun. The lay of the land is flatter than St.
Thomas and less irregular. In the distance is the huge Hess Oil refinery.
Out the other side of the plane lie the rugged contours of Ham's Bluff
where Merced and friends are believed to have hidden after the crime.

Dipping a wing and angling back in from the west, St. Croix lies
sprawled like a partially submerged creature, its green hide still showing
the scars of Hurricane Hugo. From the plane window my eye follows the
arm of the bay, the brow of the hill, the belly of the harbor, an inclina-
tion of mine to view islands as organisms: on St. Thomas when the
excesses of a bulldozer cause the topsoil to hemorrhage rusty billows into
the harbor when it rains, I think of blood; a development spreading
unchecked across a lush hillside and pockmarking the landscape brings
leprosy to mind; and in the morning, the bright cruise ships entering the
harbor to disgorge their tourists seem like a time-release medicine that is
both cure and affliction. And when I see two or three youths chilling at
the corner with trouble in their eyes, I wonder too whether something
small like a single cancer cell is dividing in the island's spleen.

In 1972 there were many such corners, particularly on St. Croix and
most notably, in Frederiksted. Some of the more hardened idlers were
Vietnam vets who had lost buddies in the war, back now on the streets,
many of them jobless. Recent Vietnam protests in the States and race

riots in places like Watts and Detroit had emboldened them, as had their ancestry, their history of uprising. To these men the first and most obvious injustice was that the same Virgin Islanders who were made to serve and sometimes die for their country were not allowed to vote for its President. But more insidious were the tales of racial occurrences that Vietnam vets returned with. In some ways Jimmy Merced typified these veterans. He had been taught to kill and had done so with distinction. The fact that he had carried a machine gun, survived a jungle ambush and been decorated for heroism gave him a certain mystique. That he had later been imprisoned and discharged after beating up a white officer, only added to it. In the view of many Vietnam vets, Merced had found an honorable way out.

When the military chose to get rid of Jimmy Merced rather than have to deal with him, he returned to the islands. He went first to St. Thomas but after a few months chose to move to St. Croix to live with his Uncle Hugo, the man who fought my father approximately twelve years earlier and who had, by that time, lived on St. Croix for five years. Jimmy Merced had always been close to his Uncle Hugo, even, at times, closer than he was to his own father. Anton acknowledges this. Jimmy Merced may have felt there were more job possibilities on St. Croix where Hugo was a heavy equipment operator who had a little land and some horses. Jimmy Merced (or "Ali" as he had come to call himself since his stint in the slammer) may have looked for employment, but his service discharge probably worked against him.

It did not take him long to get into trouble and to challenge authority. In the months before Sweet Bottom, Merced had already assaulted a member of the Home Guard, shot at a policeman, been sent to jail and escaped. He had also, during this time, come into possession of a machine gun stolen from a National Guard locker the year before. It was a gun quite similar to the one he'd carried tracking North Vietnamese in the Central Highlands.

In the four months he'd been on the lam from his earlier troubles, Jimmy Merced had set up a network of safe houses along with two or three bush hangouts. The first of these camps was in a cluster of tamarind trees only a few hundred yards up the flank of Blue Mountain. Merced and his fugitive buddy and fellow Frederiksted bad boy Sonny Rapsatt kept beans and rice and some canned food tucked into a hollow of one tree. There were some blankets as well, pots and pans. When it rained the gut there ran a steady stream for hours and formed two good pools. Sometimes they went to and from this encampment on horses — owned by his Uncle Hugo — left tied in the shadows. There was another hide-out they alternated with nearer to Creque Dam and a third, accessible only by foot, at Ham's Bluff in the rugged northwest landscape. There was also a certain farm in Caledonia and a cave near Maroon Ridge. But as often as not these men slept in a bed in houses of sympathetic friends.

And these were not few. Although Merced and Rapsatt were known by the police and by many in the community, not all were ill-disposed towards them. There were, for instance, new police recruits who were also Vietnam vets. There was a network of Frederiksted family and friends. It is hard to believe the authorities were truly unable to capture Merced. Some have even suggested that police sympathizers may have turned a blind eye to the theft of the machine gun or even made his escape from jail possible. It is the same cultural kinship which, years later, may have placed a small gun in the lavatory of the DC-10 Merced hijacked to Cuba. The unseen hand.

But evidence suggests that Merced and friends were, by mid-November, wearing out their welcome — particularly with those not wanting to be convicted of aiding and abetting a fugitive. Food and funds were getting harder to come by and sleeping in the bush had become the rule rather than the exception. Recently, Merced and Rapsatt had hooked up with Dexter Lettsome and Tyronne Pascalam to get use of a car. But the day before Sweet Bottom a police tow truck had been called to move it from a side street where it had run out of gas. Also joining the group the day before was Angel Santana, who no longer had a place to crash since his girlfriend had been evicted from her apartment. Those two things — the towed car and the evicted girlfriend — may have tripped the switch.

One seldom noted fact about the Sweet Bottom Massacre is that Jimmy Merced was spotted in the vicinity of the golf course earlier on the day of the crime and this was reported to the police. Merced was already wanted for attempted murder and had escaped from custody four months earlier while awaiting trial, so why did the police fail to respond to the call? Perhaps a responding officer, knowing Sweet Bottom to be surrounded by bush, may have seen the futility and chosen to ignore it. One wonders how different things might have been had a squad car or two shown up to put Merced and the others on notice.

At the trial, Athenial Rapsatt, grandfather of Sonny Rapsatt, testified that he had overheard his grandson the night before the crime planning with two others a raid of some sort to be staged the following morning. Mr. Rapsatt, accustomed to occasional visitations by his fugitive grandson who was wanted for attempted murder, knew better than to make this knowledge public. His wife of 50 years was sometimes required to cook for Sonny or to send a shopping bag full of food with her taxi driver nephew to be left at a drop-off point in the rainforest near Creque Dam. Mr. Rapsatt also testified that the day of the crime he saw his nephew and several others dressed in fatigues pass by his pigpen in Upper Love just downwind from the golf course. This was late in the morning, about eleven o'clock, Mr. Rapsatt figured.

What he had seen was the five men arriving in the area from the southwest flank of Blue Mountain where Merced was said to have had a campsite. From the campsite, the men would have been able to see the distant emerald fairways of the Sweet Bottom Resort. They had viewed it as a tempting target because it had been hit successfully a few months earlier by associates. The clubhouse was far enough from the main part of the resort and close enough to the bush to make it an easy job. The day of the crime all five moved through the bushes along the west edge of the 18th fairway waiting to make their move. They had planned to stage the robbery in the morning but gave way to thoughts of a fatter cash box after lunch. At one point Merced actually strolled through the parking lot to get a better look at the rear area of the kitchen and the pro shop out back. It was this stroll that caught the eye of one employee and prompted the call to the police, the call that went unheeded.

Just after three in the afternoon, the kitchen crew was cleaning up and a table of diners was preparing to leave. Up the fairway a foursome was teeing off for the 18th green. Behind them, in the distance, two golf carts were moving up the fairway to the 17th.

The plan was to go in quickly and get the cash boxes at the bar and the pro shop and the wallets of anyone who happened to be there at the time. There would not likely be any need for bloodshed. Each man was armed — two 45s, a sawed-off shot gun, a .33, and Merced would cover the whole operation with his shoulder-slung 50-caliber machine gun. With that much firepower, no one expected to have any trouble. After the heist, it was agreed, they'd go south into the bush and double back along the ridge where Rapsatt's grandfather kept his pigs. There they'd divide the money and go in opposite directions — Merced, Rapsatt and Santana west toward Ham's Bluff and Lettsome and Pascalam east toward Blue Mountain. They agreed not to remove the hoods they'd fashioned from black cloth until they were completely out of sight of the golf course.

When the visiting golfers from Florida finished their round they went to the Pro Shop to drop off a set of clubs and to say goodbye to the club pro, Gil Sanders. Gil was out on the course so they left a note and headed toward the parking lot to their rental jeep. Both couples were heading to the beach. As they were loading their gear into the back, armed men appeared dressed in fatigues with black hoods over their heads. The tall one with a machine gun told them they weren't going anywhere and ordered them back to the clubhouse.

On the terrace of the restaurant the bartender, Isaac Richards, was drying daiquiri glasses, and Thelma Daniels, the cocktail waitress, was totaling the beverage take. In the corner a waitress was sponging off the tables, and in the kitchen behind her several others were cleaning up. Just off the edge of the terrace was an electrician, Sam Elders, and his Kittitian helper, young Winston Bram. It was the last terrace lamp they had to rewire before heading home for the day. The setting was a routine day at the18th hole. Then the four tourists who'd just left reappeared followed by five armed men who fanned out from behind them and yelled for no one to move.

The tourists were herded into a corner beside a wall and covered by the man with the machine gun. To one side, the two electricians lay face down in the grass covered by a second gunman. A third bandit rifled through the pockets of the tourists and removed watches, necklaces, bracelets and rings. At the bar the fourth man covered the employees and the kitchen door while the fifth had Isaac Richards empty the cash register. That done, the money man went out back to hold up the Pro Shop. Everything seemed to be going as planned.

At the trial a witness recalled one of the tourists saying, "Please just take what you want and go."

To this the tall one with the machine gun said, "No. I am going to kill every one of you white motherfuckers."

Several of the restaurant employees who survived the terrifying seconds that followed, later testified that the tall one with the machine gun started to spray the place. At that instant, Gil Sanders, the club pro was on the final fairway helping his partner find a sliced drive. Sanders later reported looking up at the clubhouse when he heard what sounded like a long string of firecrackers and even when a crazed cook's helper came running toward him, he could scarcely make out what he was saying. The minutes spent looking for that sliced drive had probably saved their lives.

One waitress who had plunged over a nearby wall and hidden in a clump of bushes said that in the silence that followed the machine gun burst she heard other shots. Then came the sound of frantic voices and movement. There was also the agonizing wail of one of the victims.

Then she heard the words, "What? Your ass ain' dead yet?" followed by a final burst of fire.

When the police arrived a few minutes later a sergeant leaned over one of the victims and heard his dying words, "Such a beautiful island."

The photo the next day in *The Daily News* showed pools of blood across the terrace, and I wonder if the photographer got to the scene after the ambulances or the paper wisely chose not to publish photos of crumpled bodies. In all, over 100 rounds were fired from the machine gun alone. Eight were killed and others were wounded. The four tourists, both electricians, the lady in the pro shop and a groundskeeper died. One who lived long enough to see the ambulance arrive, screamed as they moved him to the stretcher, "Please, God, let me die." On the operating table an hour later that wish was granted. When the police showed up a few minutes after the murders, the five intruders had long since slipped back into the bush. A SWAT team assembled and, with dogs, tried to pick up the scent. All roads were closed off. The manhunt that would last a full seven days had begun.

— ҉ —

Most Virgin Islanders who were alive at the time of Sweet Bottom can tell you exactly where they were when they first heard about the crime. About an hour after the shooting, Anton Merced was just returning from work at the St. Thomas Post Office when his second wife, Armelle, told him what she had just heard on the radio.

"I bet Jimmy is involved," she said under her breath.

The remark led to an argument. She was not the mother of Jimmy, Anton pointed out, so what did she know? She should just shut her mouth about things she doesn't know about. She is here on St. Thomas talking about what's going on on St. Croix. And so on. Armelle bit her lip and went into the kitchen. Anton admitted to me that he went to bed that night fearing his wife might be right.

The next day the crime is all over the newspaper and the authorities want to know the whereabouts of three individuals. Jimmy Merced is the first one mentioned. Then Rapsatt and Lettsome. By the following morning the crime is world news with major pieces in the *New York Times* and the *Miami Herald*.

When I went to Sweet Bottom itself — now a resort of another name — I was struck by the beauty of the place, the setting, the course, the physical plant, the structures. I drove into the hills above the course and studied the layout, the approach, the likely avenues of escape. I tried to imagine a burst of gunfire echoing through the hills but it was hard, given the pastoral tranquillity of the scene, to bring such a thing to mind.

On the fringes of the course are various ruins of plantation days — mills, cook houses, the crumbling walls of the plantation factory — all studded now with purposeful plantings that augment the crushing work of roots and vines that are slowly bringing the memory of those times to a close. Flanking the parking lot with its golf carts and taxi vans is the curved wall of an old plantation cistern. The cistern overlooks the parking lot and the fairways beyond and the valley, settled since pre-Columbian times, the valley from which the cistern's stones were quarried.

The clubhouse is larger and more elegant than the Sweet Bottom clubhouse destroyed in 1989 by Hurricane Hugo. I was there after lunch, about the same hour the crime occurred. Standing around, I began to feel unexpectedly self-conscious and secretive, the way I'd felt when I drew the Sweet Bottom microfilm from the library file. I study the tiles wondering if they are the same tiles that were pooled with blood, the ones on the cover of *The Daily News.* They seem to be larger and of a darker hue. I look out at the hills, at the bush beyond the fairway, looking for escape routes, for the suggestion of a trail. A young caddie spotting me on the verandah imagines my interest to be that of a golfer. He can take me right now, he calls up to me. I hesitate. Or tomorrow if that would be better, he smiles. I start to tell him that I am interested in something else but do not. A row of golf carts are idle; it is late April, off season. I lie and tell him I may be back tomorrow for a round and this seems to please him. I back away from the verandah and take in the surroundings: the bar, an airy lounge, photos on the wall of famous pros and movie stars who have played here. Nothing, of course, to bring less pleasant memories to mind.

I stop at the pro shop, which sells resort wear as well as golf accessories, and wonder if this is the same place that was robbed during the crime, the shop where the lady clerk was killed. The place seems too contemporary, either remodeled or rebuilt. There is a saleslady, West Indian, at the counter who smiles at me but does not come over trying to make a sale, and I am thankful. Soon I pick out a few postcards and we strike up a conversation. When I slip in a bit of West Indian accent it brings a smile to her face; she thought I was a guest. I explain that I live on St. Thomas and ask her if she has worked at Sweet Bottom very long.

"This month makes 30 years," she says but adds that these days she only works afternoons two or three days a week. Retired. Just something to keep busy.

"So you must have been working here at the time of the Sweet Bottom affair," I venture.

There is a pause now as our conversation takes a new tack.

"Oh, yes."

It is the oh yes of someone returning to the forbidden cocktail. I do not press her but she falls easily into the memory. She was working the day of the crime and would have likely been shot had her cousin not shown up a half-hour early to give her a lift. She asked the woman, Mrs. Roberts, who was filling in for her vacationing boss, if it was all right. Things were slow, the shop empty and they closed at four.

" 'You run along, Sweetie' — those were her last words to me."

The saleslady, Mrs. Benjamin, made the added point that Mrs. Roberts didn't need to work. Her husband was wealthy. She was only doing her friend a favor.

"She was a nice lady. Very nice."

About 15 minutes after her cousin dropped her at her house, her brother-in-law came roaring up the drive and told her he'd heard something on the car radio about a shooting but had found the entrance to Sweet Bottom blocked off. She was certain there was some mistake because she had just come from there. Within the hour the radio confirmed that eight people had been killed and others wounded. By nightfall she learned that a woman had been killed in the Pro Shop and a few days later, when she was allowed to return, she saw the large darkened stain on the rug where the nice lady's life had drained away.

Three days after the Sweet Bottom Massacre, the largest manhunt in Virgin Islands' history had netted only two fugitives, one cornered in a house in nearby Orange Grove and a second in Frederiksted. These were Dexter Lettsome and Tyronne Pascalam. Meanwhile the event continued to be world news with further stories in the *New York Times* and a series in the *Miami Herald*. Both papers raise questions about the root causes of racism and resentment. The local government goes into damage control with the Governor issuing statements that the crime was not racially motivated (though seven of the eight dead are white and wounds are execution-style). Certain letters to the editor are not totally unsympathetic with the assassins, and even our own paper runs an editorial, which asks, "Can we face the facts now?"

Within 48 hours, the manhunt had expanded to include 150 men, dogs flown in from Puerto Rico and the States, helicopters, low-flying airplanes, SWAT teams and sharp shooters. There is just so much territory on St. Croix. About the only terrain that could still forestall capture was the steep and uncharted bush and ravines in Ham's Bluff.

I can picture the helicopters from Roosevelt Roads naval base running up and down along the bluffs, pulling right alongside those wind-sculpted tree tufts. But one can hear the rotors coming from miles away and I can see Merced and company duck behind a genip tree or tuck into a fold of rock. In this imagined memory he is the same boy I once knew, and if this were a movie he would be the bad guy part of me wants to get away. Right now the helicopters are not a problem although food, almost a week into the manhunt, has become one. They put in a call for food to their contacts in Caledonia but when Rapsatt goes solo back to the road no food has been left. He gets a jug of water from the stream then returns to their encampment by moonlight. Half way back he hears dogs down in Annaly, and he races the final mile back to the encampment waking the others with the news that a dog team is assembling to the east. The fugitives go down Maroon Ridge to a pre-arranged site where they have fished before and enter the water to swim and walk across a waist-deep stretch and come out downwind and to the west. There, they try wrapping seaweed to their shoes in an attempt to cover their scent and once again strike into the bush and head up a ravine on the western slope of Mt. Prospect.

All afternoon and into the night, they wait for the sound of the dogs but the sounds never come. They have been driven to the end of the island. The only hope is to steal a boat and get to Vieques or, better, the east coast of Puerto Rico, approximately 40 miles away. Merced proposes that they steal a small fishing boat from Frederiksted but Rapsatt feels certain the boats are under surveillance. They decide to risk going south after midnight and before the moon rise — maybe through the water — and get to

Frederiksted where they can hold up in one of the abandoned shacks near Rapsatts' grandparents' house. Merced proposes he make an anonymous call from a public phone near the ballpark and claim to have spotted the Sweet Bottom fugitives out east near Grapetree Bay, to help take heat off Frederiksted long enough to get food and look into cutting a mooring on one of the local fishing boats. In his pocket Merced has a knife. He also has a hand line but he has been unable to catch a fish. By the time they head down through the bush they have not eaten in two days.

The following morning a tip is phoned in. Someone has seen the three men moving through the pre-dawn streets of Frederiksted after emerging from the graveyard at the end of King Cross Street. Within 15 minutes of the report an eight-block section of the town has been cordoned off. At the center of this perimeter is a small abandoned shack on Prince Street. Just before dawn 100 police and FBI are on the scene and a crowd has begun to gather. When everything is in position, a 10-man SWAT team silently breaks into an abandoned store and, by going through the back, gains access to the boarded-up shack said by the informant to house the fugitives.

The three men, still sleeping, are caught completely by surprise.

"Don't shoot! Don't shoot!" they yell, hands in the air.

The Daily News for 1972, around the time of the trial, shows an island on fast forward. The paper is 20 pages long with syndicated columns and plenty of national news, much of it about Nixon, Vietnam, and race riots. There are also plenty of items that are local in nature. Because I'd been away for the better part of seven years (except for Christmas visits and an occasional summer), the pages create a memory of a time I never knew. It is one I am content to file away, a memory of a community at odds with itself, and an island being overwhelmed by change.

In the closing months of 1972 — after Newark and Watts, Attica and Detroit — the Virgin Islands was experiencing the cultural aftershocks of the final poisons of the Vietnam War. And Sweet Bottom was a salt in certain wounds. Some of the local resentment was related to Sweet Bottom itself and to uncertainties about the five suspects' actual guilt.

Over a period of two months various incidents, depicted in local news accounts, contributed to seething tensions leading up to the trial. Twice, cops are pelted with rocks and bottles and inmates are beaten by prison guards. There is a stabbing at the hospital and a tourist is raped at the synagogue. U.S. sailors are routinely robbed or attacked. There is a kidnapping-murder trial in the news and a newspaper editorial from a Market Square radical calling for a "guerrilla-type revolution." Beside it, is a story about local "ruffians." In St. Croix they are investigating a shooting and a robbery. A store manager is stabbed in the chest and a man, 27, strangles a man, 67, to death. Then the Attorney General commits suicide. All this while a month-long column features excerpts from *The Rape of the Virgin*, a book exposé on private and public corruption. By year's end, there will have been 21 murders, 16 of the victims whites killed by blacks, a fact noted in several stateside newspapers. The New Year is rung in with the news that a 16-year-old has been raped and her throat slashed with a machete.

A hearing date is set roughly a month after the crime. The case has attracted a retinue of heavyweight stateside lawyers including familiar names associated with high-profile radical causes. During this month the suspects are transferred to St. Thomas for detention to avoid setting off further conflict. The five Sweet Bottom suspects are incarcerated in Fort Christian on St. Thomas where, it is hoped, the air of hostility will be less virulent. But Merced is a hard-core St. Thomian with a bottomless supply of contacts. The Sweet Bottom five issue reports to the press of the Fort Christian "torture chamber" and of harassment by guards referred to as the "Goon Squad." The guards deny it. Within weeks of his transfer to Fort Christian, Merced has the guards, who are fearful of reprisals on their families, cowed. Merced requests and receives the southwest room, breezy, well lit with its view of the harbor, where things can be yelled to the street. He steals a radio and threatens to kill anyone who tries to take it from him. Judge Stout receives reports that sexual intercourse is occurring in the jail reception area. This leads to a hearing in which conjugal rights are demanded, and the court sets Tuesday and Thursday nights aside. The jailhouse at Fort Christian seems to reflect the larger schizophrenia of the community. An anonymous inmate tells a reporter that "Everyone has Gillettes."

In this kind of environment the trial, originally slated to begin in October, finally got under way in July. This after a number of pretrial motions including ones from the defense for a new trial, for the judge to recuse himself, one related to jury tampering and another protesting the judge's decision not to allow brutality testimony. At one point Judge Stout, tired of being harangued by big league media lawyers, threatened to walk out of the courtroom. Eventually, all formal motions were denied by an appellate court.

The day the trial opened, Jimmy Merced chose to wear a leopard-spotted yellow shirt open down the front with a black liberation symbol on the back. Rapsatt wore a camouflage shirt. All wore whiskers and either sneakers or sandals. The decision to show contempt was a conscious one; there would be no sense of remorse despite the fact that the legal deck was stacked against them. I wonder whether their attorneys advised them against this or whether they were playing to the jury's local sympathies, to the local sensitivity to racial injustice and to the possibility of a reasonable doubt. But not even a local jury would look kindly on outbursts of profanity and to courtroom scuffles. Perhaps Merced imagined that his sins would be overlooked and, like the cowboy movies of his youth, the crowd would surge into the courtroom and carry him away. He may have hoped he could out-street tough the court, play to a reasonable doubt, and through a little theatre carry the day.

The first witness for the prosecution is immediately interrupted by Merced who asks how much the government is paying her to lie. Then he turns to the gallery, his chest and stomach exposed and says, "Fuck the court. No one can judge me."

Judge Stout adjourns for the day.

The next day of the trial, a waitress identifies Merced as the one who shot the tourists in the stomach. Later a scuffle breaks out when marshalls attempt to subdue Rapsatt from making remarks. The outbreak occurs just as Merced, the first defendant, is leaving the stand. Merced does not join in the fray which lasts several minutes and occurs while the jury is out of the room. The judge peeks from his chamber's door. The day is notable also because Merced admits under oath that he told agents the machine gun was in the outhouse. It is a turning point.

The next day, a two-dollar bill, a Kennedy half dollar and an 1899 silver dollar are entered into evidence. The items were found in the Frederiksted shack where the three were arrested. An attorney for the estate of one of the slain tourists identifies the bill as a good luck token his client carried in his wallet, and the bartender identifies the coin as one he kept in the register. The items strongly link the men to the crime, but they are seen joking and talking to the Marshalls who are guarding them. That same day in a famous trial in Trinidad, Stanley Abbott and Steve Chadee, accused of bludgeoning an English woman to death, are sentenced to hang.

In the closing days of prosecution testimony, the FBI presents the signed confession of Pascalam and Lettsome and also matches 12 machine gun bullets and fragments from the 9mm German Lugar found on the roof of the house where Lettsome and Pascalam were captured. One day, the eleventh of the trial, is devoted entirely to the grisly description of the various fatal wounds suffered by the eight victims. After a total of 40 witnesses and 180 exhibits, the government rested its case.

The long-awaited defense starts with FBI testimony that confirms that there was no fingerprint match. The prosecution gets the same witness to also acknowledge that Merced admitted shooting four or five people against the wall. The judge has ruled that the defense is not free to call the confessions suspect due to rumors of brutality. The question of identification still remains since all had hoods. An earlier defense witness who claimed to have seen some defendants "terrified and beaten," reverses herself. But a former cop testifies he and others beat Merced. In the paper that day is a photo of about 20 people on the street keeping a vigil outside the courtroom. Merced, it seems, was beginning to comprehend the futility of the defense and the looming probability that he was heading for a life term.

In the end there were several facts that threw doubt on the equal guilt of all the defendants, at least in the minds of some. It seems extremely unlikely that all were equally guilty of firing weapons. One of the suspects in prison for life may not even have fired a shot. It also seems possible that there may have been a degree of brutality involved in the questioning carried out at Sweet Bottom. There is a shadowy Colonel Anders who appears in testimony as having been involved in the interrogation. He is described as wearing military riding boots and carrying a horse crop, and is, we later learn, a specialist in military counter-intelligence. There is much talk of the comings and goings of this Colonel from a certain storage area, where interrogations were said to have been conducted.

By the time the defense had rested its case, and the jury had heard final arguments, the Sweet Bottom trial was entering its 21st day after 70 witnesses and 200 exhibits. During the ten days the jury took to decide on a verdict, the defense tried again to have the judge declare a mistrial. The motion was denied. On the day the jury handed down the verdict (after much deliberation and accusations of jury tampering) Judge Stout wasted no time and handed down the sentences only ten minutes later. Individually, each of the defendants was led, shackled, into the courtroom to receive his eight consecutive life terms. For the occasion, Merced wore his black liberation shirt and a large black hat with a floppy brim. When all had received their sentences, they were hustled into waiting vans and taken to the airport where a chartered plane was to take them to a federal prison in Puerto Rico for later transfer to the States.

The plane that took Jimmy Merced away offered him a last glimpse of his island. It is one that we all see flying away. Whatever reasons one has for leaving St. Thomas, it is hard to do so without some lingering affection. I have left other places and been glad to see them slip beneath the wing, layered over with clouds. But St. Thomas from the air beckons even as it sends you away. First, the green mountains slide by the runway, then the harbor teeming with life causes you to stare: There are the cruise ships tied to the dock, the sailboats at their moorings, the turquoise swirl of reefs, the red roofs of town, the familiar contours of the coast. The vista from the air gives one the sense — whether one is inclined to believe it or not — that, from a distance at least, it all seems, remarkably, to work. And banking south and then west out of the harbor, one can see Hassel Island, the abandoned coaling station, the defunct signal station, the old fort guarding the harbor's mouth and, if the tilt of the wing is just right, the graveyard, all serving to remind one that centuries before man had taken to the skies there were comings and goings, adventure, longing, treachery. It seems always that the plane pulls away a bit too fast to allow the passenger a final moment to admire the gem, even with its flaws, to see how this patch of earth jutting out of the blue sea manages to work. Perhaps it is because the landscape is so finite and surrenders itself so quickly to the sea that the longing to hold on to it, to some ephemeral memory of the place, is so real.

There is no way of knowing what Jimmy Merced thought as his plane left. There must have been at least some degree of disbelief that things, after all these months, had happened so fast and gone so wrong. There had been no returning to the cell to gather belongings, no tearful farewells from friend or family. Perhaps he still didn't believe that this was happening to him; certain public comments he made in the closing days of the trial seem to suggest some lingering sense that he would be exonerated. Whatever his thoughts as the plane rose into the sky, it seems unlikely that they were tempered with remorse. Not yet, at least. He would know only that he was in a terrible bind, worse than any he had ever faced, worse even than combat situations. For in this case there was very, very little hope of escape.

Flight 109

In 1963, the year we moved from town to Contant, the glassbottom business went under — literally. It had been in a state of decline — my father farming it out to one of the glassbottom captains so he could work for a car rental agency and a paint store to feed us — but nothing could really have prepared us for the end.

The V. I. Port Authority, in an effort to extend the waterfront over to Crown Bay, was in the process of dredging the main harbor to allow for larger cruise ships, and using the dredged material to create a landfill. Pop was told by engineers and politicians that this landfill would increase the value of his lease, because the boatyard would be on "prime waterfront area." My father, with little choice, signed — like other area leaseholders — the necessary documents to give them permission to bring in the fill.

For weeks we watched the dredging pipes spew sand into the bay. Niles, seeing the opportunity this presented, made a wire mesh screen to sift the sand coming from the mouth of the dredge pipe. Things that had fallen overboard in the harbor and lain motionless for hundreds of years, were sucked suddenly into a rushing pipe, an aquatic black hole, and deposited in Crown Bay and into the blinding light of the twentieth century. Artifacts from the harbor — coins, bottles, spoons, bits of rigging — abounded. One of the bottles, dark green and tear-shaped, I placed on my dresser beside my model of the aircraft carrier U.S.S. Enterprise. I imagined the bottle to be imbued with certain Aladdin-like qualities and to have fallen, perhaps, from a pirate vessel. A week after placing it on the bureau beside the aircraft carrier, the curtain — billowed by a freak gust — caught on the flight deck and sent all 90 planes and three feet of plastic crashing to the terrazzo floor. The curtain missed the bottle.

While Niles and I were making a game of the dredging, my father was keeping his eye on the encroaching sand. The water east of the boatyard was getting increasingly shallow. Where was the bulkhead he had been told was to be built to prevent the sands from encroaching on the business? He was getting the run-around. Then, one Friday, the dredging stopped.

What happened next was made clearer to me recently — 30 years after the fact — by an intriguing discovery in a most unlikely place: McDonalds. It was the island's second McDonalds recently installed at the entrance to Frenchtown, one of the quainter harbor locations. We were spared the golden arches and the decor echoed to a degree the West Indian architecture around it. The first time I went there, I noticed a number of large, old photos of St. Thomas, nicely framed, on the walls. All appeared to have been taken in the 50s and 60s, and to have come from government archives because most depicted Public Works projects — most notably, the construction of the waterfront. On my way out, a photo on the far wall caught my attention. It appeared to have been taken from Contant hill looking southeast, and in it the boatyard is visible as a tiny nub of dock made blurry from the photo's enlargement. On closer inspection, I can see that the Calypso is tied to its mooring and the *Love Junk* is still impacted in clumps of bush. The tracings of the old road are visible along the coastline and, hazy in the distance, is town. But the most interesting feature of the photograph is that it shows a large, submerged bar of sand from the distant dredges forming a wide hook around the boatyard. The water is transparent, shallowing. The glassbottom boat business is about to be swallowed.

When we next went to the boatyard, it wasn't there. The water around the dock had been displaced and the boats, still tied to it had been largely buried with sand. Scuba gear from the shed and various cushions and flotation devices were a hundred yards to the west fanned out across the leading edge of the fill forming a delta of boatyard debris.

When I pass that area, now filled in with various warehouses, shipping terminals, automotive supply stores, it is hard to recreate the geography, to remember just exactly where the boatyard was. I know the bend in the highway where the road went in — across from the big tamarind tree and just up the road from the carwash where youths now sell crack — but how far into the new maze of warehouses was the dock itself? My closest estimate is that the glassbottoms came to rest, the light gone from its glass, near the container port or, perhaps, a few feet beneath the repair garage of the Manassah Bus Line.

—⚏—

In the 12 years Jimmy Merced spent in prison he accrued an impressive record of misconduct. Although prison officials dealt with him roughly — putting him in isolation on a number of occasions — he still had a knack for setting up networks, for intimidation. Each time his influence became too pervasive he was transferred to another prison, six prisons in all. During his last stay he seemed to be settling down, spending more time in the prison law library. It is during this time, presumably, that he was working on his book, looking into his legal rights and angling for a way out. It was also from this institution that he sent the birthday card to Anton we'd found in the picture album, the one about Allah and redemption that may have been designed to be read by prison officials.

Among the documents in the Sweet Bottom file at the Christiansted courthouse are Merced's letters from jail to Judge Stout talking about his innocence and his renewed faith and his interest in having another day in court to pursue a suit against the Virgin Islands Government seeking restitution for improperly incarcerating him prior to the trial. The dates on these letters coincided, ironically, with other reports detailing Merced's involvement in a disturbance in the prison cafeteria that exploded into a riot where chairs were thrown and tables overturned. Despite his words to the contrary, Jimmy Merced had not completely disavowed violence or learned to control his temper.

Nonetheless, in 1984, after 12 years in prison, Merced was granted permission to pursue his suit against Virgin Islands prison officials for unlawful incarceration in isolation while awaiting trial. He claimed to have been denied due process when he was placed in isolation (with cable TV) for disruptive behavior and instigating a riot. V.I. prison officials were within their rights to hold him in isolation, but federal guidelines limit such isolation to a total of only 25 days. Merced had been held for 90. He had done his homework on this one and knew he had a case, even if it was on a technicality. He was suing for $30,000.

For most people in the Virgin Islands, news that Jimmy Merced, after 12 years, was back in the territory for a court date was greeted with equal measures of annoyance and disbelief. Why was a man, sentenced to eight consecutive life terms, being coddled and allowed this privilege? What was the point? There were others, however, who were intrigued by the return of Merced, others, like Vietnam vets, who watched the proceedings with interest and some who undoubtedly visited him in jail. To these people the whys of his return were not nearly so mysterious. A person is behind bars for life. Why not take advantage of an opportunity to see the sun, to return to the place of one's birth, to see family and friends, even to take a ride on a plane? What person with the intellect and resourcefulness would not avail themselves of a similar opportunity?

One of the people who visited Merced in jail was a *Daily News* reporter, Felicia Lloyd, who interviewed him shortly after his return to the territory. There is in her article a surprisingly sympathetic tone. We hear for instance that Mr. Merced is only 20 hours away from attaining his degree in business administration with an emphasis on personal and corporate tax. We hear also that Mr. Merced is serving as a teacher to other prisoners and that he hopes, one day, to be able to teach his own people — youths in particular — to form corporations. Before the reader can wonder how he plans to do that from a federal penitentiary, we read how he hopes to one day walk out a free man in his own land and that he feels this is his "birthright." At one point in *The Daily News* article the reporter attempts to compliment Merced by saying he seems to have made a "360 degree turn" since his conviction. Because the sentence appears to be intended in praise I'm sure the reporter got her degrees wrong and did not mean to put Merced right back where he started. Soon enough her unintended inaccuracy would seem strangely prophetic.

When next we see anything in the press about the trial it is to learn that Merced has actually won his case and been awarded $12,000. That is on the 28th of December. Plans are then put into action by the authorities to transfer him back to the federal pen in Lewisburg, Pennsylvania. He will be flown by 727 to St. Croix where he will be transferred to the larger DC-10 for the flight to JFK and on to the Metropolitan Correctional Center until arrangements can be made for his ground transfer to Pennsylvania. Accompanying him on the flight will be three armed guards. The first leg of the journey will depart St. Thomas at 9:15 a.m. on New Year's Day. Just who made those reservations and who was privy to the flight plans will become the intense focus of an FBI investigation.

—⚹—

At the time of this flight and of the preceding trial, I was living in New York and unaware that Merced was pursuing a court case on St. Thomas. Additionally, I was at that time only vaguely aware of the circumstances of the Sweet Bottom Massacre. My degree of interest was about to take a quantum leap.

That evening when I sat down to watch the network evening news, the first thing out of the CBS anchorman's mouth was that Jimmy Merced — "The Virgin Islands' most notorious criminal" — had hijacked an airliner to Cuba. The report was brief because details were still sketchy. I was full of questions. How in the world could Merced have been in the position to board a jetliner was the first.

The next morning I was up at dawn to see if there was any mention of it in the *New York Times.* There, to my astonishment, was the face of Jimmy Merced right on the front page. I studied it closely. It was a handsome, chiseled face with intelligent, challenging eyes. The prison haircut made him look younger than I might have imagined him. But it was unquestionably the Jimmy Merced I'd known as a child. I read the article over and over. I studied the face again and again. That day, in disbelieving tones, I spoke to my wife and friends about it. I cut the article and photo out and the next day read the follow-up article, which explained why he had been in the Virgin Islands for a trial. I cut it out too. This guy was a murderer of the most treacherous and contemptuous kind, I kept reminding myself, trying to temper my fascination, to restrain my curiosity. Because, truth be told, there was a part of me — a part not far beneath the surface — that admired Merced's moxie, that hoped simultaneously that he would both get his comeuppance and that he would somehow get away. It is hard to explain or justify such feelings. It was as if the junkyard dog who had once tormented you but later been beaten and shamed and made to suffer all nature of indignity, it was as if that tortured dog had endured and gained your sympathy finally and, against incredible odds, broken its chains and left the junkyard of its past behind. That is the best I can do in explaining my feelings, the way anyone and everyone wants to believe, in the brighter corners of one's soul, that life can be better.

Part of my empathy was also, I now realize, the Virgins Islander in me. The part that is quietly jubilant that the Virgin Island boxer has won a world title, that the ballplayer has made the big league, that the diplomat has received high praise. Proud that the surgeon has achieved international recognition, that the writer has won the award, that the dancer has made it in New York, that the sailor has triumphed in Australia, that the soldier, trapped in a distant jungle and pinned down by enemy crossfire in a war not of his own making, has, by his wits, survived. It is the kinship one feels for any Virgin Islander who has played the game by the rules — or made up a few as they went along — and come out on top. It is the emotion, in the case of Jimmy Merced, that in the recesses of my soul says You Mother Fucker, and means it half in praise.

Just how Merced managed to hijack American Flight 113 is still a mystery, this despite years of FBI investigations. What is known is that the flight to St. Croix aboard the 727 was uneventful and the transfer to the DC-10 across the tarmac — none of the transferring passengers ever entering the terminal — also went off without a hitch. Merced, unhandcuffed by federal regulations, was accompanied by three armed guards, two of whom were black belts in karate. That the guards were armed was not apparent to other passengers because of airline policy about carrying firearms onboard. The flight was carrying 183 passengers and a crew of 13. The plane departed St. Croix at 11:15 a.m.

A flight to New York from St. Croix takes about three and a half hours. Within a half hour of departure Cuba is already slipping away 500 miles to the west. In an hour the entire archipelago of the West Indies is gone and the coast of the U.S. is drawing closer. According to the log of the flight plan, the plane did not turn around and head for Havana until it was off the coast of North Carolina. If the gun was in place, hiding in the lavatory, I wonder why Merced waited that long — long enough, perhaps, to have raised questions as to the amount of jet fuel remaining. Perhaps he chose to wait until lunch had been served in order to have the aisles cleared of serving carts. Newspapers all reported that he made four trips to the lavatory, each time complaining of intense stomach pains, each time accompanied by a guard. Perhaps he didn't know in which of the lavatories the gun was stashed. I try to imagine him frantically cramming his arm into the garbage receptacle, the paper towel dispenser, the sanitary napkin dispenser searching — and coming up empty-handed, only to return to his seat and a few minutes later once again stage the stomach pains, complaining — of what? Airline food?

An editorial in *The Daily News* two days after the hijacking asks the critical questions related to the gun and to someone leaking the flight plans to conspirators. It asks who had contact with the plane and posits food service handlers, baggage handlers, cleaning people, refuelers. It wonders if the conspirator or conspirators were actually aboard the plane, had bought tickets for the flight at the last moment. The travel plans for the transfer could not have been decided upon, it seems to me, until the trial was over and that could not have been certain until the jury reached their verdict on the 28th. How many people could possibly have known that flight plan — the date and time and airline? Quite a few, really: The person or persons who made the decision, the one who made the reservation, the guards who traveled with Merced, certain airline personnel, certain travel agents, the brothers, sisters, cousins of any of these people.

And there is the other possibility. Perhaps the gun wasn't in the lavatory at all, but slipped to him by one of the guards — either out of sympathy or as a result of being paid off or, possibly, after having threats made on his life or the lives of his family. Were final negotiations or threats or assurances being furtively whispered during those repeated trips to the lavatories? One thing seems certain. The plan — at least the basic framework of it — dating all the way back to Merced's repeated requests to come to the territory for a trial, had been years in the making.

On the fourth and fatal trip to the lavatory Merced emerged, still doubled over in pretended pain, only to straighten up with a gun in his guard's ribs. Then using the guard as a shield, the two returned to their seats to hold up the other two guards. After disarming them all, Merced had two pistols jammed in his waist and one in each hand where he, "brandished two of them Western-style" according to one passenger. In the news the following day, the warden called Merced "vicious" and the Corrections Director labeled him "a desperado." In the instant Jimmy Merced gained control of that airliner, he had become the Cisco Kid of his childhood, and Jesse James and Durango, and the Buffalo Soldier — all rolled into one.

What happened when the plane landed is not known beyond the fact that Merced surrendered to Cuban military authorities. The FBI, trying to put a good face on things, informed the public that Castro did not take kindly to hijackers — or, for that matter, American aircraft entering Cuban airspace — and that Merced, far from escaping imprisonment, could look forward to the even bleaker prospect of a Cuban jail, or being extradited back to the U.S. But this may in part be wishful thinking. In the five years prior to Merced's hijacking, there had been 15 other hijackers — and not one of them, whatever their circumstances, had been returned to the U.S. At least one well-known radical wanted for murder had gotten out of jail in only a few years. Again, Jimmy Merced had done his homework.

Now, over 15 years after the hijacking, there is still no official word on what has become of Jimmy Merced. When I have talked with Anton I have always steered clear of asking him questions directly relating to his son's whereabouts. But occasionally he will let slip — not accidentally it seems — some word of his son, some news that suggests strongly that Jimmy Merced is not sitting in a jail. And when he does, I make certain not to show too much curiosity, to ask, for instance, how he received this news, how he knows these things to be true. I have asked him whether he visited Jimmy when he was in the territory prior to the hijacking and he assures me he visited almost every day and was allowed to perambulate the Fort Christian courtyard during visiting hours, which would have provided plenty of opportunity for discussion. I do not ask Anton whether he was privy to any escape plans (I doubt he was) even though the FBI has asked him this over and over and, for years, traced his movements and, Anton is certain, tapped his phone.

My own feelings are that it is unlikely that Jimmy Merced is still in jail, and I am uncertain that he is even in Cuba. He would certainly have used his smooth tongue and knowledge of Spanish to try to convince Cuban authorities that he had not killed anyone on a golf course but had been framed for his political beliefs. This claim could be buttressed by pointing to his less-than-dishonorable discharge from the military and even, perhaps, by showing a certain editorial he had written calling for revolution and the freeing of all political prisoners. The American authorities had framed him, Merced might have argued, because they feared his combat experience might cause him to foment rebellion. And that same military experience, he might also have pointed out, could be of use to the Cubans. He may have offered to reveal tactics used by U.S. counter-insurgency units, or, if they were interested, to allow him to teach those tactics to Cuban troops or even employ his skills in Angola where Cubans were at the time fighting a guerrilla war. That would have been a good ploy, to be willing to put his own life on the line for the Marxist cause. All power to the people, and so on.

If the Cubans took this bait, Merced could have gone to Africa and, when the opportunity presented itself, gone AWOL. He could still be in Africa. Or, he could have returned to Cuba and remained in the military, or left it to become — what? A teacher, perhaps, or an agent of state security? There are countless possible scenarios, of course, including the possibility that Anton's words are mere wishful thinking or play acting and his son is still in jail. But I seriously doubt it.

—ιαν—

OLD BONES

—ɱ—

Something Unexpected

In the years since Sweet Bottom and the hijacking, changes have continued to flood St. Thomas. Fortunately, the same island that invites that change has managed at the same time to resist it. The new hotel goes up and the road widens, but beneath it is the same land, comfortable in its own skin and in no particular hurry to be something it is not. Once in a while, though, the island reveals something unexpected that forces us all to sit up and take note.

One afternoon in April of 1992, a bulldozer operator clearing ground for a new shopping mall in the Tutu Valley uncovered something unexpected. About two feet below the surface he kept seeing dark rings in the otherwise clay-colored soil. At one point he got out of the dozer and went for a closer look. The dark surfaces appeared to be the carbonized remains of tree trunks or posts, evenly spaced and in a line. The driver, Ezroy Phipps, wondered at this. Having grown up in the Fort Mylner area just across the valley, he knew this patch of land had never, to his knowledge, been inhabited. Then, walking back to the dozer he noticed clay shards embedded in the dozer track. He picked up one shard and saw the tracings of a design. Later, when interviewed by a reporter, Mr. Phipps said his decision to stop moving earth that day had to do with his belief in God. "I start to wonder," he explained, "whether I disturbing someone rest."

Because there were not, at the time, any antiquities laws on the books, the developer was not required to desist. But to placate various environmental groups and to avoid possible bad press, Kmart — the principal tenant of the planned shopping mall — agreed to delay further construction until archaeologists could evaluate the extent of the site. To the developer's dismay, it quickly became clear that the bulldozer had begun to unearth what was by far the most significant ceramic site ever found on St. Thomas. Initial dating suggested the site may have been continuously inhabited — first by Arawak and later by Carib indians — for over 1,000 years before the arrival of Columbus. Fortunately, the bulldozer had only cut into a corner of the settlement which, it would turn out, had dozens of structures surrounding a central plaza or, possibly, a ball court. To adequately and correctly conduct the appropriate archeological investigation would, experts agreed, take years.

The developer, unbound by legal restrictions, refused to abandon the project and agreed only to postpone further construction as long as it took to clear the legal obstacles. One resident, who claimed to have Carib ancestry, tried to halt excavation on the grounds that it would violate a burial ground. Many residents were hopeful. At about the same time a 40 million dollar skyscraper in Manhattan had been aborted when digging revealed part of an old Negro burial ground. If a Manhattan skyscraper could be halted by a few graves, they reasoned, certainly something as significant as an entire pre-Columbian culture could not be lost to something as mundane as a Kmart.

Or could it?

There is a vein of rock crossing through this same Tutu Valley and running into Smith Bay to Coki Point that has been identified by geologists as one of the oldest formations in the Virgin Islands — over 100 million years. The layer is light in color, rocks created by volcanic uplifting to form a kind of submarine shelf, a platform for later eruptions and one largely obscured by subsequent accretions. Core samples from 400-foot deep drill sites give a sedimentary history of the island, its outlines altering over time with the rise and fall of the ocean. Less than 40,000 years ago, we were part of a larger platform that would have made it possible to walk to Puerto Rico.

It is hard to think of St. Thomas 40,000 years ago (much less a hundred million), to think clearly of it before Man, to remember that this island has a life of its own. In the larger scheme of things, the island is on the leading edge of the Caribbean Plate, the prow of which has been grinding the Atlantic Plate for some eons. Just to the north of St. Thomas lies the icy defile of the Puerto Rican Trench, the deepest point in the Atlantic, where big pressures are building. New volcanoes form. On the shores of the island — whether seated at the beach bar or fossilized in stone — are life forms that have come to these shores. Some are now extinct. Others soon will be. New forms of life — dogs, deer, coconut palms, people — have, in recent years, made their mark on the landscape, as has the bulldozer and human imagination. But we are, in the long book of this island's life, little more than a word.

The island abides us. When the bulldozer rips open a new swath of soil and it runs red in the first rain, I feel that there is little hope. But six months later in the same spot there is a culvert and a terraced wall which, within a year, suggests the future with young royal palms, tasteful anthurium and tyer palm, boulders left in the landscape. In two years, the turn in the road appeals to the eye and we forget exactly what that stretch of raw bush once looked like. If the island were flat, the change would overwhelm it. But there are endless folds and pockets, convolutions of geography that tuft everything in green, the hard edges made soft. The grace with which the island itself has absorbed change holds a lesson, perhaps.

—⟆⟆—

In 1986 I took a trip to the States to attend a memorial service for my father at St. George's. I flew first to New York and arranged to visit an old friend I had known before I moved from Rye and with whom I had spent a summer while in college. His house had been on Grace Church Street just up from my uncle's and the church where I had learned that Jesus had blue eyes. That house was typical of Rye in that it rambled, had three stories and during the summers of our school years contained the endless comings and goings of young blood.

Peter no longer lived in Rye but had settled in an apartment with his wife a few miles away in Mamaroneck. Of all our old friends, Peter knew of only one — a hippie radical-turned stockbroker — who still could afford to live in Rye. He picked me up at the Mamaroneck station and, knowing I would want to do a bit of reminiscing, drove over to Rye. We went by One Overlook and it looked small, very small. The dogwood tree was still out front and the neighborhood looked tamer than the neighborhood I had remembered. It was not 1958, and I had difficulty imagining myself as a child on that street.

"Want to knock on the door?" Peter asked.

"Yes, but let's not."

We went on to Playland and walked the boardwalk. It was October so the rides were all closed down, but I was glad to see the Dragon Coaster — with a new name — still there. And I was heartened to see the ponds and weeping willows, the well-kept lawns. Glad, also, for October, to see the crazy twists of the Wild Mouse totally silent, the maples and oaks framing it in autumn colors.

We drove over to Milton School and then on to the Manursing Island Club and Apawamis, and up Purchase Street through the center of town. There was scarcely a new building — more traffic, newer cars but otherwise a kind of time warp. Even the air was the same. Unlike St. Thomas, change had come to Rye in whispers.

There were a couple racquets in the car, and I asked Peter if there was someplace we could play tennis. He no longer belonged to any clubs but knew old family friends in Rye who had a court. On the way there, Bob Marley was on the tape deck — *Redemption Song, Three Little Birds, No Woman No Cry* — and I remember feeling, rolling under the elms and oaks, an abiding kinship with that other world, feeling the meaning of those island songs in ways Peter could not. But they are his tapes and I doubt the irony of their surroundings is lost on him either.

The court is on an estate belonging to an old classmate's parents. The court is clay, separated from a small swimming pool by a high dense hedge. The main house sits on a grass slope behind a cluster of willows and pines. Neither of us has hit a ball often in recent years, but there still is, in the *pock-a, pock-a, pock-a* sound of our volley an echo that resonates in me like cold water, like a mountain stream. Suddenly I am in the Catskills. My father stands at the top of the falls at Fawn's Leap about to do a swan dive into the frigid shallows and walking away from that court and toward the car I feel the familiar twinge that this life, this affluence is what my father really would have wanted for me, for me to have suc-ceeded where he had not, and pulling away from the place I think of my father who had died that year and I ask him why that is. Why he wanted for me what he had chosen to leave behind.

Before I left Rye that day I asked Peter to pull over by the greenhouse on Milton Road. We crossed over to the Blind Brook side, through the cemetery, over the little bridge with my "alligator," to where the path forks — left to Disbrow Park, right through the old Purdy gravesite. Peter had never seen these graves of the founding fathers of Rye. I asked him if he thought they had buckles on their shoes and whether there might still be a buckle or two down in the roots. He thought a moment, adding the centuries. He figured there might just be.

The following day I left for the memorial service at St. George's. The serv-ice was held almost a year after my father's death in the beautiful chapel with its Gothic spires. I was to give the eulogy and did and even now won-der how. There were maybe 20 people — old friends, classmates — most faces recognizable but not all. Leaving the church, a man with an unfamil-iar name approached me. He wouldn't be going to the reception because he had to get a plane back to South Carolina. Besides, he didn't know these folks who all knew my father longer and in happier times.

"Where did you know him from?"

"Prisoner of war camp."

The man's name was H.D. Stevens. He too had flown bombers and been shot down — hit by flack not by a fighter. Mr. Stevens and I walked an ivied passage to the baseball field where St. George's was playing vis-iting Groton. Standing a few yards from the first base line I heard how Mr. Stevens had been a prisoner in Stalag III for several months before my father and several other bomber pilots showed up. It was an officers' camp, and they bunked in the same barracks. Mr. Stevens told how Pop had started a softball league and, later, touch football. He'd also put together a bridge tournament. Being the camp barber was more than it appeared. He had indirect access to a radio, Mr. Stevens explained, and, if there wasn't any good news, he'd make some up.

"Even the German guards and officers liked your old man."

A roar and groan went up from the St. George's sideline for a towering drive that has curved foul. The scoreboard says we are in the bottom of the fifth. Visitors lead Home, 7-2. I notice girls with St. George's letter sweaters and realize, remember rather, that things are coed these days. I am thinking how my father could have lived with that. There are several groups of girls hanging out. I have one eye on the game and the other on a lovely schoolgirl with chestnut hair and a beautiful figure. She is, what? Fifteen?

"Do you think my father would have approved of co-education?"

"Strongly, I suspect."

Mr. Stevens tells me he knows I need to be getting over to the reception, but he wants to leave me with one memory. He tells of how, through the Red Cross, the barracks had come into the possession of a quantity of ice skates and when winter came, the men cleared an area and created a skating pond. Soon, a group of American prisoners started playing regular hockey games. A German officer, seeing how well the American airmen played, came upon the idea of the prisoners putting on a Sunday exhibition for German officers from a nearby camp.

During warm-ups that day, skaters hustled up and down the ice passing the puck. Half the camp was there, standing and sitting around the ice. In one section near a goal, chairs were set up and the German officers took their places. It was a show of good cheer one might say — officers showing respect for other officers, fair play and all that. And in that spirit — and this was the point of Mr. Stevens' story — my father carved up the ice during their warm-up, received a passed puck and swept around the backside of the goal and came to a sharp stop, the blades of his skates sending an intentional spray of shaved ice onto the laps of the German officers. One could hear, Mr. Stevens said in a whisper, a pin drop. But my father, in good spirits, passed off the puck and continued to skate as if nothing had happened.

"I will never forget," Mr. Stevens concluded, "the sight of those Germans officers dusting ice crystals off their laps."

Groton was at bat, its base runners stealing second with impunity, the runners coming in standing up. We were probably both thinking that they wouldn't have gotten away with it if my father were behind the plate. There is nothing so unusual about standing on a ballfield where one's father once played as a young man, nor was it unusual to talk to a person who knew my father before I was born. But the man with the soft Carolina accent had been a young man at a time when young men were called upon to do extraordinary things. I thought for an instant of a story my father once told of a missed field goal and looked for the goal posts. On what field was that kick, I wondered. Perhaps the very one I am standing on. And St. George's was staging a rally in the top of the sixth.

"Good wood."

"Nice catch."

"Doubleplay depth."

"Fielder's choice."

After the inning we walk back to Mr. Stevens' car, our feet crunching the gravel drive. He had a plane to catch and I a reception to attend. When he pulled away in that sky blue rental, it occurred to me that the circle of the drive was making him drive down a road he'd never been on before. Never be on again. He had never been to St. George's or even to Rhode Island. When I turned away I imagined, wrongly, that I would never see him again.

—⦙⦙⦙—

Looking through the microfilmed pages of *The Daily News* for 1958 the year we moved to the islands, I was surprised to see a small item about two men and a woman colliding at five o'clock in the morning with one of the waterfront's historic cannons. The names of the injured are Hugo and Anton Merced and Anton's wife, Esther.

When I mentioned this to Anton he told the story of how they were coming from the Bambooshay Club in Willy's jeep. Four o'clock in the morning. His brother Hugo was driving. When they missed the waterfront intersection going 40 or 50, they wrapped around one of the upright 2-ton cannons. Hugo went through the windshield. Anton, in the rear seat, did a flip and landed on the hood with a broken neck. I remember as he tells me this that he has had 19 broken bones. How many of them did this accident account for? I ask.

"Only two."

Anton describes in heroic measures the role Hugo played in helping get him to the hospital. I feel this is very generous considering Hugo's less than heroic driving, but I keep this thought to myself. We talk instead of broken bones — this fight, that accident, the time he fell off a roof. My questions help fuel this talk because broken bones interest me (the idea of the white bone snapping, the marrow exposed) and because I have not a single broken bone story of my own to tell.

But I think of one bone story to tell Anton — not a broken one but a bone that had a cyst in it when I was five. Limping home from kindergarten in Rye led to an X-ray, which led, two weeks later, to an operation. The rotted bone of the cyst was carved back to healthy bone and a good piece grafted into the cavity. The bone selected to replace mine was my father's, cut from his pelvis.

Anton, after a moment's contemplation, informs me that as far as he is concerned, this qualifies as a broken bone story. I tell him the part I like best is that a part of my father, gone now over 15 years, is still living, still a part of me. Anton smiles. The thought had already occurred to him.

—⟋⟍—

Looking back now on those early years, I see how the glassbottom — the actual well with the glass in it — was like life itself, floating over vast reaches of possible experience, but passing within a narrow and quickly moving path of sight. What we see is a spectacle, but our grasp, like the parable of the blind men and the elephant, is limited to our experience. We see it but are removed. Once, motoring between the reef and the first wreck, the glassbottom passed through a school of sprat and I saw a barracuda slice through a jack. At least I *think* that is what I saw — the head, a glitter of scales, the blood a pink film. But it was too fast. I looked up at the person across from me to see if she had seen what the person beside her, looking toward Sub Base, had not. The captain was lining us up for the wreck. He had seen nothing. Had he, we might have backed up to see, what? Maybe the head lying on the floor? Not likely. The blood would have vanished, the event complete, and the bubbles from the reversing props would have served only to further erase or distort the memory. Too soon we are drawn back to the glass, into shipwreck wonders, into convolutions of coral, into the memory of a dream of a crossing deer, into whether that was a snapper beneath the brain coral, or a shadow.

In returning to the events of my childhood it is as if I am, in effect, turning the boat around, going back. In that turning back I am looking for certain spots in the reef, certain events. But often when the boat goes back over that spot in the reef you wanted to return to, you don't at first recognize it because you are entering it from a different angle. For years the fight my father had with Anton Merced served in my memory as a defining point in my life as an island boy. But returning to the fight, it was as if I was approaching the reef from a different angle, seeing things upside down. From that angle an obvious but unthought of aspect of the fight occurred to me: If the fight was a determining event in the story of my own family, how might it have acted on the Merced family? Although Jimmy Merced, then twelve, had doubtless heard tales of his father's and his uncle's fights, it is less likely that he had witnessed one first hand — much less been a participant. That fight on Crystal Gade — a fight with a white man, a fight his uncle had, for all intents and purposes, lost — could only have contributed as a source of racial resentment. And the audacious act of throwing a brick, the brick that brought my father to his knees, was a likely lesson in the efficacy of bold personal acts, a lesson that would be repeated five years later with a man on a golf course riding his horse. Another white man, another rock. But that time, the brash impulse earned him a tour in Vietnam, a crash course on big league racism, and a life spiraling out of control. There is danger reading into such events more connection than is actually there. After all, Jimmy Merced had an edge to him well before the fight his uncle had with my father. The very first time I recall meeting him (about a month before the fight), was the day with Pam when he called me a dirty white cat scunt for no apparent reason.

But, again, why *was* that? Why did Jimmy Merced say what he did to my sister and me that day in 1958? Like the question of Hugo Merced's opening remark about my father hitting his wife, I hadn't really given the origins much thought. I began to wonder if my memory had, as memories will, selectively forgotten some bit of information. Was this actually a case of unprovoked name-calling or was there, possibly, some underlying reason? Perhaps my father had antagonized the Merced family in some unseen way — maybe even *before* Mom and Pam and I came to the islands, some history unknown to us. At times my father was quick to anger and like Anton Merced, not incapable of taking offense. They may have run into each other at some bar or another. When I asked Anton whether he thought there was any truth to his brother's claim that my father hit his wife, he smiled and said he doubted it because he and his brother were always inventing reasons to get into fights. But that didn't settle it for me. While it should be enough to know the fight had happened and that the two combatants had carried the cause of it to their graves, I could not easily put the matter to rest. There was, at the bottom, a need to discover if, at the very origin of things, someone was at fault.

Then, during a 1998 trip to Puerto Rico to visit my sister, new insights into the possible origins of the fight emerged. She remembered an event that might have helped antagonize the Merced family and as she spoke of it, I remembered too. One day the parking brake on the jeep failed and it crashed into a small wall outside their house. I only remembered seeing the jeep, its fender bent, and a few concrete blocks in pieces. What I didn't remember was that words were exchanged. Pam recalled members of the Merced clan charging out of the house and yelling at my parents who were indignant because no one asked if anyone was hurt. Did we pay them for the damages, I wonder? If one was looking for origins, for the beginnings of blame, is this as far as it goes? Or does it go back further, really, having to do with the causes of a worn brake pad or a leaking master cylinder, or a millimeter of rust?

Memory, like the tide, works the surface of other memories, the wave washing back the pebbles, each time exposing new surfaces. The morning following this discussion, Pam said she'd thought of something else in the middle of the night, something that occurred before the fight that might have helped things along. The Merceds had a small island mutt, a terrier of sorts, unchained, who did not like anyone to pass the house. One kept a watchful eye. Pam recounted an instance — she was sure it was around the time of the fight — when my father chose to take Scheorn, our German shepherd, for a walk past their house. Scheorn was on a rope but almost broke free and there was a bit of snarling and yelping. Pam remembers their dog having run beneath their house and people coming out on the porch. I don't recall my father ever taking Scheorn for a walk. To the beach, yes, but not through town. Might my father, weary of the unchained dog's attacks, have decided to mosey on by the Merced's with a dog that, given the chance, could have torn their dog to shreds? That kind of act — slyly provocative — would not have been beyond my father's reach.

Then there is the other thought, the other speculation that has surfaced most recently. Perhaps the fault lay not with something my father did, but with an act of my own: Perhaps all those rocks I fired at cats resulted in some errant ricochets I am unaware of. That might explain my being called a cat scunt and, later, being ambushed with rocks on my way home from school, a kind of payback.

Who can say where fault finally lies. As with pool shots and pebbles in ponds, actions have unexpected consequences and uncertain beginnings. I look for origins. I find a dogfight, a catfight, a rockstone, a millimeter of rust. I find fossils in the marl.

Almost Invisible

I n 1989 our house, at the time under construction, was destroyed by Hurricane Hugo. For sixteen months my wife and I lived in a tent that rested on a deck built from the debris of the house. Federal disaster aid and loans enabled us to build back a house that was in every way better than the one that was destroyed. In the end, a blessing in a rude disguise.

In the following years, the hurricane season brought a few more close calls. Then in 1995 we were hit by Marilyn. A few hours before the storm, I went out to a certain isolated peninsula of bush to pick up Niles who had become more-or-less destitute in recent years (though never lacking in dignity) living in the bush under a tarp tucked into an outcropping of rock. When I got there that day, he was ready with his small green sack of belongings. This was not the first time I had picked Niles up before an approaching storm. On the ride to the house I filled him in on the direction and speed of the storm and he told me what he'd just heard on his transistor radio. He was full of things to say this day, this hour. The conversation was remarkable. In recent years, Niles seldom has had much to say and sometimes, riding along in the truck, he might say things to someone not present, answering voices he hears in his head. Often, he is addressing certain unspecified suspicions having to do with things like microwave towers, men in uniform, a person he saw who was the spitting image of the person we once knew in, say, Boston or Peru. Could Jorge, the architect in Lima, be working on a garbage truck in Magens Bay? Was the blonde lady he saw passing in a taxi actually Sheila, the old girlfriend who was said to have died back in 1975?

Nile's abrupt departure from Peru was followed by three months spent in a mental institution in Connecticut. After that came a series of jobs in Manhattan, San Francisco, Seattle and St. Thomas, which alternated with bouts of illness, usually because he refused to take his medication, the side-effects of which were worse than the phantoms the medicine was meant to keep at bay. On St. Thomas, he worked for the best architects but always according to his own rules and relaxed pace no matter how pressing the client or the deadline. Most architects valued his abilities and creativity enough to let him get away with it for a while. One architect was willing to keep him on just to do renderings of the proposed projects until Niles started drawing things that weren't part of the blueprints, whimsical departures of his own. Eventually he wore out his welcome.

For a brief period in the mid-80s he was hospitalized in the local mental health wing. After that, he gave up on paying rent and accepted the generosity of an acquaintance who owns a vacant piece of property with a nice view. Here, with occasional care packages and gifts of cash from father and sister, Niles has been able to achieve a certain balance, however precarious, between not having to take medication and not exhibiting any untoward behavior. Although the owner gave him permission to build a small shed, Niles has chosen the exquisite simplicity of a hammock, a tarp and an outcropping of rock, the architect surrendering to the sturdy and sensible structures of nature.

When I picked him up that day it was the third storm of the season that my wife and I had offered him refuge. The first storm, Iris, had brought little more than rain. The next, Hurricane Luis, had given us something to think about with gusts of at least 75 mph. Now Marilyn, which had been little more than a tropical storm crossing the Atlantic, had been upgraded to a hurricane only the day before when it crossed into the Caribbean north of Trinidad, far to the south of us. But its westerly track had then taken a sudden, unlikely turn to the north the same day. Forecasters viewed this as instability, a sign that the hurricane might be downgraded later in the day to a tropical storm. Little chance in any case that it would hit us with much force.

This kind of thinking had prevailed prior to Hugo in 1989 due to a couple of near misses that passed us just before. All that battening down for nothing tends to lull people into a sense that it really isn't necessary. Having lost our home in Hurricane Hugo, we were taking nothing for granted. Our wooden West Indian-style house situated at an elevation of 1,000 feet (hip roof, gallery on three sides, a kind of tree house up on posts) had been cross-braced with large beams to prevent the whole structure from racking. Every beam is hurricane-clipped and through-bolted, and the galvanized roof is held down with hundreds of three-inch roof screws. All the openings are designed with hurricane shutters and all the timbers are calculated to take the best (which is to say, worst) nature has to offer. Still, experience has taught that sustained gusts over, say, 150 mph can destroy almost anything, as can breeder tornadoes tearing across the eye wall. The hope is not to allow an opening, not even the slightest breach — the structure, like a chain, only as strong as the weakest link.

Because she had made a promise to do so, my wife, Karen, prepares to go stay with my 80-year-old aunt who lives three miles east in Rosendahl. Before she leaves, we gather our cats and put them in the laundry room. At that time the radio is still predicting winds between 60 and 80 mph. This is serious but something we feel our own house can sustain, though we are less certain of the studio out back that has a shed roof. There is also the unstated hope that the authorities, always eager to prepare for the worst, are actually overstating the likely severity of the storm.

Niles and I set to some additional bracing of the porch uprights and to tying off some of the larger trees. The tall mahogany that could conceivably come down on the house comes first. I go into the higher limbs and tie them together and then run the two-inch rope and tie it to the base of the mango tree to prevent the mahogany from swaying more than a few feet to either side. We do the same to several other trees and then start to secure anything that might become airborne. By noon the wind has already begun to pick up. Usually forecasters have the storm arriving hours before it actually does, but this time it is the forecasters who seem to have fallen behind.

Working beside Niles I am a child again. He is frightfully thin from his subsistence years in the bush but in the sinews is a strength that is familiar. The hunting and diving of his youth, the gymnastics of his first years in college are still much in evidence and it occurs to me that, even now, he would be hard to subdue. He ties knots with the same efficiency, the same authority he always has. He casts his eye over the structure seeing, perhaps, things I do not. The corner of the gallery where the rafters tie to the crossbeams and the crossbeams in turn tie to the corner 4x4 have his attention.

"How come they didn't through-bolt this overlap?" he asks.

I look to see what he is referring to. It seems with the bolt coming from the other side that they didn't have enough clearance. Instead, the overlap is secured with five four-inch nails. It seems solid enough and I say so.

"You might want to consider a brace out there in the future."

He may be right though it seems a brace would look incongruous where he is suggesting. And it annoys me. Him living in a rock crevice complaining about the accommodations. This is the way my emotions see-saw with Niles; on the one hand annoyance, on the other, a nameless comfort.

By three in the afternoon, it is no longer wise to venture out on the east porch. Gust are up to 50, I guess. It is still possible to leave a door open on the north side of the porch just to watch the way the wind works the hillside, to witness the raw power, the sense of something greater, the sheer abnormality of things. A termite nest, tumescent in a tamarind tree, is lurching wild parabolas, the termites on the ride of their short lives. The trees seem at first to welcome the bending, the testing, the crazy horizontal rain. Or is it we who welcome it? Our memories are short, and we revel in the momentary pedal to the medal, the passing of the hand through the flame. There is still the comfort, when the wind is only blowing 50, of knowing one is safe.

Niles tells me to come in and close the door. I resist a while longer to preserve on my senses the storm's dazzling display. I resist also because I do not welcome being closed in for the next eight hours with Niles. When I go in we begin to fill containers with water since it is certain the electricity will go off soon. We can always throw a bucket into the cistern. We have the radio on and plenty of back-up batteries. By five o'clock, they are recording gusts of 70 mph and a note of alarm is creeping into the announcer's voice; the track of the hurricane is now looking like a direct hit and the winds we are experiencing, he informs us, are only the beginning, only the outer edges of the storm. Now I am thinking about Karen. My aunt's house in Rosendahl, though at a lower elevation, is not nearly as sturdy.

As night falls, we disconnect the propane gas tanks that we have already lashed to a 6x6 column and cut all the circuit breakers in case of a freak overload. We rig a couple of hurricane lanterns and battery-powered lights in different corners of the house. As the wind really starts to pick up Niles, grows silent and then hunkers down in a chair by the computer. This is a bit odd because he usually avoids that corner of the house particularly when the computer is on (fearing what? Radiation or microwaves, mind-reading beams?), but now, with the electricity off, that corner is the safest in the house. Even if all the doors blew off, Niles would still have a kind of blast wall to crouch behind. He draws a comforter completely over his head to cocoon himself from reality.

I continue to walk around the space trying to find things to occupy the time. I am wondering how the studio-storage shed is holding up. By midnight the winds are clearly over a hundred and I know the shed roof can not take much more. If a gust goes over a hundred it is bad enough but now the gusts are sustained blasts lasting ten or 15 seconds. The air is blowing large bubbles under the door on the east side of the house, and the floor is wet just about everywhere. The last of half a dozen radio stations is blown off the air at 12:27 a.m. shortly after an update that concedes forecasters wrongly predicted the track and intensity of the storm. Niles is in his cocoon, out of reach.

At about one o'clock a series of gusts hit the house and cause me to drop to the floor. All bets are off. These gusts are over 150 I am sure, and there is a sense that the entire house could go airborne. One gust produces a ripping sound and a muffled pop. The studio roof. I look at the ceiling above to see if there are any signs of separation and see none. Air is poring in through cracks in the floor and the pressure from the gusts is causing the water in the toilet to disappear and reappear. I wander about with my flashlight, shoving towels under doors, cracking shutters in the lee of the house to vent pressure, comforting the cats, checking on the unmoving Niles cocoon, waiting for dawn.

When day finally breaks, the winds are still too strong to risk much more than a peek. I am also afraid of what I will see. At first I take only a glancing peek through a partially opened shutter. The boulder at the end of the porch is still there and so, I seem to realize, am I. Fortified by this dose of reality, I open the front door and venture onto the porch.

The studio roof, a half ton of lumber and galvanize is gone. I discover an hour later that it has come to rest 150 feet up the mountainside, its wild trajectory visible in the broken tree limbs, the path where it cartwheeled like a colossal frisbee through the trees. The sides of the house are plastered with a stucco of mulch. On the driveway below is a large section of an unfamiliar roof. In a rock outcropping beside the stairs, a section of a Bible belonging to God knows who. More disturbing is the blasted leafless landscape of a nuclear winter, the mountainside strewn with the debris of people's lives. Sheets of galvanize lie like giant cards from a deck scattered across the valley. Below, on Crown Mountain Road, not a single telephone pole still stands, and wires, like a cat's cradle, crisscross the road.

By mid-day we are using a chainsaw to clear the road and later are reunited with Karen. My aunt's house had collapsed early on and they had retreated to the one room still standing — the bathroom. For eight hours in 100 plus mile winds, the three — Karen, my octogenarian aunt and a large black retriever — huddled in a shower stall.

The following day I returned Niles to the bush, something I do fairly regularly — usually when I pick him up hitching. There was some small talk on the ride back about fixing his surfboard and getting back in the water, familiar terrain, but he must have been more talked out than usual, having been under a roof for 48-hours with other humans. Or perhaps he was carrying on one of those other conversations. Leaving, he gathers up his few things including his bag — green canvas tending toward ratty — which contains his compact world of belongings, folded or sealed, each item perfectly in its place. And soon, through the window, I am telling him how I have some resin for his ding if a swell comes up. And he mumbles something that someone less knowledgeable might let go as agreement and I make a similar sound but we both know that it isn't likely to happen. He waves and starts down the trail that was once a steep drive cut by a bulldozer but has become rutted and grassed over. I notice how he has chosen to leave tufts of wild tamarind and casha at bends in the trail rendering the trail, like Niles himself, almost invisible.

The One That Got Away

In 1994 the community was rocked by the news that the retiring governor had chosen to commute the sentences of seven convicted felons. Most controversial was the pardon of one of the Sweet Bottom Five who had been serving his eight consecutive life terms in a Washington State pen. The pardons, along with a recent case of missing cocaine and an execution-style murder of a police officer, was much in the news at the time. The issue of Sweet Bottom, a new name to many of this generation, has been raised again. With it has come renewed curiosity about Jimmy Merced.

Where *is* Jimmy Merced? An article asks more than a decade after his disappearance. Is Merced in Cuba? If so, what are his circumstances? Or did he go to Angola with Cuban troops as some have suggested, where he could have slipped away? One day coming from pool with Anton, I brought up the business of recent extradition of a certain international financier from Cuba, and the thawing of Cuban-American relations. Wasn't he concerned that a noose might be in the making for his son? He was not. And he left it to me to figure whether this was because his son was in Cuba or elsewhere. Although there were many opportunities to ask Anton if he had any word from his son, I didn't. I was still afraid if I showed too much interest in that subject, he might fall again to wondering if I was a Federal Agent. There were still, truth be told, some lingering uncertainties on both our parts.

One day when I went to pick Anton up to play pool I was surprised to find him out. His beautiful amber-eyed granddaughter, Carmelita, called from the porch that he was out back. When she went to get him I noticed that the Merced sign was down and that the side gate was hooked and barred. Strange. A few minutes later Carmelita returned to inform me that, no, Anton had stepped out and she wasn't sure when he would return. For some reason I didn't believe her and, continuing down Bunker Hill toward the post office, I had a sudden dark feeling. It was the holiday season; could it be that Jimmy Merced had quietly slipped into town?

This was not the first time I had feelings of foreboding. A few months before, I had tried to make contact with Jimmy's mother feeling certain that she could help me understand certain things better than Anton. At first, a year before, Anton had discouraged such a meeting and to preserve our relationship, I had agreed not to call her unless I had spoken to him first. Why didn't he want me to talk to Esther, his first wife? He claimed it was because she was too volatile and suspicious, a potential Pandora's box. I wondered if that was really it or whether there might be some other reason he wanted to prevent our meeting. Might there be something she could reveal that Anton wanted kept secret? When Anton finally agreed to call her for me as a way of setting up a meeting and allaying any suspicions she might have, I was encouraged. But the weeks went by and Anton never made the call.

Finally, I decided to do it myself. Esther Merced's phone number was in the phone book — along with her address in Bournefield — and I had by that time already driven by the house, a concrete box almost completely overgrown with bush. I had even imagined myself entering this house with some trepidation and sitting on a porch talking with her. When I finally phoned, there was no answer. A few hours later I tried again and a young, gruff male answered.

"Good afternoon. Mrs. Merced home?"

There was a pause.

"No."

"You know when she go reach back?"

Another pause.

"No."

"Well, I go check back later."

"Who calling?"

I gave my name, grimacing to myself.

"She off-island. You can't speak to she."

I put down the receiver and have to walk around the house to quell the nerves. The intonations sounded Rasta and I imagine dreadlocks in that little concrete box and I wondered if he is in on it, and if Esther Merced might be in Cuba. It is possible now to fly to Santo Domingo and from there to Cuba without Customs problems. What would Jimmy

Merced make of someone stirring up curiosity about his crime and his whereabouts? I imagine, as I sometimes have, his appearing on my porch, unannounced, with friends. After that phone call I decide perhaps Anton is right. A cage I decided it best not to rattle.

In Virgin Islands' history we celebrate the 1733 slave revolt on St. John. We look to the heroes of the Emancipation who threatened to burn the island to its foundations and to General "Buddhoe" Gottlieb who led the rebellion. Like other cultures we sometimes honor those who have taken a stand against injustice by using violence or the threat of violence to achieve an end. Jimmy Merced bears little resemblance to these heroic — and brave — ancestors and few islanders would think to utter his name in the same company. But, if pressed, some locals might concede that Merced and the others were to the 1970s what other firebrands were to their times. In the context of the racial and social dislocations of those Vietnam years, Sweet Bottom, some might argue, acted like a lance to the festering boil. In a similar light Jimmy Merced is viewed by some as our inevitable outlaw, our bad boy, our Jesse James. And years later, after the hijacking, Merced has added to that image by disappearing, by creating a mystery, by becoming the one who got away.

If I had anything to say to Jimmy Merced it might be in the nature of saying I'm sorry. Not that I have done him any wrong, personally, or that he would even remember who I am. He would remember, however, the fight his uncle had with the white man on Crystal Gade, and he would also know that he had connected with the brick. I am sorry in the way of, say, being sorry about the death of a child. Sorry that your house burned down. Sorry that these things happened to you. In your case, Jimmy, my being sorry has underlying, personal regrets. Suppose there was some history — beyond the jeep crashing into the wall or our dog fighting your dog or my throwing rocks at nighttime cats — something that my family did, intentionally or otherwise, to contribute to the tensions that already existed in your family and on the street. If there was, I am sorry. Not contrite. Not needing forgiveness. Sorry in the same helpless way one might be sorry that certain cowboy films may have seduced you. Sorry that in my family's case a misunderstanding of some kind may have occurred to bring a child to the point of hurling a brick. Sorry also for whatever might have been said in passing — on both sides. Sorry that your father and your uncle glorified fighting. Sorry that with a black mother and a white father you were at odds with that part of yourself. Sorry that a man chose to ride your horse and that a judge sent you to the jungle. Sorry for the discrimination you experienced in the military, for the machine gun you learned to use, for the lives lost when you pulled the trigger. Sorry that after being wounded, they wanted to send you back. Sorry you had to be the bad ass and hit an officer. Sorry that you got in trouble with the police. Sorry I don't really know for certain which or how many of the Sweet Bottom Five actually did what. Sorriest, ultimately, that eight innocent people died.

I would also want you to be sorry, Jimmy Merced, yet I wonder if you have been humbled by your imprisonment, your religious convictions, the life you have squandered, the opportunities denied — humbled enough to be able to say that. To say I am sorry.

Am I sorry that you hijacked a plane, that you have become The One That Got Away? If I thought that apprehending you would solve some problem, I might. The victims of Sweet Bottom and their families and the people of the Virgin Islands have so far received over one hundred years of imprisonment, only twelve of it yours. Some of those serving a life sentence may never have fired a shot. If you were still in the can we could add, at this point, another 15 years.

On the other side of the equation, there may be something to be gained by your disappearance, some aspect of your freedom from captivity that acts on the viscera of some Virgin Islanders. Something that equates with a local sense of justice. In the minds of some, you are the runaway slave, unshackled, with a chance, the bloodhounds close behind. In the minds of others, there is the wonder that your crime, the senseless slaughter of innocents, does not happen more often. Now, over a quarter of a century after the crime, the boil that was lanced shows only a faint scar, barely visible, but one that reminds. So that even on a balmy, sun-drenched day we can be reminded that such a thing happened. And can happen again.

The memory of Sweet Bottom is, to my mind, like a jackspaniard nest in a soursop tree. Soursop is a local fruit tree. The fruit offers a tart and succulent pulp. If one grows in your yard you go to the tree when it is in season and regularly twist the fruit from the stem. But the day may come when, unthinking, you reach for a fruit from a particular branch that is concealing a large jackspaniard nest, and a day later, after the swelling from the wasps has begun to subside, you can laugh at the experience. Laugh even at yourself. But it will be a very long time before you reach for that fruit without thinking what might be on the other side.

One day I arranged to pick up Anton to shoot pool with plans to eat dinner afterwards with my wife. It had been almost two months since we had last played partly because I'd been busy and partly because he had failed to pay his phone bill and had his line cut. Or so he said. I wondered about this choice. Had he really forgotten to pay the bill or was there something more? Anton almost always had phone problems and I wondered if the real reason it was cut was because he was afraid the phone was tapped. When I picked him up that day, I learned that his wife and children were out of town, gone indefinitely to Florida, and that he was now living alone in a house that was in a semi-board-ed up state. I noticed a nasty cut on his elbow and he informed me he had just that morning been to the hospital to have the bandage removed. A few days earlier he had been mugged on his return from his afternoon walk to the post office, jumped from behind by two young thugs. Anton thought they were both in their late teens or early 20s. He pantomimed how he had almost caught one of them with a good fist, but at the age of 70 and change, there wasn't much chance. I couldn't help take account of the poetic justice of this attack on a man who had always prided himself on hitting first and who had, in his youth, often sought unsuspecting prey. I doubt the connection was lost on Anton either. He seemed to take the beating philosophically, though he assured me he would kill either of them if ever given the chance. He didn't even seem to begrudge the 20 or so dollars that they had gotten along with his wallet. The only thing he regretted was the loss of a few cherished photos including the two of Jimmy as a boy. The two-bit criminals, not finding any credit cards along with bills would have passed over the photos of the young boy, and the ratty wallet probably ended up in the trash.

Later over dinner we are reminded that tomorrow is Father's Day. This leads to the trading of tales. Anton tells of the time his father rode a horse up the staircase and into the ballroom of the Grand Hotel to collect his wife who had gone there without him. I reciprocate with the story told me by friends of the time my father buzzed the first fairway of the Apawamis Country Club in a B-24.

In a question that is designed, perhaps, to move our masculine memories away from bombers and horseback abductions, my wife asks Anton what his tenderest memory is of Jimmy as a child. Anton does not have a quick answer to this. He puts his fork down and takes a sip of his glass of water. My own mind, trying to anticipate his answer, rifles through stock tender moments — a babe in arms, a hurt feeling, a school play, a birthday, a ball game — but I am having difficulties making a connection.

When Anton speaks he recounts with a wry smile the tender moment he and Jimmy fought a couple of U.S. sailors on Main Street. Shoulder to shoulder, each giving his best.

"How old was he at the time?" my wife asks.

"Fourteen," Anton answers.

The following morning I arrange to meet Anton at the post office in the morning so I can take him to Kmart. He is seated on the post office steps, the same steps my father once stood on when he first got the urge to move to St. Thomas. Anton often sits there mornings with *The Daily News* when the air is still cool and the shadows long, hailing the passersby, so many of whom call to him by name. I run in to check my box and we return to the truck together. I am taking him to Kmart because his own car has been out of commission for over a year and, though the bus does go into the

252 Glassbottom Days

country, it is a bothersome affair. He needs a new antenna for his TV, which, with the wife and children gone, has become a more important part of his day. I'd avoided going to Kmart since its construction, still miffed at the fact that its creation prevented a proper analysis of the pre-Columbian culture unearthed by the bulldozers. Three quarters of the archeological site covering an area of over three acres has surrendered after a thousand years to a treeless, blacktop parking lot.

On the way to Kmart we pass the former site of an old restaurant and bar called Rusty's Roost, and I discover that this was one of Anton's preferred watering holes. When I inform him that my father also frequented the Roost, other memories surface. Anton describes a fight he once had with a local at the Roost and brags about how he knocked the man out with one fist. That's all it took in those days. One good fist, Anton explains, would send a man across the street. He raises his fist above the dashboard like a trophy, but I have some difficulty imagining it sending a man across the street. The comment seems tinged with hyperbole as if it has been melded with some cinematic John Wayne punches that Anton's memory imagines to have been his own. It is also, after talk the night before of beating up unsuspecting sailors with his 14-year-old son, a bit tiresome.

Hearing it, I surrender to the temptation I had resisted on more than one occasion. Has it not occurred to him, I ask, that his violent nature was the legacy he handed down to his son? It has occurred to him. The question produces a bit of silence, and I am sorry at once that I have allowed myself to ask it. But he does not take offense. It is such an obvious question, really, one that most who have known Anton would ask — though perhaps not out loud.

I recall how the day before Anton had twice referred to saying his prayers at night. This had never come up before but then, in the space of two or three hours, the subject had come up twice. I remember thinking the empty house had brought this out in him, that with his wife gone and the commotion of the children not present, his own thoughts, his own life had begun to crowd in on him.

When we enter Kmart I am stunned by the size of the place, the sheer volume of merchandise. I am not on St. Thomas, suddenly, but in some metropolitan suburb and the feeling is not altogether unwelcome. To get to the TV antennas we have to pass through Lingerie, Housewares, Sporting Goods, Power Tools, Appliances, and my resistance is weakening. The same router on display here I had almost bought the week before for twice the Kmart price. And there is an efficient, well-stocked pharmacy. Anton asks the salesman something about an antenna, and I see the place is teeming with locals with shopping carts piled high. They are the greatest beneficiaries of the store, and they are not thinking about archeological consequences, about Arawak pottery or Carib bones. At the checkout counter I even see Mrs. Desmond, wife of the chief planner for the Department of Conservation and Cultural Affairs. Her shopping cart is piled high with disposable diapers.

Back in the parking lot, as Anton is situating the antenna box in the back of the truck, I notice the ten-foot drop of the embankment in front of us where the bulldozer cut away to level the parking. Beneath the ten inches of topsoil, where most of the Indian relics once lay, is a layer of clay that descends a foot or two to become a crumbly kind of brown basalt. Between the basalt and the bottom layer of harder volcanic blue bit is an irregular smear of whitish marl — two or three feet of it — old ocean bottom here before the island, matter composed of ancient life millions of years old. And, for some reason, it occurs to me, sitting there in that Kmart parking lot, that those extinct creatures who lived all those million years ago, those creatures wanted to survive on this earth as much as I want to, that their lives were as important to them as mine is to me.

When Anton tries to get into the door he has to struggle with the lock a bit and when he tries to fasten the seatbelt his hands tremble trying to make the buckle fit. I help him. On his knuckles are old scars. And I think that these things, these scars, this parking lot, those layers of earth are, in the end, no one's fault. At the end of the day there is no one to blame.

One recent evening returning home after dark, I rounded a downhill slope of the Bonne Esperance road and my headlights hit on a deer, a good-sized doe. It has been at least 20 years since I last saw one and my unbelieving brain tells my eyes — not a deer, donkey. And then, not donkey, cow. And finally, the car slowing, my mind running out of options, out of reason — not cow, goat? By now the car is stopped and the catalog of possibilities exhausted and the deer — for that is what it was — saunters across the road in no particular hurry, gives my headlights a parting glance, and with legs that seem spring-loaded, shoots up into the bush on the uphill side of the road.

I sit in the car in the middle of the road, idling, the bush and the night crowding in from both sides. The sound of the engine and the insistent luminescent dials of the dashboard seem, after the deer, intensely real. How do the deer do it? With all these roads and houses, with all these dogs and droughts and guns. Where on this small island do they hide, what corner of the bush do they call their own? And driving on down the road, I am moving slowly with these thoughts, but my heart is gathering momentum and my mind is racing ahead to how I will share this moment with the person I love, and soon the accelerator is pushed to the floor and I am flying. It is as if I have seen God in the middle of the road, God in my headlights. And so well-fed, so sleek, so damn sassy.

There are, on the hillside around our house, a number of large boulders that look as if they have been here since the beginning of time — probably only for a few million years, really, but time enough. And if I choose to push through the bush beyond the area that has been cut back, I can sit on one of these boulders and feel with a certain degree of confidence that I am sitting where no other mortal has sat, and looking out to the horizon to a scattering of uninhabited cays, I can imagine that what I am seeing is no different from what the earliest man on these shores might have seen. It is a strange little exercise and I don't know exactly why I do it or why these thoughts give me a certain comfort. If I look a few degrees to one side or the other, the illusion is dashed by the assorted houses nestled into the hillside, or by the swooshing sound of a car passing on the road below, or by a dog barking at the wind.

At night it is easier to get that primordial other-eon feeling. At night, atop a 20-ton boulder surrounded by dense bush, one is in the province of the iguana. Crickets and tree toads lend their voices to a sense of earth and root and rock being one. And above are the stars, the light that has been traveling our way since before we were born.

I was surprised one night not long ago to see one of those distant pin-pricks of light appear to move. Or was it the tree limbs causing that illusion?

No, it was the starlight that was moving.

Possibly a plane, a high altitude jet. But what a strange track — due north — and no blinking tail light. I realized then that what I was seeing was not a plane or a star but the faint reflected light and lonely circling of an orbiting satellite. And when it disappeared behind an invisible night cloud, I scrambled down the boulder I was on and up another, higher boulder to see if I could find it, to recapture it once more. And when I did, when I saw again its dark and silent trajectory, my heart felt a connection to it, a kind of kinship. It was, I realized, a feeling of kinship not unlike the feeling I had felt for that deer in the dark.

How to explain such a thing? One, blood and bone. The other, metal-lic, spinning, lifeless. Perhaps hope explains it, the dominion of hope.

The Grandfather Clock

When my mother died unexpectedly of heart-lung complica-tions I returned to the island to attend the service and to settle her will. That year, 1983, was her 25th on the island. She, who had resisted the move most, had lived on the island (at that point) longer than anyone else. She knew St. Thomas too well. It was in her blood, a force of habit, so that even after the divorce she never expressed an inkling of interest to be anywhere else, to return, say, to Greenwich or Rye. She had come way too far for that.

If a nurse had been attending her properly, her doctor said, she might not have slipped away. It was one of those things. At the service, which was hastily arranged, the officiating minister who was new to the island and had never met her, tried his best but was limited to platitudes and benign generalities. He even referred to her as Sarah — the name on her birth certificate. Sarah this and Sarah that. Mom had not been called Sarah since she was three. But it is just the kind of thing that she would have smiled at.

During the service, afternoon sunlight slanted in through a high window above the choir loft and I remember feeling her presence in that light. Soft, indirect. The old boards warmed in the light, and I suddenly felt, as the minister talked on about Sarah, that I was, in a way that window; the boards that surrounded the light and gave it form was my father and the light that gave the window reason was my mother. I was both of them, light and dark, body and spirit.

There was not much of an estate to tie up beyond the selling of the house and getting the grandfather clock shipped off to my father on Vieques. Her possessions were few — some tired antiques, the silverware, a bit of jewelry, china, a few beach chairs, a dog, a cat, a small car. When all my mother's outstanding bills were settled, she still had $26.87 in her bank account. Her working clothes, sensible and sturdy, and a few nice dresses she hadn't worn in ages went off to the Humane Society flea market and are probably hanging in various closets and walking about today. A bathrobe that still had her scent I kept. Strange the way things seem to acquire and transmit the spirit of the one gone, for me at least. In a drawer of family keepsakes I have saved, along with more valuable items, is a pair of her reading glasses and a blue plastic cigarette lighter. To my mind her glasses still see the way she saw, and the lighter, which is transparent and half-full of lighter fluid, still works. I don't light it often, but I take pleasure in knowing I can.

After my father's death in 1986, the grandfather clock, which had been on Vieques for a few years, was sent to Pam's home in Puerto Rico, not far from the rainforests of El Yunque. It was really mine to inherit but because there was no direct route from Vieques to St. Thomas at the time and because I had no place to keep it, Pam agreed to hold on to it until I did.

For five years it lay in her carport in a long coffin-like box she'd had made. I felt sorry for the clock. Though I didn't know for certain how old it was or for how many generations it had been in the family, I knew it had at least belonged to my great grandfather and, as such, had existed for at least a century and had stood (if not always ticking) in Brooklyn, Manhattan, Rye, St. Thomas and Vieques. It had endured all nature of indignity including hurricanes and termites and would no doubt outlive me. Most recently it had survived five years of being entombed in plywood and things were getting a bit moldy. I felt I owed the clock an explanation. I also felt at times that my father was looking down from the Great Beyond with diminishing patience.

So I was relieved in 1992 when our house, rebuilt after Hurricane Hugo, at last had a corner high enough to accommodate the clock. Elaborate preparations were made, which included a chartered private plane and adaptations and reinforcements to the box by the shipping company located in Rio Piedras. It was there in the cargo bay of the shipping company where crow bars pried open the box for the first time in five years and the clock face — to my mind looking a bit beleaguered — seemed to look up at the unpromising sight of our staring faces in the florescent lights of the cargo bay. This was followed by the placing of certain padding and by a vacuum hose pressure-pumping thousands of Styrofoam bubbles into every last crevice as well as into the abdomen of the clock, the hollow housing where the pendulum and weights, (disassembled now and wrapped in paper like the organs of a pharaoh), usually hang. With these final preparations accomplished, the lid was again nailed shut and bands of copper bailing wire were corseted and cinched around the sarcophagus.

A week later, after time spent in another warehouse where Customs officials poked and prodded it, we managed with friends to lug it up our steep driveway and steps and onto the porch. There, we cut the bailing bands and pried open the top with a crow bar. One of our cats, Ishmael, rounded the corner and stopped in mid-stride startled by the crate's mighty presence where normally his bowl is situated. The other cat was not taking any chances with a thing so big and chose to sit in the mango tree and worry from afar.

In time the clock was back on its feet again and no longer a mystery to the cats. But first we had to tend to the business of termites that had been living in the apron of its base for a long time having come on board, my guess would be, back in Vieques where they had turned other antiques into hollow sticks. In this case they hadn't done too much visible damage, so I fashioned a small platform at the base so none of the clock's weight rests on the apron. Only a careful observer would notice that the entire clock is suspended a quarter of an inch off the floor.

One night recently, Anton came to dinner and was dutifully impressed by the clock's age and size. He was talkative this evening and even allowed himself a beer. It was perhaps this that caused him to let slip word that Jimmy had a new child, a baby girl, and I didn't ask how he knew this to be true but sidestepped it with something that the mention of Jimmy brought to mind.

I'd been wondering, I explained to Anton, about those rocks I used to throw from my window at alley cats. Anton was familiar enough with my probing for causes, so I asked him if those rocks I'd thrown at alley cats might have contributed in some way to hard feelings between our families? Could he remember any time when stones had whistled by or ricocheted in the gutter beside their house? He didn't recall anything like that except that his own kids were always throwing rocks at one thing or another. But wouldn't it be odd, I pressed, if the problems between our families originated not with something my father had done, but something I had. Unwittingly, with those stones I threw at cats my first few days on the island. Anton thought about this. He allowed as how stranger things have happened, but said he'd rather place the blame with the damn cats.

He stood looking a bit at the grandfather clock and asked if he could hear it tick. I told him it had been some years since it had functioned and I wasn't at all sure how to fix it, and it was then he reminded me of Benlow, a fix-it fellow on Back Street who used to be a dentist. And as he spoke I remembered him. Remembered also his having a less than glowing dental reputation and a penchant for extractions.

"He quit with teeth," Anton explained. "But he start up with clock. The man could fix anything."

It's a handsome clock and when I open the door that houses the pendulum and weights and stick my head in there and breathe deeply, I can smell my childhood and the scent of things before I was born. And like a child, I find myself imagining the clock having thoughts of its own and wondering what those thoughts might be. Hopeful ones, I suspect, after all those years in a box. The clock that, years ago, seemed so out of place to me here, now belongs to this island, and the mahogany trees outside seem to confirm that judgement. The corner it stands in is, to my way of thinking, about as pleasant a corner as a clock could hope for. To one side of it is an arched window beside a portrait of my mother as a child and to the other side is a shuttered porch door. The clock's corner looks out upon a very open room with wide open doors so that all nature of green can be seen, and beyond there is the tumbling mountain and beyond that a horizon of blue. In the morning the trees are filled with bird song. It's an excellent corner. There is still the matter of my setting the weights and the pendulum. With a little luck, and maybe a visit from the clock guy, we should be able to get it ticking again before too long.

Willie Wilson lives and works on St. Thomas, Virgin Islands where he teaches writing and theater. He is the author of the novel *Up Mountain One Time* that was originally a play he wrote and directed for stage and television. Wilson is the recipient of a Christa McAuliffe Fellowship Award for outstanding teaching. He and his wife, Karen, live high on a green St. Thomas hillside where, each morning, birds start to sing at an early hour.